The Concept of Development

The Concept of
DEVELOPMENT

AN ISSUE IN THE STUDY OF HUMAN BEHAVIOR

EDITED BY DALE B. HARRIS

University of Minnesota Press · Minneapolis

PRINTED AT THE JONES PRESS, INC., MINNEAPOLIS

3 2

Library of Congress Catalog Card Number: 57-7009

PUBLISHED IN GREAT BRITAIN, INDIA, AND PAKISTAN BY THE
OXFORD UNIVERSITY PRESS, LONDON, BOMBAY, AND KARACHI

FOREWORD

For thirty years the Institute of Child Welfare at the University of Minnesota has been a vigorous research center, studying aspects of child growth and development. In a day when the social sciences, and especially the behavioral sciences, are the focus of many research funds and much intellectual effort, it seems appropriate to consider the concept of development and its usefulness in the various disciplines studying human affairs. Such a conference was held at the University of Minnesota, December 8–10, 1955, to recognize the Institute's productive work of three decades.

Initially the Institute was nothing more than a grant from the Laura Spellman Rockefeller Foundation. It took someone with the vision, the scientific competence, and the organizational skill of John E. Anderson, for thirty years the director of the Institute, to transform dollars into one of the most distinguished centers of child study in the United States, if not the world.

The effectiveness of such an organization as the Minnesota Institute of Child Welfare is not measured in terms of staff size or magnitude of budget. The only valid measure is the output — the quality of the students who have been trained, and the quality of the research results that have become part of the literature.

The conference permitted many scholars to trace the evolution of a concept that has been central in the teaching and research activities of the Institute. Along with the scientific aspects of this occasion there was a special dinner at which a citation, formally adopted by the Board of Regents, was presented to Dr. Anderson.

But it was not ceremonialism that made the conference the unique affair that it was; its value stemmed from the willing participation of the scholars who deemed it an honor to come and present papers that contained analyses pertinent to the major theme. So carefully planned had these contributions been that, when completed, they constituted a body of thought that clearly justified wider dissemination. As an integrated set of chapters, they represent a further contribution to the literature of the concept of development. It is an especially happy occurrence that publication can be accomplished through the University of Minnesota Press, for the Press has been a channel through which many of the research studies of the staff of the Institute of Child Welfare have reached a wide audience.

This volume, therefore, is issued because of its contribution to scholarly thought in one significant area of scientific study and research; and because it symbolizes all that the Institute and John E. Anderson have meant, both on the campus of the University of Minnesota and in the world of scholarship at large.

MALCOLM M. WILLEY
Vice President, Academic Administration
University of Minnesota

ACKNOWLEDGMENTS

Pʀᴇsɪᴅᴇɴᴛ Jᴀᴍᴇs L. Mᴏʀʀɪʟʟ and Vice President Malcolm M. Willey of the University of Minnesota were most instrumental in making possible the Conference on the Concept of Development. They also extended financial aid, advice, and encouragement to the publication of these papers, which were presented at the Conference. The general interest and support of the Regents is also acknowledged.

Dr. James S. Lombard, Director of the Division of Concerts and Lectures, who co-sponsored the Conference, and the staff of the Institute of Child Welfare, who aided in planning and arrangements, contributed most significantly to the occasion.

The following distinguished scholars of the University served as chairmen and participated in the discussions when the papers were presented, December 8, 9, and 10, 1955: T. C. Blegen, Dean of the Graduate School; Herbert Feigl, Chairman of the Department of Philosophy; Donald W. Hastings, M.D., Head of the Department of Psychiatry and Neurology; Dwight Minnich, Chairman of the Department of Zoology; and Paul E. Meehl, Chairman of the Department of Psychology.

D. B. H.

TABLE OF CONTENTS

Issues in the Study of Development

Dale B. Harris

PROBLEMS IN FORMULATING A SCIENTIFIC CONCEPT OF DEVELOPMENT

ONE contribution to this volume refers to the protean meanings of development. Like the Old Man of the Sea, development has a significant reference to the future. However, each person who laid hold on Proteus to make him yield the secret of the future found him assuming a different shape. Few were those who mastered him in his many forms. The concept of development has impressed scholars as being equally slippery, and of limited usefulness. Few are those who attempt to master it in its many aspects.

The concept of development is fundamentally biological. While a concept of development may be used in respect to physical systems, and while it may refer also to systems of ideas, the term has been most commonly associated with the organization of living structures and life processes.

The functions which distinguish living from nonliving matter are usually expressed as irritability, or responsiveness to stimulation; motility or self-movement; self-regulation, or maintenance of a balance between input and output of energy; and reproduction. Discussions of development commonly include as essential the ideas of (1) organism conceived as living system; (2) time; (3) movement over time toward complexity of organization; (4) "hierarchization," or the comprehension of parts or part-systems into larger units or "wholes"; and (5) an end-state of organization which is maintained with some stability or self-regulation. These last ideas inevitably bring up the troublesome issue of "purpose," so easy to dispose of in simple mechanical systems, but so difficult to avoid in one guise or another in discussions of biological systems.

3

These elements, essential for describing the growth and organization of the biological individual, have been applied to processes of organization of phenomena in other fields. By analogy, the concept of development has been applied to psychological, sociological, economic, political, and even artistic and esthetic events.

The varied uses of the concept have in the main been based on descriptive and inductive approaches. But the tremendous gains in modern physics, and the dissolving of matter itself in the face of such gains, have suggested for all science an approach quite different from yesterday's descriptive empiricism. In theory construction the observation and verification of fact is replaced by sets of postulates and theorems from which may be deduced larger sets of empirical laws to be tested in crucial experiments. Good theory defines the widest possible array of empirical laws in terms of the fewest simple theorems. Within the network of these laws scientists should seek to define the hypotheses and to predict phenomena by purely logical-mathematical procedures.

The philosophers of science, in particular, look to this hypothetico-deductive method as an effective way to establish the unity of all science, including the study of behavior. Can the phenomena of development be reduced to physical terms and subjected to hypothetico-deductive logic, or do they represent an order of affairs peculiar to living organisms, too complex for known analytical models? As yet, only a few biologists, of whom Sommerhoff (19) is an eminent example, have essayed a systematic application of the hypothetico-deductive method to biological theory.

But many accept this approach with reservations. Many empirical scientists, also interested in bridging the gap between the living and nonliving, expect to do so by manipulating materials in the laboratory rather than symbols. While recognizing the rigor and power of deductive logic, many biologists and behavior scientists believe that we are a long way from establishing a unity of science which will embrace developmental phenomena on this basis. Most biologists today take an "organismic" position which holds that while organisms are one with nature in being composed of matter, there is "something more" which is yet not disjunctive with matter. Living organisms exhibit characteristics which appear to defy immediate reduction to physicochemical terms. Irritability and locomotion, growth and reproduction, development and progressive organization, maintenance and decay, are difficult to account for specifically in the language of physics and chemistry. The organismic view suggests epigenesis, the emergence of new phenomena and new properties not contained in miniature, or preformed as of descriptive if not fully explanatory value. Thus, organisms as organized systems show in the *relations* among their material constituents properties which cannot be reduced to physical and chemical terms. Such scientists incorporate concepts like "wholeness," "system," "process," and "purpose" into their theoretical discussions.

Various compromises have been offered to attempt to bridge this gap. Some ten years ago Schroedinger (16), a physicist, established the expectation that further developments of physics and chemistry would permit the reduction of biological phenomena to the terms of physical science. Biologists, of whom Haldane (10) is an example, agree with that position as the ultimate solution, but hold that "we are not ready for it yet."

An organismic biologist (3, 5) and, more recently, a psychologist (13) boldly propose to envelop the physical sciences by a more comprehensive system. General System Theory offers concepts of kinetics and thermodynamics for the "steady state" (self-regulation) maintained by the organism through the import and export of energy. It views the kinetics and thermodynamics of equilibrium of the "closed" physicochemical system as a special case of the more general theory.

From the field of physics also comes a double-aspect solution. Bohr (6) suggests the principle of complementarity, which holds that just as classical mechanics and quantum physics are both appropriate and complementary ways of viewing matter, so we may discover a complementarity in physics and biology. This principle avoids a simple "psychophysical parallelism" by showing that to gain knowledge concerning one aspect of reality one may have to sacrifice knowledge concerning another aspect. The Heisenberg principle solved a similar problem in physics by affirming that knowledge of the momentum of a particle can be gained only by sacrificing knowledge concerning its position, and vice versa.

Students of animal and human growth and behavior who attempt to fit the developmental phenomena they observe into systematic relationships with other data, have frequently had recourse, in one manner or another, to the "levels of organization" doctrine. Granted that science or knowledge may have a basic unity, it is easier, for the moment, to view experimental embryology as constituting one level of phenomena, the behavior of the rat in a maze as another, the juvenile delinquent in the stolen car as another, and the emergence of mercantile capitalism as still another. Each of these orders of phenomena can be described and some rules or generalizations formulated that will predict (within a margin of error) the course an individual member of the order will likely follow over time. This prediction will fall far short of the scientific standard of *explanation.*

One popular treatment of the levels of organization solution to the continuity of disciplines likens the relationship of adjacent areas of phenomena to a flight of broad steps (12). Viewing from above, the scientist sees the areas of phenomena as a spectrum separated by thin lines, and remarks on the continuity of the several adjacent "levels." Viewing from directly in front, the completely unsophisticated person can be overwhelmed by the faces of the risers, and see only the massive jumps or "discontinuities," reckoning not at all the areas of knowledge which lie at each level. To him everything is an unexplained mystery.

One interpretation of this levels of organization position holds that the laws of a given level cannot be reduced to, nor predicted from, those of the lower level, although the laws of the lower level are implied in those of the higher order. Another position affirms general laws that apply at all levels, plus specific laws at each level that can only be formulated by studying the phenomena at each level. The unity of science viewpoint holds, of course, that a true continuity across these levels exists, could we but formulate theorems capable of embracing all orders of phenomena.

Not only do the biologist and the student of behavior development have difficulty fitting phenomena of growth or development into physical concepts, but they have a fundamental difficulty with the symbolic system into which their concepts and constructs must be cast. What order of symbols can best express the complex relations exhibited by the living organism traveling its course of development? The symbolic system an investigator adopts often limits his results or defines the scope of his achievement. Thought has a reticulate character and seldom flows steadily from point to point. Rather it makes many side excursions, linking old observations and related data to new observations in a most complex manner. Ordinary language is linear and moves from word to word, from idea to idea. Being unidimensional, it often is a poor representational device for complex concepts, particularly those dealing with organic phenomena.

Arber (1) argues that the student of biological development (and by inference the student of human behavior) should deliberately make more use of the literary, descriptive aspects of language than does the physicist. This position represents scientists who work from a descriptive, empirical, inductive position. Sommerhoff (19) illustrates the opposed position, that the language and logic of physical science can be adapted to scientific purposes more profitably than customary descriptive terms. Although they are good English words, such terms as "system," "differentiation," and "wholeness" are far too vague for an intricate axiomatic and deductive system. The semantic error, the extended multiplicity of meanings which is carried by terms from common expression, gets in the way of scientific communication. Such symbols are untrustworthy for science; the unambiguity of mathematical symbols is necessary.

But an explanation satisfactory for the hypothetico-deductive approach would, for the descriptive biologist, introduce such gross oversimplification that no "meaning" would be left. Phenomena of life and behavior are "intelligible but not explicable in physicochemical terms" (10). For many of those espousing the organismic point of view, explanation is a matter of *describing* a phenomenon in all its relationships. This procedure inclines toward a connotative language. The hypothetico-deductive position requires precise denotation. Such precision may in turn require severe limitation of the conditions investigated. Indeed, the attempt to develop an analytic model by restricting the system to one independent and one associated or dependent variable at a time, leads to the very oversimplification most biologists decry.

Certain contemporary philosophers of science acknowledge the intricate character of the antecedent-consequent relationships in causality, and look to "information theory" and to "cybernetics" for models and techniques of handling, on an analytic basis, great masses of data involving patterns of interrelations (9). For such philosophers, high levels of explanation require that we move from objects and their complex interrelations, as they are given at the level of perception, to more symbolic representations, from molar to molecular analyses. At the present time, certainly, scientific rigor requires precision in formulating or describing any system; the organismic position is necessarily defensive in this regard.

The formal structure of one's statements is another source of difficulty in scientific explanation. We are perhaps more alert to errors of logic than to semantic errors; consequently the problems of correct prediction and reasoning may be less insidious, but no less significant, than the problem of meaning. Can the concept of development, applied to living organisms and to behavior, be used to achieve scientific explanation? Or is the concept too inexact for use in scientific logic?

Workers who take their models from physics to achieve scientific explanation affirm the power of the hypothetico-deductive approach. A system of axioms, a set of mutually consistent and general formulae, is established solely on the ground that a larger group of given and less general formulae can be deduced from them. The axioms need have no relationship to matters of fact; it is unimportant whether they can be known to be true or false. However, this axiom system can be interpreted when the deduced formulae do refer to matters of fact and consist of propositions which may be true or false. An empirical fact is explained by a scientific theory when the propositions which express it can be shown to be a consequence of the axioms of the theory. Whereas induction can lead both to truth and to error, deduction is a formal process in which one proposition follows as a necessary consequence from another. When properly tested, such a process leads only to truth, hence its advantage in science.

Another kind of scientific explanation consists in presenting the actual conditions and factors under which phenomena will occur together with the specific laws which are illustrated by the productive interaction of these conditions and factors. This is the view that many biologically oriented students of development hold today. To explain is to demonstrate a phenomenon simultaneously in all its relationships. Obviously this is essentially a problem of prediction, of specifying antecedent-consequent chains. Applying this view, Bertalanffy (4) believes we may be a long time in arriving at explanations of life phenomena, unless we are willing to work with logical homologies — similarities between two phenomena in respect to the isomorphy of their governing laws, even though the factors involved in the two may be different. Thus, when quite different sets of data (e.g., increase in size of bodily organs and change in prices under the principle of economic competition), can be fitted to the same mathematical curve, the "laws" expressed are said to be isomorphic. While warning against serious limitations in analogical reasoning, some authorities hold that it may be useful in biology and behavior science generally (1, 15, 18). However, to affirm that analogy may be useful in empirical research is quite a different matter from asserting it to be a model for theory construction. The distinction between analogy and homology may be only one of degree; the latter may suffer from all the limitations of the former. Although this phenomenal approach will give working principles for "laws" of limited usefulness, it is claimed that such an approach does not afford scientific explanation, and hence does not advance our effort materially (8).

The empirical scientist frequently distrusts the deductive approach. His theory grows out of an intimate knowledge of observed data. Scientists occupied in their laboratories are usually too busy to make more than occasional ventures into the philosophy of science. This they defer to their later, more reflective years. They are too immersed in basic problems, finding solutions, testing hunches, amassing the materials out of which theories can be built or extended. While the logic of science asserts that we need to frame an exact intellectual system in order to ask the proper questions and make scientific progress most economically, research biochemists, geneticists, embryologists, and physiologists have been making considerable progress in the absence of such a system. The chemistry of viruses and genes, the process of photosynthesis, and the composition and action of hormones are today much better understood than they were ten years ago. One physicist calls frankly for a pluralistic approach in science with continued use of naturalistic and descriptive methods for "sorting out an immensely vast experience" (15).

Certainly, the empirical approach in science is still vigorous. Selye (17) points out that while one's basic facts must be correct, theories need not be; they are useful principally in helping us to discover new facts. Indeed, theories often are proved to be wrong. It has been frequently remarked that an accurate, scientific observation has a much longer useful life than most theories. This gives a certain primacy to the empirical investigation. Dobzhansky (7) described such a position to the American Society of Naturalists in these words:

"The best view of a mountain range is usually obtained from a distance; at close quarters minor peaks, and even hills obstruct the vista of the whole range. To understand man and his universe is the goal of the scientific movement; this goal must always be kept in view, in order that we do not mistake means for the end. Well authenticated facts are the life blood of science, and gathering them will always remain the principal function of scientific research. But science is more than a mass of facts; it is a meaningful system of significant facts. Facts taken out of their context, showy methods to solve meaningless problems, and learned terminologies for conceptual trivialities are often amusing to play with, but they stultify the work of a scientist. Integration of the results obtained by individual scientists and by various disciplines is therefore an important function which should be performed. The stones should be fitted to form an intelligible mosaic. The general view of the world unfolded by science should be kept before our eyes in order that scientific work be directed purposefully and effectively. Now, experience has shown that, at least in biology, generalization and integration can best be made by scientists who are also fact-gatherers, rather than by specialists in biological speculation."

If a unity of science is to be achieved, embraced in one general theory or system, the facts of biological development — of the living system organizing its structure and behavior over the time toward greater complexity, and maintaining a unity or "wholeness" with some stability — must ultimately be accounted for. Ultimately the problems of semantics and logic must be solved. And once the principles have been developed to explain the organizing processes in structure and behavior in living systems generally, perhaps we shall be able to account scientifically by the same system for the organizing processes in individual and group behavior which is mediated symbolically.

But this is, apparently, a considerable reach into the future. A pluralistic rather than a unified approach still seems necessary if not desirable. The data gatherers working in a variety of fields and with many phenomena, even in the absence of a common theoretical design, are pushing the boundaries of their knowledge toward one another.

It was in the spirit of Dobzhansky's words quoted above that the present volume was planned. The contributors, eminent scientific investigators, were asked to consider the concept of development defined broadly to include the following elements: (a) a process of organization of elements or parts into a larger functional unit or "whole," and (b) a process which occurs over an extension of time rather than in a short interval. They were invited to state the concept in their own terms and to assess its usefulness to their fields as they saw it; they were not admonished either to reduce their terms or to generalize them to more broad and inclusive principles. Thus, there was no plan here to demonstrate the unity of science on a physicalist basis, nor to expound general system theory, though it was thought desirable to have a contribution from a keen and critical philosopher of science to keep the group from too irresponsible excursions. Nor was there any intention to encourage extension of the concept from biological to supra-individual levels into a mystical frame of reference, to find in it a solution to the riddle of the universe. Nevertheless, the papers do illustrate many of the controversial problems outlined in this introduction. No solutions to these problems were intended, and no solutions were found. The papers are offered as evidence that concepts of development variously conceived are fruitful in research work in many fields, and of great value in the study of human behavior.

The concept of development usually has reference to ontogeny. Representatives of disciplines which deal with individual organisms were asked to present their understanding of the term and to assess its usefulness in their several fields.

In the field of psychology the developmental point of view has been commanding increased attention with the publication of several recent works (2, 11, 14). As clinical practice has grown within psychology, the importance of early growth has impressed itself upon those working with disturbed individuals, and those concerned with theories of personality organization. Several different fields of psychology were, therefore, asked to present their use of developmental concepts.

Because the concept of development is sometimes used in reference to products of the human mind, representatives from history and literature were asked to examine their use of the idea. Practical applications of ideas of growth and development in several applied professional fields dealing with human behavior rounded out the discussion.

When one views the spectrum of disciplines represented in this volume, he can scarcely escape the convenient doctrine of levels; the concepts of development considered in these papers are perhaps best viewed from a perspective which notes both the treads and the risers in the grand staircase of "levels of organization."

Among the contributors to this volume, Nagel affirms a unity of science in which reduction of concepts brings about one system of theorems to explain the observable phenomena of nature. Schneirla, while sympathetic to this position, cannot escape the discontinuities, in structure and behavior, in the various phyla and species he has observed. He, with Hamburger, Scott, and Werner, affirms a "levels of organization" position more or less explicitly. Although in presenting a Freudian theory of personality development Lippman does not openly acknowledge the "levels" solution to the problem of apparent phenomenal discontinuity, this resolution is apparent in his treatment of the normal versus the neurotic, and the phases of ego development.

Meredith, who discusses physical growth of children, takes a frankly empiristic and descriptive position, but Sears, who considers behavior of children, affirms a theoretical position to some extent based on observed phenomena, but also requiring many constructs removed at some distance from the world of phenomena. Sears is basically sympathetic to the unity-in-continuity position. The position closest to the unity-in-discontinuity view of the organismic biologist is that of John E. Anderson, though Schneirla and Scott most certainly use such formulations also. Hamburger is sympathetic to this position but comes into direct conflict with Schneirla and with Scott concerning the significance of exercise in the organization and elaboration both of structural and behavioral patterns. In discussing psychological phenomena of perception, Werner likewise follows the organismic position of biology. Experimental psychology, represented by Russell, speaks from the hypothetico-deductive position of behavior theory. However, Russell reconciles developmental to experimental psychology by contrasting their observational methods, and by recognizing certain fundamental differences in concern or outlook, which he finds differing more in degree than in kind.

In contrast with the effort to define phenomena of development in more elementary units and ultimately in physical terms, Heaton, Spencer, and DeWitt consider extensions of the concepts to larger units and to more inclusive meanings. But Heaton and DeWitt, in particular, do so with great caution and no little skepticism concerning the validity of such extensions.

Those concerned with the practical management of people use the concept of development in quite a different way. An "explantion" (description) in the language of phenomena is generally sufficient. Kidneigh's approach to the repair and facilitation of human relationships in the practice of social work is boldly eclectic. Some general notion of a growth process suffices, and parts of this notion are freely borrowed from various schools of behavior theory. Medicine's spokesman, John A. Anderson, takes linear and ponderal physical growth as his working model and uses it heuristically to demonstrate the variable nature of individual differences and the limited predictability of growth and developmental trends which are nonetheless sufficiently conclusive to help people grasp the general principles of physical and mental health. Education, as represented by Olson, is struggling to fit the observables of classroom learning into a "theory" which is just beginning to incorporate explanatory principles. This is yet a long distance from a theory which would satisfy Nagel.

Such is the scope of the papers which follow. In the attention currently being given the behavior sciences, a concept of development seems necessary to order the complex processes of organization, adaptation, and learning which are the focus of these sciences. Rather than attesting to theoretical confusion, the varied substance of the papers represents the efforts of scholars working in a pluralistic system, with the hope of attaining a unified system ultimately. They attest the belief that a multiple attack on a complex problem will be fruitful, and that empirically based concepts may have scientific as well as heuristic value. Each paper is a scholarly statement in its own right. Taken together they give full play to Proteus. And the sea, we recall, is the purported original home of the stuff which gives rise to all this concern with the Concept of Development!

REFERENCES

1. Arber, Agnes. *The Mind and the Eye.* Cambridge: Cambridge University Press, 1954.
2. Baldwin, A. L. *Behavior Development in Childhood.* New York: Dryden Press, 1955.
3. Bertalanffy, L. "Problems of General Systems Theory," *Human Biology,* Vol. 23 (1951), pp. 302–12.
4. ———. *Problems of Life.* London: Watts, 1952.
5. ———. "The Theory of Open Systems in Physics and Biology," *Science,* Vol. 111 (1950), pp. 23–29.
6. Bohr, N. "Light and Life," *Nature,* Vol. 131 (1933), pp. 421–23, 457–59.
7. Dobzhansky, T. "Mendelian Populations and their Evolution," in L. D. Dunn, ed., *Genetics in the Twentieth Century,* pp. 573–89. New York: Macmillan, 1951.
8. Feigl, H. "Functionalism, Psychological Theory, and the Sciences: Some Discussion Remarks," *Psychol. Rev.,* Vol. 62 (1955), pp. 232–35.

9. ———. "Principles and Problems of Theory Construction in Psychology," in Wayne Dennis, ed., *Current Trends in Psychological Theory*, pp. 179–213. Pittsburgh: University of Pittsburgh Press, 1951.

10. Haldane, J. B. S. "Interaction of Physics, Chemistry, and Biology," in R. W. Sellars, ed., *Philosophy for the Future*, pp. 202–21. New York: Macmillan, 1949.

11. Jersild, A. T. *Child Psychology*, 4th ed. New York: Prentice-Hall, 1954.

12. Koestler, A. *The Yogi and the Commissar*. New York: Macmillan, 1945.

13. Miller, J. G. "Toward a General Theory for the Behavioral Sciences," *Amer. Psychologist*, Vol. 10 (1955), pp. 513–31.

14. Munn, N. L. *The Evolution and Growth of Human Behavior*. Boston: Houghton, 1955.

15. Oppenheimer, R. "Analogy in Science," *Amer. Psychologist*, Vol. 11 (1956), pp. 127–35.

16. Schroedinger, E. *What is Life?* New York: Macmillan, 1945.

17. Selye, H. "Stress and Disease," *Science*, Vol. 122 (1955), pp. 625–31.

18. Sinnott, E. W. *Cell and Psyche*. Chapel Hill: University of North Carolina Press, 1950.

19. Sommerhoff, G. *Analytical Biology*. New York: Oxford University Press, 1950.

Ernest Nagel

DETERMINISM AND DEVELOPMENT

THE word *development* is notoriously one with protean meanings. It is sometimes used to connote a process, sometimes the product of a process. It is frequently employed as a purely descriptive term to characterize several types of change; but it also functions in many contexts as a eulogistic label. An analogous though perhaps less disturbing plurality of connotations is associated also with the word *determinism*. Prefatory to discussing the ostensible theme of this paper, something must be said to identify, if only in a loose way, the senses in which these words are to be understood in the sequel.

Even if, as in the present paper, the term *development* is used to signify a temporal process rather than its product, a number of its more specialized meanings, or components in its meaning require to be distinguished. In many of its current uses the word carries the suggestion that developmental processes make progressively manifest something latent or hidden, a suggestion that is reinforced if we recall the original meaning of the word as connoting an unfolding or unwrapping. We still speak of the development of heat in a wire, of the development of a photographic plate, of the development of a fertilized egg, or of the development of a human personality, understanding in each case a sequence of continuous changes eventuating in some outcome, however vaguely specified, which is somehow potentially present in the earlier stages of the process.

It is not difficult to appreciate why so many writers both past and present, who have perhaps been influenced by the etymology of the word, have been unable to conceive of genuine alternatives to preformationist theories of development, and why they have therefore rejected epigenesis as "incomprehensible." But in addition to this backward reference, the designation of a process as developmental also has a prospective one, as the above examples of usage indicate. No change per se is commonly counted as a developmental one, though it may be so labeled if it is referred to an explicitly or tacitly assumed consequence of the change. The word thus possesses a strong teleological flavor. The teleology intended does not, of course, assume the operation of purposes or final causes; the imputation signifies only that a sequence of change is designated as developmental only if it contributes to the generation of some more or less specifically characterized system of things or property of things.

But a still further component in the notion of development needs explicit mention. There are contexts in which the word is applied to systems undergoing cyclic or repetitive alterations — as when the periodic return of the seasons, or the rhythmic motion of the heart, is counted as a case of development. On the other hand, many students often decline to apply the term to merely repetitive changes. For example, the descent of the weight in a pendulum clock is frequently not regarded as a genuine developmental process, though the slow wearing away of the cogs which eventually results in the irremediable stoppage of the mechanism may be so classified. In this usage, changes must be cumulative and irreversible if they are to be labeled *development*. Moreover, in a somewhat narrower sense, the term is reserved for changes which are not merely irreversible, or which yield only a greater numerical complexity; those changes must in addition eventuate in modes of organization not previously manifested in the history of the developing system, such that the system acquires an increased capacity for self-regulation, a larger measure of relative independence from environmental fluctuations. This is, at any rate, what embryologists and evolutionists have in mind when they take progressive differentiation and self-maintaining organization as the essential marks of development. (For reasons of space, the use of the word to denote "retrogressive" as well as "progressive" changes will be ignored.) In discussions of moral growth the word is employed in what is perhaps only an analogous sense. But here, too, an individual is commonly said to be developing only if he is progressively exhibiting greater sensitivity and coordinated response to various cultural stimuli, and if his responses and attitudes fall into a stable pattern that is adapted to the vicissitudes of external fortune.

The connotation of *development* thus involves two essential components: the notion of a system possessing a definite structure and a definite set of pre-existing capacities; and the notion of a sequential set of changes in the system, yielding relatively permanent but novel increments not only in its structure but in its modes of operation as well.

Although this account is patently imprecise, it must suffice for my purposes; and I must be even briefer in explicating the meaning of *determinism*. In the loosest relevant sense of this word, it is a label for the claim that all things, events, processes, and traits come into existence, endure, or pass out of it, only under fixed and definite conditions. This claim can be stated more precisely as follows: Let S be any system of things occurring in an environment E; and suppose that at an arbitrary time, S is in a certain "state" A (i.e., the components of S, their organization, and the specific traits of S at that time are described by A). One part of the deterministic assumption then maintains that if at a later time S should be in state B, the change from A to B is a consequence of some alteration either in S, or in E, or in both. Moreover, let S_1 and S_2 be two systems occurring in environments E_1 and E_2 respectively; and suppose that S_1 changes from state A_1 to state B_1, while S_2 alters from state A_2 to state B_2. Then determinism also maintains that if B_1 and B_2 differ in some respects, this difference is the consequence of some difference either in the intrinsic composition of the two systems, or in the environments of the systems, or in the initial states of the systems, or in the changes initiating the transitions from the initial states, or in all of these together. If determinism is assumed, alterations in a system which do not appear to occur as the consequence of the presence or operation of antecedent factors or conditions, must be regarded as belonging to a more inclusive system which is deterministic. On the other hand, since we are admittedly ignorant of the conditions upon which many occurrences are contingent, determinism in effect functions as a maxim that formulates the formal objective of empirical inquiry. Moreover, since in its general formulation the deterministic assumption does not specify upon which definite conditions a given type of occurrence is contingent, the content of this assumption is meager and cannot be unambiguously controverted by factual inquiry. Despite these difficulties, I wish nevertheless, to discuss the import for determinism of two areas of inquiry in which developmental notions play important roles, one of the areas being biology and the other human personality.

On the surface at any rate, there seems to be no incompatibility between the findings of developmental studies and determinism broadly construed. For on the one hand, determinism merely expresses in general form that component in the meaning of *development* which connects the outcome of developmental process with antecedent structure and latent capacity. On the other hand, determinism does not deny that many systems manifest in their development novel traits and new levels of organization. For the deterministic formula is silent on the question whether traits exhibited at later stages of development are novel or not, nor does it prescribe the kind of materials and changes which must concur as the condition for the appearance of diversified structure and function.

Nevertheless, a closer look does reveal sources for the equivocal attitude of many students of biology toward determinism. For according to determinism, if in the parallel development of two organisms existing in identical environments, one exhibits traits which the other does not, the difference must be accounted for in terms of differences in the constitution of the two organisms, or in their initial states. As Driesch put it, determinism assumes that "no states and no events in nature are without a sufficient reason for their being such as they are at such a place and time," so that determinism implies the "univocal determination of being and becoming." To cite but one familiar example, however, it has apparently been established that despite an initial homogeneity, or equality, in the intrinsic composition of certain embryonic parts, those parts are eventually transformed into inhomogeneous, or unequal, parts of the adult organism. Such findings are often felt to raise difficulties for the deterministic assumption.

I am not qualified to discuss the factual issues raised by these embryological experiments. I do want to consider, however, the three main lines of the effort which has been made to save determinism in the face of such apparently fatal experimental findings. One of them is *vitalism*, according to which differences in development from allegedly identical antecedents must be explained in terms of the operation of non-spatio-temporal determinants or entelechies. But vitalism has not proved to be a fruitful notion, and it no longer seems to present a live issue in the philosophy of biology. A second defense of determinism is based on the hypothesis that the apparent equality of organic parts which develop differently, is really only apparent, and that a fuller study will eventually reveal subtle but still obscure physicochemical differences between them. This is the standpoint of what is commonly known as *mechanism* in biology, a standpoint that has been rejected not only by vitalism but also more recently by so-called *organismic* biologists. According to the organismic approach, which is the third way mentioned of saving determinism, the mechanistic conception rests on a "machine theory" of living organisms, and subscribes to an *additive* notion of organic structure. Mechanism is therefore said to be in principle incapable of explaining vital phenomena in their totality, since the additive point of view cannot do justice to the hierarchically organized structure of living organisms, and cannot account for the distinctive traits which are manifested on each level of the hierarchy, or for the integrated, self-maintaining character of the whole organism. In substance, therefore, the organismic standpoint is a variant of the doctrine of emergent evolution, for like the latter it maintains that traits exhibited by a hierarchically organized system cannot be reduced to, or explained by, the properties of parts of the system whose mode of organization occurs on a lower rung of the hierarchy.

I cannot here discuss in detail the mechanist and organismic standpoints; I can offer only a few brief remarks toward evaluating their respective claims, and I hope to show that both positions overlook important points in the logic of explanation. Let me begin by noting that systems can undoubtedly be distinguished from one another according to the degree in which they possess a self-maintaining or self-regulative character. This distinction can be made in an objective way, without introducing assumptions about purposive agents or self-realizing ends in view. Indeed, the distinction is entirely neutral to the difference between the living and the inanimate. Even systems whose detailed modes of operation can be completely understood in terms of the principles of classical mechanics may be self-regulative with respect to certain of their manifest traits. It is, therefore, clearly a mistake to claim that mechanistic explanations of living organisms are in principle impossible, merely on the ground that such systems are adaptive and self-maintaining.

In the second place, the question whether a given trait of a system, which it manifests as the outcome of a developmental process, is "novel" or "emergent," requires to be so formulated that the attribution of novelty is relative to some specific explanatory theory. Let S be some given system which is being studied with respect to a certain set of its "global" properties P_1 . . . P_n; and suppose a number of laws or regularities L_1 . . . L_k have been established between some if not all of these properties. Suppose, moreover, that a comprehensive theory T has been devised which analyzes S into a set of parts X_1 . . . X_y, and which is formulated entirely in terms of traits Q_1 . . . X_j, characterizing those parts. Assume, finally that the theory stipulates certain relations between P's and Q's, so that when appropriate boundary and initial conditions are supplied, the occurrence of a number of the P's can be predicted and a number of the laws L can be deduced. Two main cases can now be distinguished; all the laws can be deduced; the occurrence of all the P's can be predicted; or this can be done only for some of the L's and P's. In the first case, the system S with respect to the properties P and laws L is deterministic relative to the theory T; in the second case, S is only partly deterministic, and those of its properties and regularities which cannot be predicted on the basis of T, are emergent properties and regularities *relative* to T. Nevertheless, a different theory T' might be found, which is formulated in terms of an alternative set of parts of S and their traits, such that relative to T' the system S is deterministic in respect to its properties P and laws L. In short, whether a system is deterministic in respect to a given set of its features is a question that requires to be put relative to some specific set of theoretical assumptions.

In the third place, the question whether a system S is an additive one or not must be made relative in a similar manner. Continuing the above notation, suppose that a theory T can explain the occurrence of the properties Q of the parts X of S, when these parts occur in a certain set of relations R, but that it cannot do this when those parts stand to each other in some other set of relations, and in particular when they stand to each other in just those relations that constitute the organization of S itself. In this event, S is not deterministic with respect to the theory T, and it can be said to possess various "holistic" traits which are not reducible to the traits of its parts. On the other hand, some other theory T' may be invented, which is formulated on the basis of an alternative analysis of S into parts X' and their properties Q', such that T' does make it possible to predict the occurrence of the global properties P of S when the parts X' stand to each other in just those relations which constitute the structure of S itself. Accordingly, S can then be said to be an additive system relative to T', though not relative to T, so that whether or not the system is an additive or organic one depends on which theory is being assumed.

The possibilities just outlined are not introduced simply as a formal exercise. They represent schematically what I believe are actual situations in the history of science. For example, relative to Dalton's atomic theory, many of the properties of chemical compounds are emergents, and with respect to these properties chemical compounds are organic or nonadditive systems relative to that theory. But relative to current quantum theory, a number of those properties which are emergents for Dalton's theory no longer are emergents; and with respect to these properties chemical compounds are additive systems relative to quantum mechanics, though not additive relative to the older theory.

Let me now state briefly what I think is the outcome of this discussion. The main conclusion is that determinism is compatible with the known facts of experimental biology, not only if determinism is stated in its most general form, but also if it is made more specific by construing it to postulate physicochemical determinants for all occurrences. It is, of course, quite evident that if a mechanistic theory in biology does not include in its vocabulary, either as a basic or as in some sense a "defined" term, an expression which describes a distinctive outcome of a developmental process, that theory cannot possibly predict or explain the manifestation of such a feature; and if that feature is a novel one in the history of the developing organism, the theory cannot account for this novelty. All this is just a logical truism. But none of this can be taken to imply that an alternative theory could not possibly be devised, which would be mechanistic by common consent, such that it would contain the previously missing term in its vocabulary and so be in the logical position to account systematically for the novel property. Transformations of this sort which mechanistic theories have undergone in the history of science provide sufficient evidence to the contrary. On the other hand, there is no a priori proof that a mechanistic theory (or for that matter, a theory of a different type) can always be found which will explain the occurrence of what is assumed to be novel; nor is there plausible ground for the supposition that some day men will construct a complete and final theory which will account for every trait that may ever be manifested. The chief point upon which I am insisting is that the notion of novelty, as it enters into the meaning of *development*, needs to be explicated relative to a specific theory, and that there are no substantial grounds for the thesis that deterministic theories of the mechanistic type are in principle incapable of dealing adequately with developmental processes. Nevertheless, the question whether a mechanistic theory of biological development can in fact be constructed, and the question whether the cause of knowledge is advanced by current proposals of such theories, are issues whose answers depend partly on the character of biological subject matter, partly on the ingenuity of men, and partly on the strategy of research at a given stage of inquiry.

The influence of the belief in a universal determinism upon conceptions of human personality has been of acute concern to students of ethics and morals, and I would like in conclusion to touch briefly upon one of the issues that have been raised. There is today an extensive literature whose main burden is that as a consequence of the current extensions of causal analyses to human behavior, and especially as the result of seeking physiological and social determinants for individual actions, the possibility of autonomous personal development is being challenged, and the sense of personal responsibility is being gradually undermined. As one recent writer has put it, methods are being employed in studying men which are at best adequate for understanding the nature of machines and rats; and since in consequence men are being viewed simply as the products of the conditions to which they have been exposed, it has become fashionable to hold no individual responsible for anything that he does because the locus of responsibility has been shifted to the conditions which allegedly have made men what they are. And as another commentator has claimed, from the determinist view the notion of human responsibility as commonly understood is inapplicable to actual individuals. Eloquent pleas have therefore been made to cease viewing men as nothing but machines subject to deterministic laws, and to recognize that men are capable both of making choices which are not completely determined and of undergoing a free autonomous development.

It must be admitted that it is easy to find in current social and psychological discussions much that supports the fears which such complaints illustrate; and it is not my intention to support the amoralism professed by many contemporary students of the human scene. Nonetheless, it is far from clear that commitment to any form of determinism is incompatible with the facts of moral life or with imputations of individual responsibility. If it is the case that men engage in deliberation and make choices only under determinate conditons — whether these conditions be physical, physiological, psychological, or social — the discovery that this is so, and the identification of those conditions, do not, on pain of a radical incoherence in our thought, eliminate from existence those very features of human behavior which the discovered conditions for their occurrence ostensibly maintain. Should we succeed, for example, in ascertaining some day the particular collocations of physical particles and their modes of interaction, upon which the occurrence of self-consciousness and acts of deliberation are contingent, we should not thereby have explained away those traits of human life that initiated the inquiry into their physical conditions. The assumption or the discovery that our acts and choices are determined in some fashion does not mean that we are being coerced when we are engaged in deliberation and decision, nor does it mean that acts of deliberation and choice are irrelevant to what we may overtly do. But the mere absence of feelings of coercion does not by itself warrant the conclusion that there are no determinants, whether physical or otherwise, for what we are and what we do. In short, the assumption that responsible choice and action are manifested as products of developmental processes which have conditions for their existence, does not convert the moral life of man into a sham and illusion.

Nor does the deterministic assumption in any of its general or specialized forms necessarily place limits upon legitimate human aspirations or undermine the grounds for imputations of personal responsibility. On the contrary, the discovery of the conditions under which various distinctive human traits occur may itself become the means for releasing or redirecting human energies. This does not deny that a specific causal hypothesis — for example, one which locates the determinants of human action exclusively within the epidermis — may be inadequate. But it is well to bear in mind that even in purely physical inquiry a theory can account for the actual operations of a system only if it is supplied with the requisite initial and boundary conditions, which may be variable for different systems; and two systems whose operations are intelligible in terms of the same general principles may nevertheless behave differently if their special structures and the special circumstances of their operation are different. In any event, as the practical problems of education and the administration of justice clearly indicate, an intelligent imputation of responsibility involves the question of where the factors are located that are simultaneously controll*ing* in human action, and also controll*able* by human intervention. We may be right or we may be mistaken in supposing that these factors are of one sort rather than another; but the question cannot be settled without detailed inquiry or by invoking the alleged autonomy of human choice. There undoubtedly are commentators on the human scene who are distressed by the suggestion that we must engage in empirical inquiry in order to establish the limits of individual responsibility, just as there are temperaments that are revolted by the idea of botanizing on one's parent's grave. But if our objective is really to know and find things out, the patent facts of moral experience present an invitation for discovering the conditions, whatever these may be, under which growth of human personality is possible, and under which the scope of moral choice may be enlarged.

John E. Anderson

DYNAMICS OF DEVELOPMENT: SYSTEM IN PROCESS

ALL of us are interested in development, in what happens to living beings and to social systems as they move forward in time. But we are only incidentally occupied with the transactions of the moment; we are much more concerned with long-time trends; with structuring, organization, system formation, whether we see it in species, in individuals, or in groups. Perhaps we can find a common language in the principles which underlie development.

For my part, as a student of human development, I have tried to break down the concept of development into dimensions which frame mutually exclusive principles, and then to explore each briefly. My former students will recognize a number of familiar principles, some of which appear here in the sections on Openness, Growth, and Selection. Let us then consider the age-bound behavior of the person as it takes on form or shape.

What manner of thing is the person whom we study from birth on to maturity? Even the most superficial observation reveals a very complex system moving forward in time by growing in complexity and size. This system receives much stimulation from the outside world and reacts to that stimulation in many and varied ways. As it grows, it contacts a wider and wider range of objects and persons; its ability to solve problems increases; it builds up many habits and skills; it gains in knowledge and self-control. It is a complex manifold of many characteristics and potentials which together make up the total shape or form we call a human being.

How shall we characterize this manifold and break it up into parts? Some idea of the complexity of our task can be gained from the recent work of Barker and Wright (6) who have recorded the experiences of children from early morning until late at night. If you have any illusions that the developing system is simple, prepare to lose them. Barker and Wright in a midwestern town of 700 people find 2,030 different behavior settings to which children are called to react. Within these behavior settings there are some 1,200,000 behavior objects to which children build specific reactions. In this quiet community the flow of life is so great that the three children who were followed for 14.5, 13.6, and 13.0 hours at the ages of 8.7, 7.4, and 7.4 years respectively, reacted to a new behavior object every 1.5, 1.2, and 1.0 minutes. And in the course of a single day they reacted to 571, 671, and 749 behavior objects, making 1,882, 2,282, and 2,490 different reactions, respectively. Long before these studies, research on language had shown the four-year-old child uttering a total of 10,000 words a day. Studies of social interactions gave similarly large figures per day, while estimates of the number of distinct visual images formed on the retina ranged from a low of 250,000 to a high of 500,000 for the waking portion of the day. We have then an amazing system in terms of its intake and its power for converting the flow of intake into behavior. It becomes quite obvious that very simple explanations in terms of single stimuli and single response patterns cannot give us a picture of this enormously facile being. Perhaps we need a concept like entropy.

In the past we have taken cross-section slices of the activities of the growing person at successive ages. More recently we have followed children over long periods in longitudinal studies, in order to picture the various aspects of growth. We have also placed children in specific situations and studied their reactions to controlled stimulation. From these studies we have come to understand much about perception and learning. Sometimes we have selected a particular characteristic which manifests itself in various ways, such as love, anger, or anxiety, and generalized it into a construct which makes possible explanations of what are on the surface very diverse types of behavior. By studying the resemblances between parents and children we have also been able to reach conclusions about the interrelations of heredity and environment for many behavior areas. We have also learned much about building a good environment for children in community, home, and school.

In breaking into this manifold, scientists have put forth a wealth of theories for the various phases of the process: genetic, cognitive, behavior, psychoanalytic, and social learning theories. We have cut across the developing organism in many ways, and we have sliced it vertically in many ways. But what of the whole, and particularly what of the whole as it moves through long segments of time? This is essentially the domain of developmental theory which asks whether or not we can abstract from the manifold, as it is transformed in time, general principles that will aid our understanding. Because these principles are encumbered by a wealth of concrete observation and fact, it is sometimes desirable to construct a theoretical model in order to obtain a generalized picture by separating the principles from their supporting data.

Models, whether laid out verbally, diagrammed visually, or constructed out of metal and wood, force the scientist toward a very clear and definite picture of the interrelations involved in whatever process is symbolized. Next they bring out new research problems or programs, and permit generalization by analogy from one type of system to another. A unifying concept which runs through studies of biological and social phenomena is that of system which changes with time. Immediately we think of mechanical systems or machines which are so fabricated that certain functions are accomplished. We may ask then, What is a machine, an organization, a structure, and how does it come to have its present shape or form?

In the models of the types of machines which are everywhere about us, form is imposed from without by a designer, engineer, or fabricator; in the living machine, design evolves within limits from the materials and relations within the organism and their interaction with the environment. Limits are imposed by the number and variety of the genes and chromosomes, the mechanical structure of the organism, and the environment, which is restricted in comparison with all possible environments.

The model of the growing person is one of an ongoing manifold passing through time with a multidimensional head, much as a tunnel-making machine moves under the river. When viewed from the front this head consists of many irregularly shaped components of various sizes with a complex series of interrelations. At the boundaries there are complex relations with the external world which involve a continuous intake and outgo at both the physiological and psychological levels. Through this interchange a dynamic or ongoing equilibrium is maintained. The system is however open-end, that is, always in imbalance. Over and above the maintenance level there is a progressive enlargement or growth with time which reaches a maximum in mature form. In the ongoing movement of the system successive levels of integration are achieved, and new properties emerge which must be studied and analyzed in and for themselves. The model has a self-propelling character and as it cumulates from its own experience, it progressively and irreversibly builds up energy from the free energy of the environment. This denies any possibility of explaining human behavior on the analogy of a physical or mechanical model which is limited to intake and outgo. In exploring this model, our concern is with its changing total shape as well as with the changing form of its parts. Analyses of these transformations in time are crucial.

Consideration of this model brings us immediately face to face with the inadequacy of the language by which we symbolize our findings. In considering the development of plants, Arber (5) points out that the one-dimensional ongoing stream of verbal language is inadequate. She suggests visual representation as preferable, and perhaps visual representation by a motion picture of growth collapsed in time, but points out the difficulties of such representation in terms of manipulability. D'Arcy Thompson (23) using Cartesian coordinates, devised a visual system which proved more effective for symbolizing species transformations than either verbal or mathematical symbols. Medawar (11) has successfully written the equations for the stretch of body form from fetal life to maturity from the frontal or two-dimensional aspect as portrayed in the celebrated Stratz figure, but states that the solution of the problem for the three-dimensional figure is beyond present mathematical equipment. In fact, those most expert in the use of mathematical methods for the analysis of growth question whether or not it will ever be possible to represent the variety of shapes and forms — the outcomes of growth — that arise from differences between species and within species, and from differences between individuals.

If the problems of symbolization are so great for structures with forms and shapes that can be measured with precision, how much greater must they be for psychological functions? At present our mathematical and statistical procedures can handle cross-sectional relations better than longitudinal ones, the relations of two-factors better than those of three, and those of three better than those of four, and so on. It would be interesting to analyze scientific problems in terms of the manner in which our analytic symbols force restrictions on the conceptualization of problems; for example, how much does the present vogue of hypothesis research force problems and analysis into the determination of two-variable relations?

Turning now from the difficulties of symbolization, we may delineate the general characteristics of the developing system. We can consider these under the general heads of openness, activation, growth, selection, learning, mechanization, cumulation, emergence, and symbolization. In my opinion these topics represent the major dimensions of the developmental process or, if not the dimensions, at least the framework within which discussions of development must be oriented. In a sense they define development. All are processes extended in time; all influence in some manner the shape or form of behavior. Despite the interaction which creates difficulties in discussing any one without bringing in the others, they seem to me to be distinct enough to constitute the parameters of evolving behavior form.

OPENNESS

The developing organism is an open system in which irreversible changes occur as a result of the relations within the system and the interactions with the environment. Contrasting with the open system is the closed system of the machine manufactured by man which likewise carries on an exchange with the environment, but which involves a fixed input and output and a series of relations which do not change except for deterioration. While machines can be built which will store information and operate over substantial periods of time in much the same way as a living system, nevertheless both the controlling and holding mechanism are laid out in minute detail in the original wiring plan. If there is to be any substantial change in the machine's operation, a new wiring diagram has to be evolved by someone outside the machine.

In an open system the control element is progressively modified in time, the wiring diagram changes itself, and the system has some capacity for self-correction or repair. Hence an outcome of momentary transactions is a modification which is carried forward in time. As a result, the changes in an open system are not reversible, a fundamental characteristic of an open system and of living as compared with mechanical systems. For example, a child who has once learned to talk can never be returned to the state of one who never has talked, as is shown in the studies that compare congenitally deaf children with those who acquire complete deafness at 18 months or two years or after even a small amount of language has been acquired.

ACTIVATION

As early as we know it, the developing organism is already an active system achieving a high level of interchange with the environment and within itself. This basic activation state is maintained by internal and external stimulation. Upon this level with its own patterns, there are superimposed the patterns initiated by the particular stimuli to which the organism reacts specifically.

The human system has been described in terms of two levels: first as a physicochemical machine which takes in food and converts it into action and waste products, and second as a sensory-neuromuscular mechanism which takes in stimulation and converts it into behavior by channeling the energy developed in the physicochemical system into specific responses. As Sherrington (21) in his concept of the final common path has shown, the muscular system is so organized that only one major activity can be conducted at a time, and that energy goes to specific points in space time.

One implication of this principle often made in the literature emphasizes the energy output of young organisms in various species and leads to the surplus energy theories of play which have been current for centuries. And a practical conclusion sometimes drawn is that rather than looking upon the energy of the child as harmful and therefore seeking to repress it, we should concern ourselves with the guidance and direction of this valuable possession.

Recent work by Hebb (13) indicates the existence of an arousal or activation level which is a function of the amount of stimulation rather than of its specific character. To this sum of stimulation, all forms of sensitivity contribute. Above this level there is the cue level, or the precise stimulation from specific items, objects, or elements within the range of "its" sensory equipment to which the organism builds specific reactions. If the activation level is lowered by a drastic reduction in stimulation, severe disturbances of the perception and action of the person soon appear. Evidence is also piling up from other fields that any marked reduction in activity level over a substantial period of time realigns the functions of the organism and may be more disturbing than the disorder which brought about the reduction. Immobility, prolonged rest, nonuse of parts or functions, bring their own particular type of deterioration. There is, then, a psychological tonus like the physiological tonus which must be maintained in order to keep organ systems ready for functioning. To use Hebb's analogy, the human mechanism is more like a steam engine with some steam always in its boilers than like an automobile engine which starts from a complete stop. Electroencephalograms show activity in the nervous system even when the person is at rest and indicate that specific stimulation sets up waves which are superimposed upon a going pattern.

From the standpoint both of practice and theory, then, a fundamental problem arises. Are we talking about a machine into which we pour a specific stimulation and out of which comes a specific response, or are we talking about an organization already moving under its own power, with its own patterns, upon which we are superimposing new patterns? The first point of view makes of the growing person a passive recipient of forces from the outer world. The second makes him an active agent with something to say about the imposition. Psychologists develop drive theories on the assumption that we have to explain activity as something which arises from without; whereas the second point of view recognizes activity as a property of a living system, and makes the explanation of inactivity or lack of drive the important problem.

At any moment in time much behavior consists of transactions within and without the organism which are concerned with the steady state and have little or no significance in terms of forward and backward reference. Thus we may set apart moment-by-moment transactions which do not modify the system. For example, we take in oxygen and expel it, take in food and convert it into energy, tissue, and waste. By analogy we can develop the same concept of behavior for social systems or for phylogenetic development and separate the inflow and output on a transactional level from the cumulative changes which affect later functioning. Some learning is also transactional in that it occurs in a relatively brief time and involves acts or products which are not carried forward. Hence there are quotation marks about "permanence" because of the difficulty of drawing a hard and fast line between a transactional and a cumulative process.

As time passes the living organism increases in size and in complexity in a manner that can be described accurately and in detail. Growth begins with the fertilized egg and continues until maturity or a terminal point is reached. Psychologists have devoted some attention to a hypothetical zero point at which behavior originates, but while some study fetal behavior, for most the study of behavior begins with an organism already far along the developmental course.

With growth the shape of the organism changes in such a way that it moves progressively away from its initial state and progressively nearer its final state. As a result the correlations between the primal shape of the organism or any part and the shape at any later period decrease with growth, and the correlations with the final shape increase (2). This holds for mental as well as physical functions.

With increase in physical size, significant changes take place in bodily structure and function. Since volume increases as the cube, surface as the square, and linear dimensions in the power of 1, changes are forced within the differentiated structures in order to make possible the carrying on of functions. For example, the cortex, which is a surface, must be folded to accommodate the number of neurons necessary for functioning in the complex system.

Some physical size relations clearly limit or modify function. Because of differences in the length of the arms and legs relative to the total body length, the adult cannot put his foot in his mouth as can the infant. This instance, however facetious, covers a wide territory, since back of it there lie quite substantial variations in motor patterns and adjustments with age.

For behavior it is difficult to separate increase in size from differentiation. Nevertheless, we describe the change in the range and level of activities as an enlargement of the life space. With age the organism reacts to more and varied stimuli; has available many more skills and more complex patterns of reactions; reacts to objects which are more remote in space and in time; and adjusts to situations and solves problems of greater altitude or complexity. Several years ago, Thorndike, in a study of the dimensions of intellect (24), found very high, almost perfect correlation between range, speed, and altitude, which point to the existence of a general underlying factor in mental growth that manifests itself in different ways. More recently an entropy theory of intelligence has appeared (12) that distinguishes between levels of intelligence, not so much by quality of performance as by the rate at which information moves through the nervous system. Theoretically, the higher the rate the more completely explored is the situation, and the greater is the likelihood of obtaining a good response. This suggests a developmental relation between size and function within broad limits.

SELECTION

With development, the growing person purchases efficiency at the cost of versatility. Facing time limitations and choice points, the organism loses the multipotentiality of the infant and gains the efficiency of the adult. Involved in this modification are whole series of processes which we divide among growth, learning, and cumulation.

Various observers have described the very young organism as fluid, polymorphous perverse, multipotential, and plastic; all are terms which indicate that subsequent development can go in any one of many directions. But once a choice is made and direction is set, cumulative and irreversible changes take place which determine the major aspects of subsequent form. These choice points are not points in the mathematical sense as they may be extended in time. Much more typical than the dramatic episode or trauma, which may be momentary, is oscillation for a week, a month, or a year before direction appears.

In his life the growing individual meets successively many choice points, at which decisions between alternatives are made. Modern computers are based upon a similar principle in reverse; complex problems are broken down into a series of binary choices for purposes of analysis. In ongoing behavior such choices are made in a forward sequence with complex form or behavior as the outcome. Needham (18) gives as an example of this phenomenon the switching yard which makes up railroad trains by means of electrically controlled switches. At each switch the car can go in either of two directions. From a line of incoming cars that are jumbled or randomized many trains may be put together, each of which will differ in make-up from every other. Viewed from the air these assembled trains on their tracks have a distinct shape which varies from day to day and which is produced by a relatively simple process of consecutive binary choices. The choice point may be illustrated in human terms by two fourteen-year-old boys who receive chemistry sets for Christmas and are equally interested for several weeks. One boy then tosses the set aside, whereas the other over the next eight years receives professional training, and devotes the remainder of his life to chemistry. Although he begins with an interest in chemistry, he soon chooses between chemical engineering and chemistry; then between inorganic and organic chemistry; and then, within organic chemistry, he makes further choices. Considering the developmental significance of these choices for the subsequent behavior of the person, we know astonishingly little about the mechanism involved.

3. Similarly the pattern of social relations may operate to determine the final forms of behavior in what is known as the vicious circle. A child is delinquent in a minor fashion; his escapade becomes known in his neighborhood; the neighbors expect him to be delinquent and take precautions against him. Over a period of time, a combination of personal and social expectancies is built up and culminates in a form of behavior which we call delinquency. Later, when society steps in, it usually attempts correction or punishment for a time, but then returns the person to the same environment in which the cumulative expectancies have created an atmosphere that makes good adjustment unlikely. Some students of social problems point out how difficult it is to undercut or eliminate the context of expectancies which determine the shape of such behavior. Similar expectancies and atmospheres operate at successive choice points to shape desirable behavior.

It should be noted that there are difficulties in predicting the outcome of choice points at the moment the choice is made. Retrospectively we can describe the factors involved in great detail and can develop a number of explanatory systems, as is well illustrated by the variety of theories advanced for the causes of particular wars by historians. But because experience is assimilated, and because successive choices bring greater involvement of the system, it is difficult, if not impossible, to make firm predictions at the moment of choice. This principle has sometimes been generalized into a distinction between significant and nonsignificant events. The significant event for the individual is the one which modifies the subsequent amount of energy or practice devoted to the activity, or which modifies the subsequent current of social relations and their feedback into the individual.

As the growing person meets choice points, his behavior becomes more structured and multipotentiality is lost. Supporting evidence comes from studies of children's interests, which have the widest range at eight years and progressively narrow until the age of twenty-two. But the study of particular interest patterns shows greater involvement on the part of the adolescent and young adult, and indicates a shift from breadth of interest to depth of concern. In this shift, the fact that the time available to the growing person is limited forces choice. The boy cannot practice the piano while he plays baseball, as many parents know. Since the person lives only so many hours a day and is a creature that can do only one thing at a time, selection becomes necessary and shape evolves. Moreover, the more complex and advanced the organism, the more limited becomes the time available for realizing potentialities.

This progressive specialization of function within the person parallels the specific roles that characterize our complex society, which is composed of a series of interlocking roles giving individuals specific functions upon which other persons depend. In a sense, the capacity of the person to structure his available energy makes possible this differentiation of roles. In turn, the specialized roles offer him the possibilities upon which subsequent behavior depends. As a result of specialization and role playing, the growing person becomes more sensitive to some aspects and less sensitive to other aspects of his environment. Choice comes to be made more and more in terms of the availability in the environment of materials and events which resemble the system already operating. From this principle, which has been called the principle of congruence, emerge the projective methods for evaluating personality structure which theoretically should operate better in the older and more differentiated person.

An important question arises for all the developmental phenomena. Why do they not continue indefinitely? If left to themselves the factors we describe would make for an indefinite progression. Among the various explanations for the stoppage of development the best for our purpose seems to be the principle that the limiting factors are not within growth itself, but comprise an inhibition of growth.

If the concept of inhibitors of growth is broken down we find, first of all, competition among growth processes within the person which limits each component. Since the person is a very complex collection of structures and functions within a single whole, one subsystem will limit or circumscribe another. A second type of inhibitor is external, and arises from relations with other persons and the demands made by them. A third inhibitor arises out of restrictions in opportunity, and constitutes what is now known as deprivation. The deprivation studies imply limitations which have effect over a very long period of time; in some degree they fail to recognize the capability of the organism for self-repair or readjustment when appropriate facilities are made available. A fourth and very important inhibitor already mentioned is that all psychological processes take time, and time is limited.

If we turn to learning we find so-called task limits — those inherent in the tools or machines operated by the person — and physiological limits — those intrinsic to the fact that the person moves toward but never quite reaches the highest possible performance of which he is capable in terms of his genetic make-up and bodily mechanism. For very complex verbal skills involving vocabulary and language acquirements, there are limits in terms of the sheer mass of material which is to be grasped or handled within a given time.

In the past the students of development have more frequently concerned themselves with the factors that produce behavior change rather than with those that limit or restrict the organism. But the study of the limits of behavior which is implied in such phrases as "growth potential" and "developmental potential" would seem to be very important.

LEARNING

By learning we mean the modification of behavior as the result of stimulation. It is a property of the living organism which is present to an extraordinary degree in the human being. Because it can be compressed or distributed in time at the will of the experimenter or teacher, learning can be regarded as time-free in the sense of organizational time. It is not my purpose to discuss the very powerful intellectual tools and theories which psychologists (10, 15) have developed for the analysis of learning, except to point out that these are concerned with the mechanisms rather than with the products or the content of learning. Developmental theory on the other hand studies the way in which the products or results of learning are incorporated into evolving systems of behavior, and how they function as constituents in subsequent development. For example, developmental theory is not concerned with how long it takes a child to learn to read or to learn to dance, but with whether or not he can read or dance and what reading and dancing do for him in his subsequent behavior. The experimenter in learning loses interest in the child as soon as he reaches one or ten perfect trials, i.e., some defined level of proficiency. Learning theory is therefore not the equivalent of developmental theory, but deals with different phenomena.

Learning may also be viewed as a disturbance of the steady state of the organism in line with what was said earlier about the activational level. In this sense, the organism seeks to recover from the disturbance of learning by forgetting and thus to return to balance. It follows for the developmentalist that questions about the phenomena that keep what is learned active and alive within the developing system are important. Hence he speaks of reinforcement, reiteration, and overlearning.

In the life situation as distinct from the laboratory situation, research shows that reinforcements run into the thousands and millions, that they are aperiodic rather than periodic, and that they are not clean-cut and separate phenomena but appear as parts of complex patterns.

A developmental phenomenon growing out of learning becomes important for us. First, in moving from birth to maturity, the person meets a succession of situations and problems for which he builds appropriate skills. The growing person learns to handle a spoon, to lace his shoes, to read, to write, to ride a bicycle, to shave, to dance. By the time he is an adult the number of response patterns, even in a very ordinary individual, is so great as to defy enumeration. In building these response patterns, regardless of their type, we find essentially the same basic learning mechanisms operate and that the person, despite the travail of learning, moves on to competence.

Recently investigators have obtained evidence that the early life of the child, with its tremendous impulses to curiosity and the manipulation of objects, is given over to the building of hundreds of thousands of simple response patterns to hundreds of thousands of behavior objects. For example, with the appearance of the eye-hand coordinations, perception of objects advances. The movements of the body, limbs, and head, which are made almost endlessly while crawling and creeping, become the basic coordinations upon which upright locomotion is based. The vocalizings of the infant become shaped and integrated into the symbols used in speech.

In the later periods of development the growing person combines these response patterns into larger units, and we pass from the period in which learning consists of establishing what Hebb (14) calls simple cell-assemblies to the building of complex from simple cell-assemblies. To some degree, success in meeting the involved problems of adolescence and adulthood is a function of the repertoire, or the number and variety of responses that have been established in infancy. With development the number of reaction potentials increases faster than the opportunities for using them. Thus a great file of simple and complex responses and response assemblies becomes available for meeting the demands of life.

These larger systems become in some degree independent of the units of which they are constructed. This process is similar to the equipotentiality of which the biologists speak. Because one unit can be substituted for another, the behavior of a complex assembly becomes in some degree independent of its parts, and in a sense exists in its own right. Such substitution is, however, limited by the fact that if too large a section of the whole becomes inoperative, the remainder ceases to function. For behavior integration and equipotentiality are enormously facilitated by transfer, and by the mediation mechanisms of the symbolic process.

MECHANIZATION

In development the growing person mechanizes or ritualizes much of his behavior. Achieving maturity is largely a matter of successively ritualizing one series of responses after another and incorporating them into the system of behavior. Mechanization and ritualization have counterparts in many biological and social systems. From this process there are several developmental results. First, less of the available time is needed for the particular response; second, energy is freed for responding to other aspects of the situation; third, higher-level integrations become possible, as units or subsystems already organized become available for incorporating into large systems. For example, the four-year-old lacing his shoes for the first time takes thirty minutes; a year later he takes one minute for the same operation, and has thereby gained twenty-nine minutes and a residue of energy for other response patterns. He also has added a pattern to his repertoire which can be elicited upon demand by the particular situation of shoes and laces and which has partial components such as tying a knot that can be transferred to other situations. Thus the way is cleared for complex patterns and the solution of more complex problems. As the person moves toward competence his affective involvement decreases, and the stability of expertness appears. Recent work on aging persons indicates the extent to which there is emotional disorganization upon retirement, when time-filling activities and routines are lost. As a new schedule of activities is worked out, the emotional difficulties of the older person are reduced or disappear.

Mechanization, or ritualization as it is sometimes called when social systems are discussed, has a very important function in stabilizing behavior. But the process has limitations. In a real sense these products of learning, like the constituents in biology, can be viewed as residuals or debris which ultimately will choke the system and cause infirmity and death. Out of this comes a very interesting and appropriate question for the study of development at all levels, namely, that of the optimal balance between stabilizing and adjusting processes. For behavior this is related to our earlier discussion of activation level, in which the question was raised of how stimulation and activity can preserve or maintain the adjusting capacity as long as possible.

CUMULATION

Some events moving into the developmental stream modify either the internal relations or the external relations of the system. A product appears which is then carried forward in the total system as a permanent change to affect all subsequent relations. Some products are stable, as in the case of a specific skill or bit of knowledge, and are accreted. In many functions cumulation continues in such a manner that it changes the shape of the total system. Whether the product is *stable* or the function is *cumulative* depends upon its effects on the developmental stream.

In the earlier section on choice points it was said that decisions or events which modify the stream of practice or which affect the relations of individuals with other persons may exercise an influence out of all proportion to their extent and thus determine whole areas of subsequent behavior. What begins as a minor phase of the total system comes to include more and more of the system. This process resembles the cone concept which is used by Woodger to describe the fact that within the embryo some physical and functional phenomena increase out of proportion to the total system. A similar phenomenon occurs in history. Consider the example so frequently given that contrasts the discovery of America by Leif Ericson with that by Columbus. In the former the feat was greater but without consequence, whereas in the latter the series of social and economic changes which followed made it one of the outstanding events of history.

A corollary of the principle of cumulation is that of the recession of the cause. Any system moving forward in time which has a holding or memory mechanism will retain some of the effects of past action. When cumulation is possible, the origins of present behavior go far back into the life history, and it becomes difficult if not impossible to explain present behavior in terms of present stimulation even with the best of assessments. Thus arises the necessity of both an historical approach to the developing person and an approach in terms of multiple factors or causes, calling to mind the classical distinction between precipitating events and an underlying complex of causal relations.

EMERGENCE

As the person moves forward in time, changes occur in the altitude of behavior because of the emergence of new properties and new relations. The enlargement of the life space proceeds by stages, each of which may involve a varying period of time for acquisition followed by a period varying in length during which the growing person adapts to his new found functions and properties. Thus there are sudden as well as gradual transformations of behavior with each change followed by a period of gradual adaptation.

In child development controversy has raged and still does as to whether development is a continuous process with small increments out of which higher levels of behavior gradually emerge, or whether there are distinct stages through which the organism must pass in order to move on to a new level of development. That the controversy is partly a matter of how data are obtained and interpreted may be

illustrated by the Shirley (22) studies of walking behavior. By supporting the baby under the armpits and recording stepping behavior, a
continuous and gradual curve which shows increasing strength and
better coordination is obtained. If, however, locomotion is viewed
from the standpoint of what the child is doing, a four-stage picture
emerges: (a) lying prone; (b) a crawling stage in which the abdomen is
on the supporting surface; (c) a creeping stage in which the abdomen
is lifted clear of the surface and pacing movements of the arms and the
legs occur; (d) a walking stage in which the upright position is assumed and forward motion on two feet occurs. While the appearance
of these stages spreads over several months, in terms of the whole life
cycle the transitions are completed within very short periods. Criteria
for describing these separate levels can be developed, and our popular
language clearly recognizes their existence. While some investigators
concern themselves only with the development of behavior itself, it is
clear that immediately following the transition and permanently thereafter, the orientation of the child to his environment is changed. A
child who walks and runs has different properties from one who crawls
or one who lies in his crib.

Comparable instances of other relatively quick transformations can
be given. Thus the transition from reflex grasping to thumb opposition
not only modifies all responses but all perceptions as well. The most
dramatic transition, and also the most difficult one to explain, is that
from vocalizing without meaning to the use of sounds as symbols, or
the appearance of language and speech. Although more questions are
raised about the existence of later stages, the evidence suggests that the
separation out of the qualities of objects or surrogates from the objects
in which they are embedded, which occurs roughly between five and
nine years, is a somewhat similar process, and that the reorganization
in the forward reference of thinking during puberty is a comparable
stage.

A fruitful way to attack the question of stages is to ask whether or
not properties have emerged which cannot be described in terms of
earlier behavior, irrespective of whether it takes a few days or a few
years for the transformation to take place. Furthermore, the transformation which we describe in terms of properties may originate either in
a process of maturation or a process of learning. Not only is the child
who talks very different from the one who doesn't, but the child who

reads in a world of reading material is very different from one that does not.

In any complex learning process it is clear that the expert performer not only can equal all that the inexperienced performer can do — he can also accomplish many things which are beyond the beginner's reach. While it is difficult to describe these properties of the growing organism which flow out of increasing complexity, the speech of the common man is full of descriptions of behavior that are felt to be relevant. From the very beginning in developmental psychology there have been many controversies over whether or not the child's behavior is best described in terms of his bodily movements, like the number of steps taken toward another child, or in more generalized descriptive terms, like aggression and cooperation, that pertain to his social orientation. When we say a person is angry we describe a total property of a system, even though we have some difficulty in defining the term precisely. All such terms, like all others in science, need to be examined with great care in order to determine their appropriateness and their limits. In general, we describe the properties of simple organizations or systems more readily than we do those of the complex ones.

It may well be that the human being differs markedly from the animal in his capacity to build up integrations of behavior that give new properties. Learning may function with respect to behavior much as do the organizers in embryonic development that establish the gradients out of which new structures function and properties evolve. A human being is then a combination of a built-in series of stages, which he has in common with his biological ancestry, and a process of learning by means of which new stages with new properties can be built up within a single lifetime. If the stimulation for learning is set by the culture in such a way that all growing individuals meet similar stimulation at the same ages, an orderly progression is produced which, from the developmental point of view, is superimposed upon the development that is in the person by virtue of his biology. The classical instance is the imposition of the first grade upon children at six years.

SYMBOLIZATION

In one fundamental respect the human system differs from other living systems as we know them. Through the symbolic process man is able to represent his experience in units which can be dissociated from their contexts and manipulated in and for themselves. Although symbols are often identified with their primary source in speech and language, they nevertheless exist in virtually every type of stimulation and response. It is the process of symbolization rather than the particular form taken that is important for our purpose.

Symbols not only function as the means of communication with other persons and thus make possible our social life, but they also act within the individual as triggers to set off responses, as tracking devices to control the direction of responses, as holding devices to store past experiences and incorporate them into the system, and as the manipulable carriers of meaning which make thought and problem solving possible. Within the person they function as reverberating mechanisms, and in social groups as feedback mechanisms. Through their storage and carrier functions they become the devices by means of which we anticipate the future, become aware of purposes and goals, and are able to free ourselves from the immediate demands of the present.

On the one hand, the symbolic system is a system in and for itself, set within the larger system of the person, but following its own rules and developing in its own way; on the other hand, it functions parallel to the other phases of the developmental process and in time becomes so pervasive that virtually every phase of stimulation and response becomes tied in with symbols in some fashion. In terms of properties, a comparison of a deaf and dumb child of ten years with a normal child of the same age would reveal even to the most casual observer such enormous differences that he would hesitate to place them in the same category. In their nature and extent the differences would be like but greater than those between a society with and one without a written language.

Symbols appear first between twelve and eighteen months, and are to be distinguished from the responses to signals which many animals make by the fact that the child, by deliberately using them as means for controlling others and himself, frees them from their attachments and comes to manipulate them in and for themselves. Thereafter symbolic development follows its own pattern by starting very slowly, then proceeding at a very rapid or accelerated rate. For many symbolic processes curves of progress are positively accelerated, which means the more you have the greater is your gain within the next period of time. Contrary to many other growth processes, some aspects of symbolization seem to be without limits. Symbolic processes also seem to be the behavior processes which are most resistant to the effects of aging.

When what has already been said in this paper is examined, it becomes clear that throughout I have assumed a human being with symbolic capacity. The symbolic system in itself is an open system with a high activation level; it increases in size and complexity, it is selective, it facilitates learning, it is subject to mechanization, it increases by accretion and cumulation, and new properties continually emerge. A word in particular should be said about its relation to learning, since it furnishes a ready method of advance which is a great gain over the slow and progressive simplification of behavior in the animal. By substituting symbols for overt action the rate at which information flows through the system is enormously increased, the rates of selection and of mechanization are increased, and the person is freed for attacking the more complex problems which could not be attacked in any other way.

Through symbols we are able to build up the systems of thought reflected in our sciences and philosophies, to establish the records which make our histories, to make the inventions and discoveries which transform our lives, to establish and operate the societies which make up our civilization. I am not interested in creating striking images; I am concerned with calling attention to the symbolic mechanism as a basic determiner of the shape or form of the human being wherever we find him.

SUMMARY

We may now bring together into a final brief picture the factors in the development of the growing person that seem to be generalized into principles of form or shape organization. We began by pointing out that we deal with an open system with a very high rate of interchange within the system and with the environment in which it exists. The processes which evolve out of this interchange are irreversible. When we first study it the system is already a going and active concern upon which events and stimulation are superimposed. This implies that the system is itself in some degree a determiner of its experience. With age this system grows in size and differentiates. Because of limitations of time and the fact that basically only one thing can be done at a time, the entire process of development is inherently selective, and movement is in general from versatility to efficiency. In succession choice points are encountered at which the decisions are made which determine the ensuing developmental process.

Through the basic mechanism of learning which follows a describable and similar course for a wide variety of behaviors, the system acquires patterns of skill and knowledge. In the early period with its curiosity and manipulation, tens of thousands of specific reactions to stimuli are established; later, and to some degree simultaneously, these are integrated and organized into larger units. Experience may be merely transactional. Or it may result in stable products which are incorporated into the system ready for functioning. Or it may result in cumulations which acquire significance for later development by affecting the extent of practice or the system of social relations. As the system moves along it passes through successive stages out of which come new properties and accomplishments to which subsequent periods of orientation are devoted. Pervading the whole and facilitating all the factors involved in development is the symbolic process by means of which the range of communication, control, and direction, as well as the emergence of new properties, is enormously increased.

It should now be clear that development is a multi-faced process of enormous complexity. To describe it and explain it we need the efforts and thought of many investigators in many disciplines. The person interested in developmental theory hopes that in our concern with the transactional aspect of the living system, we will not lose sight of the long-term changes which will add to our understanding of the life process.

REFERENCES

1. Anderson, John E. "Freedom and Constraint or Potentiality and Environment." *Psychol. Bull.*, Vol. 41 (1944), pp. 1–29.
2. ———. "The Limitations of Infant and Preschool Tests in the Measurement of Intelligence," *J. Psychol.*, Vol. 8 (1939), pp. 351–79.
3. ———. "Personality Organization in Children," *Amer. Psychologist*, Vol. 3 (1948), pp. 409–16.
4. ———. "Methods of Child Psychology," in L. Carmichael, ed., *Manual of Child Psychology*, 2nd ed., pp. 1–59. New York: Wiley, 1954.
5. Arber, Agnes. *The Mind and the Eye.* Cambridge: Cambridge University Press, 1954.
6. Barker, R. G., and H. F. Wright. *Midwest and its Children.* Evanston: Row, 1955.
7. Bertalanffy, L. *Modern Theories of Development.* London: Oxford University Press, 1933.
8. ———. *Problems of Life.* New York: Wiley, 1952.

9. Bonner, John T. *Morphogenesis: An Essay on Development.* Princeton: Princeton University Press, 1952.
10. Bush, R. R., and F. Mosteller. *Stochastic Models for Learning.* New York: Wiley, 1955.
11. Clark, W. E., and P. B. Medawar. *Essays on Growth and Form.* London: Oxford University Press, 1945.
12. Eysenck, H. J. *Uses and Abuses of Psychology.* London, Penguin, 1953.
13. Hebb, D. O. "Drives and the Central Nervous System," *Psychol. Rev.,* Vol. 62 (1955), pp. 243–54.
14. ———. *Organization of Behavior,* New York: Wiley, 1949.
15. Hull, Clark L. *A Behavior System.* New Haven: Yale University Press, 1952.
16. Krech, D., and G. S. Klein, eds. *Theoretical Models and Personality Theory.* Durham: Duke University Press, 1952.
17. Lillie, R. S. *General Biology and Philosophy of Organism.* Chicago: University of Chicago Press, 1945.
18. Needham, J. *Order and Life.* New Haven: Yale University Press, 1936.
19. Rashevsky, N. *Mathematical Biophysics.* Chicago: University of Chicago Press, 1948.
20. Redfield, R., ed. *Levels of Integration in Biological and Social Systems,* Biological Symposia, Vol. 8. Lancaster: Jacques Cattell Press, 1942.
21. Sherrington, C. *The Integrative Action of the Nervous System.* New Haven: Yale University Press, 1906.
22. Shirley, Mary M. *Postural and Locomotor Development,* Vol. I of *The First Two Years: A study of Twenty-five Babies.* Minneapolis: University of Minnesota Press, 1931.
23. Thompson, D'Arcy W. *On Growth and Form,* 2nd ed. Cambridge: Cambridge University Press, 1952.
24. Thorndike, E. L., *et al. The Measurement of Intelligence.* New York: Teachers College, Columbia University, 1926.
25. Woodger, J. H. *Biology and Language.* Cambridge: Cambridge University Press, 1952.

Biology and Growth

Viktor Hamburger

THE CONCEPT OF "DEVELOPMENT" IN BIOLOGY

T H E term *development* is used in so many fields, and it has so many connotations, that it is difficult to find a definition common to all. There seems to be a rather general agreement among the contributors to this symposium that the term, in the most general sense, denotes a more or less continuous *process* which usually involves *progressive changes* from a more simple to a more complex structure or organizational pattern. The increase of complexity is particularly obvious in biological development, but this aspect may not be significant in other fields.

Even in biology the term has different meanings because it is applied to a variety of different phenomena at different *levels of organization*, from collectives of individuals down to the cellular and subcellular level. The collective called "species", which is probably the largest natural unit, undergoes progressive changes that fit the definition; they are usually designated as *evolution*, or evolutionary development. We are at present on the way toward a clearer understanding of the mechanisms which operate to bring about the transformation of species. We think primarily in terms of mutations and other chromosomal changes, in combination with subtle and diversified procedures of selection. In this respect, we are on somewhat safer grounds than the historian; the collectives which he deals with differ from the biological collectives in more than just the degree of complexity of social structure or of interaction with environment. The historian has to cope with a new dimension, namely, human motivation expressed in social interaction and based on value systems. These aspects do not complicate evolution on the biological level. However, the student of biological evolution

49

is also harassed by many unpredictable elements which enter into the picture; for instance, it would be impossible for him to predict which animal group would take over in case man should eliminate himself from competition. To what extent behavioral elements, such as "motivation" and "will," should be counted among these unpredictable elements in biological evolution, particularly among higher animals, remains for the comparative psychologist to decide. Nevertheless, it seems to me that when conscious human motivation and evaluation enter the scene, the concept of "development" assumes a new dimension and new connotations.

EMBRYONIC DEVELOPMENT

Some similarities and some basic differences between biological development on the one side and, on the other, postnatal development of human individuals, as well as the development of human collectives and human technical and cultural products, can be illustrated best by focusing on *embryonic development*, that is, the prenatal development of the animal organism from the fertilized egg to birth. Historically, embryology started as a descriptive science, but it has now advanced to an analytical stage with all the methodological trademarks of an analytical science. Although our main goal is a comprehension of the development of the *whole organism* — our textbook titles are Development of the Frog, of the Chick, of the Human — what we actually do, in the spirit of the analytical tradition, is a study of the development of the component parts, or the organs: of the brain, the eye, the limb, the lung. In doing so we cannot help getting involved in the differentiation of their constituent parts, the cells. For instance, development of the brain — apart from the molding of its shape in the earliest stages — is essentially a matter of differentiation of embryonic cells into brain cells and nerve fibers and the molding of these elements into nerve centers and fiber tracts. Cellular differentiation, in turn, leads inevitably to a consideration of the role of the cellular constituents in differentiation, that is, the nucleus which, among other things, is the carrier of the hereditary units or genes, and the cytoplasm. Since the differentiation of embryonic cells into nerve or muscle cells or any other type involves the synthesis of specific proteins with the aid of specific enzyme systems, we arrive eventually at the molecular level. The term development is applicable to phenomena on each of these levels.

There is no doubt about the fruitfulness of this analytical procedure which breaks up complex processes into their simpler components; it has yielded already a deep understanding of the developmental processes. But, of course, there is always the danger of losing sight of the whole. We may legitimately ask, What do we mean by development of the frog, the chick, the human? How is the integratedness and unity of the whole developing organism guaranteed in view of the fact that many partial processes go on in different parts of the embryo quite independently of one another? The two great integrating systems of the mature organism, the nervous system and the endocrine system, are not yet available; they are themselves in the making.

Of three possible answers to the question, two, I think are generally rejected. As scientists, we find the invocation of a metaphysical, vitalistic, nonmaterial principle unacceptable. Driesch's "entelechy," which was conceived as a teleological prime mover that directs all developmental processes toward a preconceived goal, has left the scientific scene forever. The other extreme viewpoint, which sees in the whole not more than the sum of its parts, really begs the question. Most embryologists would probably find a holistic or "organismic" but nonteleological view acceptable. Child, Woodger, Needham, Bertalanffy, and others have proposed different versions of this view. They contend that individuality and wholeness are manifested in the egg no less than in the mature organism or in any intermediate stage. From the beginning, *development proceeds within the framework of the whole.* (This concept establishes perhaps a common ground for embryonic development and the development of the human personality). In other words, integration does not require special devices; it is there from the beginning. Embryonic processes, like all others, have been subjected to the rigorous surveillance of evolutionary selection, and all sidetracks and superfluities which reduce viability and chance of survival have been eliminated during evolution.

Within this framework, the more complex patterns of structure and function emerge from the simpler patterns. The internal conditions change continuously and thus create ever new opportunities for molecules, cells, and cell groups to interact. A step forward sets the stage for the next step. Higher units acquire new properties in the same sense as the combination of oxygen and hydrogen under certain conditions leads to a new substance, water, with new properties that were not manifest in the constituents. In this process, the events follow each other in a rather *stereotyped sequential order*, and it is one of the concerns of the embryologist to unravel the space-time pattern of the developmental process. The large units, the organs *primordia*, are blocked out first in the rough, and the details are sculptured later. In other words, *development proceeds from the general to the specific*. For instance, the early limb *primordium*, a paddle-shaped outgrowth, looks alike in the bird and in the human embryo, and not until rather late does it become recognizable as wing or arm, respectively.

The progression from the general to the special is revealed very clearly in some classical experiments which were performed on the eggs of lower forms, such as sea urchins and amphibians. It is possible to split such eggs in half; and each half will regulate to form a whole embryo. In other words, a single egg can give rise to two individuals. These experiments demonstrate that the special features such as eyes, limbs, or brain are not yet rigidly preformed in the egg. If they were, the single egg would not be potentially capable of giving rise to two pairs of eyes or limbs, or to two complete brains, as it does in these experiments. Other experiments demonstrate the gradual transition from this state in which the different organs are not yet "determined" to the final condition in which the fate of each region of the embryo is definitely fixed.

We have briefly outlined some of the basic features of our present-day *theory of development* which can be designated as a theory of progressive or emergent differentiation. Of course, the theory is actually much more elaborate. It is well founded on a large body of experimental data which were obtained on a great variety of embryos (7). It is an epigenetic theory inasmuch as it acknowledges that organization is actually created anew in development. It has superseded older preformistic ideas according to which the detailed structure of the mature *individuum* is preformed in the egg, and development was conceived merely as the becoming visible and unfolding of this preformed organization, after the fashion of the development of a photographic plate. I think we have here, in the epigenetic theory, another agreement with the development of the human mind.

However, the analogy ends at this point. The ways and mechanisms by which new levels of maturation are achieved are fundamentally different for the embryo and the human person. The most striking contrast is perhaps in the role which the environment or external milieu plays in the two processes. The chick embryo illustrates this point well. Its seclusion in the shell symbolizes its unconcern with the outside world. Of course, the chick embryo has definite temperature, humidity, and oxygen requirements, but these three major environmental contributions do not influence the specific patterns of the developmental processes which go on inside. They are necessary prerequisites or "conditions" but not specific, determining "factors." The egg — a single cell — contains within itself not only the raw materials but also the machinery that transforms them into structure. It is a *self-contained* and *self-generating system*. The situation is not different in the human embryo which derives from the mother its nutritional material but none of the agents which determine structure or function. The blueprint for the building processes, embodying detailed specifications, is represented by the hereditary factors, or genes, which control and direct each step of the differentiation process. It is this blueprint which is handed down from generation to generation to ensure the precise replication of the norm.

However, "norm" does not mean stereotyped uniformity. On the contrary, variability is of the essence in organisms, and, actually, the expression of *individual differences* within the norm is almost unlimited. The biological basis for individual differences is found in the chance recombination of the several thousand hereditary factors, or genes, with which each cell is endowed. A reshuffling of each individual's genes occurs first during the formation of egg and sperm cells, and another chance recombination occurs at fertilization. It is at the onset of our individual life, at conception, that the foundation is laid for the uniqueness of our personality. We should be different from each other even if we were all reared in an identical environment, because each of us would respond to it in a different way. The differences in milieu and in social factors which operate from the moment of birth on, accentuate and further diversify the individual differentials and bring them to full realization. But, undoubtedly, heredity factors continue to control our development after birth, though perhaps in indirect and sometimes not too obvious ways. There is evidence for genetic differences in those components of intelligence which are rated by intelligence tests. Nobody can contest that our physiological make-up, such as the rate of our metabolism, or of hormone production, or of our visual acuity, are under the control of genes; and since physiological and psychic processes are intimately interwoven and interact with each other, one can hardly escape the implication that genes are among the many factors which determine behavior in a direct or indirect way. The question is not whether they are involved, but to what extent they are involved. We should have an open mind with respect to this question and not be influenced unduly by preconceived theoretical ideas, nor by the great difficulties which face us when we try to obtain valid data for the role of heredity in human behavioral traits. One is often persuaded to assume that factors which are methodologically difficult to assess are not important.

Exercise and learning play a paramount role in postnatal physical and mental development. The question has been asked whether *functional activity,* which would be the equivalent of exercise in the fetus, is among the factors that determine the maturation of structure and function in the prenatal period. It would be conceivable that a muscle requires actual contraction, or a joint actual movement, for the perfection of its structure during development. However, all available experimental evidence refutes this idea. By appropriate transplantation experiments in early chick embryos, it is possible to prevent the ingrowth of nerves into a limb. It grows nevertheless to almost normal size, and muscles, bones, and joints are typical in every respect, although the leg has been paralyzed from the start. Eyes develop normally in the absence of light even if the optic nerve is prevented from entering the brain; lungs and intestine are fully developed before they have had a chance to function; and so forth. One can make the general statement that organization and structure develop in forward reference to functional activity, but without its participation as a determining agent. Organs are built up first, and thereafter they are taken into use.

ORIGIN OF BEHAVIOR PATTERNS

The foregoing considerations, and particularly the last-mentioned point of the ineffectiveness of functional activity in organ formation, may serve as a background for an understanding of the origin of behavior patterns.

Behavior has its structural basis in the *nervous system*. There is no coordinated movement, no reflex, no perception without the appropriate nervous apparatus. It would be reasonable to expect that both mature synchronously and in relation to each other; which, in fact, they do. Whenever a new reflex appears on the scene, it is anticipated by a corresponding advance in the structural maturation of the nervous system, be it the outgrowth of a nerve fiber tract or the closing of a circuit by a synaptic connection. Again, structural differentiation proceeds in forward reference to functional activity.

As far as the development of the nervous system is concerned, it follows exactly the same general rules which govern the development of any other organ: there is a gradual increase in complexity of structure that follows an inherent, self-directed, sequential order. All evidence from experimental neuro-embryology shows that an advanced state of neural organization is firmly established before functional activity begins.

What are the characteristics of *behavior development?* To answer this question we have available not only studies on mammals and lower forms but a detailed week-by-week account of the sequence of human prenatal activity by D. Hooker, who had at his disposal a large number of human fetuses which were studied and filmed immediately after their surgical delivery (4). If one follows the intriguing story from the first feeble bending of the neck and upper rump at 8½ weeks to the rich pattern of reflex activity at birth that enables the infant to adjust itself to the outside world, one is impressed by the smooth, orderly sequence of events. One encounters, just as in structural differentiation, a gradual, continuous process: the emergence of complex activities from simple beginnings, and the gradual refinement of originally rather generalized, undifferentiated, and not goal-directed movements.

The very first movements are a slight bending of the trunk in the neck region, accompanied by an arm extension backward. These primitive reactions can be elicited by stimulation near the mouth, but no other skin area is sensitive at that stage. Neurological studies show that only the fifth cranial nerve which innervates this part of the face is sufficiently mature to conduct sensory impulses, and that the pathways along which the impulses travel down the body are mature only to the neck level. Very soon, however, sensory and motor areas expand, and along with maturation of nerve structure the reflex patterns become more complex. Without going into detail (see references 2 and 4), we may mention just two instances. The first is the development of the grasping reflex. At 10½ weeks the palms of the hands become sensitive to the stroke of a hair, and partial closure of the fingers ensues; but the thumb does not participate until several days later. At 14 weeks the fingers close to a fist, but no sustained grasp is possible. Not until the 27th week does the grasp become sufficiently strong to maintain the weight of the body with one hand. A second example is the upbuilding of the suckling reflex that begins with the first slight lip reaction at 12½ weeks, proceeds to a pursing of the lips at 22 weeks, and achieves perfection of the performance at 29 weeks. These instances illustrate the general picture, that is, the gradual elaboration and refinement of the reflexes which are essential immediately after birth.

G. E. Coghill, who has followed step by step the building up of the swimming, feeding, and walking activities of amphibian larvae, has contended that all behavior is at first completely integrated, involving the whole organism, and that local reflexes emancipate themselves secondarily from this total pattern (1). However, this principle is not as generally valid as he thought it to be, and the opposing view, which interprets the first movements as random movements that are gradually woven into the fabric of integrated behavior, has strong proponents. The two viewpoints are not mutually exclusive, and it seems that amphibians and mammals follow different patterns in this respect.

It is evident from the foregoing that the writer, in agreement with most investigators in this field, identifies both neural and prenatal behavioral development with embryonic development in general. This implies that the architecture of the nervous system and the concomitant behavior patterns result from self-generating growth and maturation processes that are determined entirely by inherited, intrinsic factors, to the exclusion of functional adjustment, exercise, or anything else akin to learning.

The latter point deserves perhaps more scrutiny. It is a crucial point inasmuch as it creates a basic distinction between the elaboration of prenatal and postnatal behavior patterns. Of course, we do not imply that a radical break occurs at birth. On the contrary, birth is in many respects an insignificant hiatus. The continuity of intrinsic growth and maturation of the nervous system and behavior is not interrupted. The prenatal mode of development through "maturation" persists as an essential component which constitutes the foundation of "learned" behavior. What happens is that the organism through perception of, and interaction with, the outside world acquires a new mechanism of behavior modification and adjustment. The preformed organization is sufficiently flexible to allow for this kind of adjustment.

The skeptic will rightly insist on crucial evidence and experimental proof for the contention that functional activity has no part in prenatal behavior development. It would appear quite plausible to assume, for instance, that the swimming movements of an amphibian larva are "learned" or at least facilitated by trial and error, or practice. This possibility has been tested by a simple experiment in which amphibian larvae were kept in narcosis for several days prior to the stage at which swimming normally begins. After they had recovered from the narcosis, they exhibited nearly perfect swimming movements, a result showing that neither the actual performance of the preceding steps nor practice is necessary. Similarly, one might envisage that the coordination center for limb movements in walking would be gradually built up by trial and error. Again, it can be shown experimentally that exercise or learning by trial and error plays no role in the perfection of the walking performance, at least in lower animals. Lower forms, such as amphibians, lend themselves to all kinds of embryonic transplantation experiments, and it is possible to construct odd freaks for the purpose of analyzing difficult problems like our present one. In a particular experiment (6) the left and right forelimbs *primordia* of a salamander embryo were exchanged and inverted in such a fashion that the left one grew on the right side, and vice versa, with the toes directed backward and the elbows pointing forward. When the animal began to crawl, the inverted legs operated in perfect coordination with the rest of the body, but in reverse. When hind legs and body moved forward, the forelegs counteracted this motion by pushing backward. This unadapted and useless performance was maintained for months, and there was no sign of adjustment or improvement. The conclusion is inescapable that the normal limb coordination center had been built into the central nervous system in the typical, stereotyped fashion before the onset of limb function. Once activated, it operated blindly, even if the result was ineffective or detrimental. Obviously, trial and error or practice on the part of the limbs had no share in its initial construction. Many other experiments on different types of nerve centers and organ functions could be cited (5, 6). They all lead to the conclusion that the *basic machinery for coordination is established by maturation processes in prefunctional stages*, without the benefit of learning.

CONCLUDING REMARKS

The analysis of embryonic development shows a self-contained, self-generating process which leads step by step from the simpler to the more complex organization, but always within the framework of the whole. This characterization of development may be applicable to other than biological phenomena.

Altogether we recognize three different connotations of the concept "development," on three different levels:

1. *Prenatal development,* including the origin of behavior patterns, is characterized as an intrinsic self-generating *maturation* process following rather stereotyped, inherited patterns in which exercise and learning have no share.

2. *Postnatal development* is characterized by the significant role which exercise and learning play in the elaboration and perfection of the pre-established structural and behavioral organization.

3. *Human motivation,* according to human value systems, introduces entirely new potentialities for the development of the mind and of culture. To define this type of development is beyond the scope of the biologist.

REFERENCES

1. Coghill, G. E. *Anatomy and the Problem of Behaviour.* Cambridge: Cambridge University Press, 1929.
2. Gesell, A. *The Embryology of Behavior.* New York: Harper, 1945.
3. Hamburger, V. "Experimental Embryology," in Vol. 8, *Encyclopaedia Britannica,* 1947.
4. Hooker, D. *The Prenatal Origin of Behavior.* Lawrence: University of Kansas Press, 1952.
5. Sperry, R. W. "Mechanisms of Neural Maturation," in S. S. Stevens, ed., *Handbook of Experimental Psychology.* New York: Wiley, 1951.
6. Weiss, P. "Self-Differentiation of the Basic Patterns of Coordination," *Comp. Psychol. Monogr.,* Vol. 17, No. 4, 1941.
7. Willier, B. H., P. Weiss, and V. Hamburger, eds., *Analysis of Development.* Philadelphia: Saunders, 1955.

J. P. Scott

THE GENETIC AND ENVIRONMENTAL
DIFFERENTIATION OF BEHAVIOR

I T I S now generally agreed that the concept of development in its original sense of a process of unfolding or unwrapping is too simple to fit the observed facts. The term is still useful in general description, but the actual working concepts employed in the study of the development of behavior have long been those of maturation and learning. Under maturation have been lumped all the biological factors which act during development, and learning has included all the psychological ones. This has never been a satisfactory dichotomy because in practice it has been found that it is almost impossible to make a clear experimental separation between the two.

It is now realized that maturation itself was in its original sense an oversimple concept. Maturation is more than ripening or growing older; it involves organization and differentiation as well. Since these are ideas which also can be applied to the process of learning, it is of considerable interest to examine the development of behavior in relation to the concept of differentiation.

FUNCTIONAL DIFFERENTIATION

In his chapter on embryonic development Hamburger has correctly stressed the point that a great deal of early differentiation is accomplished strictly by growth so that the embryo is structurally adapted for function long before function actually takes place. However, this should not detract from the fact that as soon as a part becomes functional its further differentiation tends to be modified by its own

59

activity. One of the first organ systems to become functional in verte-brate embryos is the circulatory system. As soon as the heart starts to beat, its development and that of the other blood vessels is modified by hydrostatic pressure. This may be called functional differentiation. D'Arcy Thompson (18) has described some beautiful examples which take place in the skeletal system, where bone cells are laid down on the lines of greatest stress and where the shape and thickness of bones may be altered to meet unusual circumstances. Perhaps the most out-standing recent example has risen out of the work of Riesen (12) on chimpanzees raised in darkness during the first year of life. So far three animals have been raised under these conditions, with the result that certain cells in the retina never develop and vision is permanently impaired.

Applying this concept more generally to the vertebrate nervous sys-tem, we find that functional differentiation is continued throughout the entire life of an individual. Memory is somewhat affected by old age, but until a person is completely incapacitated by circulatory fail-ure his brain goes on being modified and specialized by use in daily experience. The remarkable thing is not that the brain of an individu-al of eighty still responds to the effects of preceding experiences, but that some of these effects may go back almost an entire lifetime. How this can be explained in terms of physical factors has baffled the im-agination of investigators for many years, and there is still no evidence of structural change which can account for the results. We do know that nerve cells require very little energy for their function, which indicates that the chemical and physical changes involved must be very slight. Differentiation must be inferred from behavior, and cannot yet be confirmed microscopically.

Along with the organization and differentiation of the nervous sys-tem within an individual there also takes place a functional differen-tiation of behavior *between* individuals, which may be affected by genetic as well as environmental factors, and which is particularly im-portant in social organization.

GENETICS AND BEHAVIOR

From the viewpoint of genetics one of the primary questions to be asked is the nature and definition of the character to be studied. In the case of behavior this must be done largely in terms of function rather than structure.

A second primary concept which the geneticist brings to his work is the idea of *variability*. The effect of heredity is to magnify or reduce variability between individuals. When dealing with behavior, the geneticist finds that variability is also a primary constituent of any behavior character, so that he must consider variability as a characteristic of an individual as well as of populations.

Such variability can be seen even in the lower organisms. If a paramecium runs into an obstacle it does not keep repeating its behavior. It backs off and approaches from a different angle, and never does exactly the same thing again. It is apparent that variability of this type is necessary for the process of adjustment, since an animal which gave fixed and invariable responses could never adapt itself to a variety of changing conditions.

In the higher organisms there appear to be two opposing tendencies, one to behave variably and the other to form fixed habits, and the two never reach more than an unstable equilibrium. In a typical learning situation there is first a stage when the individual shows a great deal of variability of behavior. When the situation is repeated there is poor reliability of performance; i.e., it is very difficult to predict what the animal will do next. As the learning process proceeds and habits are formed, the behavior of the individual becomes increasingly predictable. However, if training is discontinued for a while, variability will tend to reappear.

What will be the effect of genetics on a character like this? Fuller (4) has analyzed an interesting example of learning in dogs. As might be expected, there is great individual variability and poor reliability during the initial phases, with greater and greater reliability as the animals proceeded in the test. When the data from different genetic populations of dogs were subjected to analysis of variance, it was found that the relative amount of variance due to heredity was the same in the beginning as in the end of the test. This means that it was just as easy to distinguish genetic differences between populations when the behavior of the animals was quite variable as when it later became invariable. It also suggests that heredity does not necessarily reduce variability of individual behavior and thus put a limit on what can be done. Rather it suggests that it is habit formation which tends to put behavior in a strait jacket and that heredity only acts to make more probable the type of behavior which will be fixed by habit formation in any given situation.

The tendency toward fixation of behavior by habit formation may occur either rapidly or slowly in different individuals, and this may be affected by heredity (16). In one of our experiments with genetics and behavior in dogs we set up a simple kind of barrier problem. At first glance this looks like a T maze with the pattern of 1 right, 2 left, and 3 right turns. However, the walls of the maze are made of wire, and the animal can solve the problem by visual inspection. Almost invariably the dogs will reduce the problem to a simple stereotyped kinetic habit of taking alternate right and left turns which inevitably involves getting into some of the blind alleys. Beagles show significantly less tendency than the other breeds which were studied to form such stereotyped habits without any subsequent change. This of course is correlated with the fact that the beagles have been selected for their ability to find rabbits, and if they readily formed stereotyped patterns of search their chances of locating game would be small.

It may be concluded that individual variability is an essential constituent of behavior and should be studied as such. There has been a tendency in the past to assume that all variability is the result of uncontrolled environmental factors, and that if these could be eliminated behavior would be perfectly consistent. It is here suggested that, on the contrary, variability of behavior is an essential part of the process of adjustment, and that the genetic results indicate that there are innate mechanisms which lead to variability of behavior.

It is convenient to think of the variability of behavior in an individual as the result of an unstable balance between two processes, one tending to increase variability of behavior and the other, habit formation, tending to decrease it.

THE TIME OF DIFFERENTIATION OF BEHAVIOR

From the above considerations it would be expected that any study of the genetic differentiation of behavior would have to include very careful control of the factor of experience, which would of course tend to produce habit formation. One might also expect that the best time to study the effects of heredity would be early in development, before there had been an opportunity for differential habit formation to take place. With this in mind, our study of genetics and social behavior in dogs was founded on a careful survey of the development of behavior (17). As will be seen from the following examples, genetic differentiation may occur at various times that cover almost the entire life span from early embryonic development until late maturity.

Morphological factors affecting the differentiation of behavior. The earliest processes affecting the differentiation of the nervous system are, of course, those of morphogenesis. (See Table 1.) The primitive

Table 1. Periods of Prenatal Development in Mammals, Based on Changes in Function

Period	Nature of Change
Cleavage	Cell division, growth begins
Implantation	Improved nutrition, leads to accelerated growth
Germ layer formation	Organization of growth
Embryonic organ formation	Nerve tube, limb buds, etc., formed by differential growth
Adult organ formation	Embryonic organs transformed by tissue formation; nerve tracts formed
Fetal	First motor behavior; organization through nervous stimulation begins

form of the nervous system and other parts of the body can be affected by both genetic and environmental factors which act by modifying differential growth. However, Oppenheimer (9) has produced some recent embryological evidence to the effect that differences in the general form of the nervous system may have little effect on behavior. Monsters of various kinds were produced by early operations on the developing eggs of the fish Fundulus. Distorted brains and even double nerve cords were produced in these animals. However, when the larval fish began to develop, many swam and coordinated their activities perfectly, a fact indicating that the primary form of the nervous system had little effect and that when it later became functional the nerve tracts tended to be laid down in a normal way, no matter what the substructure was. Of course, no complex behavior was studied in these animals, and against this kind of evidence is that of brain damage in certain human cases. However, it may be tentatively concluded that unless parts of the nervous system are completely missing, they may be organized fairly effectively even though considerably distorted.

When there is a morphological difference in sense or effector organs, there is frequently an obvious effect upon behavior. Such defects may be produced very early in development before there is any function of the nervous system, and they may be produced by either genetic or environmental factors. Of the various sense organs the eye is particularly susceptible to early embryonic injury, and occasionally the ear is also affected. The effect on behavior is not always what might be expected. The loss of the eye has very little effect upon the behavior of mice or rats, which, at least under caged conditions, normally make little use of this particular sense organ. In the dog there is a dominant gene for a peculiar kind of dappled spotting called merle, which is present in collies and Shetland sheepdogs. The homozygous condition of this gene produces an animal which is almost or completely white and which usually has defective eyes and ears. One such animal, when run through our testing program, actually performed better on certain tests than its completely normal litter mates. The point seemed to be that the normal animals were very sensitive to small noises, and consequently easily distracted from the problem at hand, whereas the deaf animal was able to concentrate without interference. Deaf human individuals have also noted the advantages of not being able to hear under certain conditions.

Another example of morphological differences that affect behavior is sex differentiation. Sex is, of course, a hereditary trait, and insofar as there is differentiation in sex behavior between males and females the behavioral differences are also inherited. The mechanisms by which this is accomplished are well known. One of these is the presence of different kinds of hormones that affect the threshold of response. In the case of the dog, both the male and female hormones will lower the threshold for the mounting response. However, as in females this occurs only at the time of estrus, this type of behavior is seen much more often in males. Furthermore, when it does occur in females the morphological differences in the sex organs make it impossible for a female to complete the male pattern of copulatory behavior.

Morphological differentiation affecting later behavior may begin very early in embryonic development, and some of the most obvious variations are produced at this stage. However, growth processes do not end at this point, and differentiation can occur relatively late in postnatal development, as in the case of the preadolescent spurt of typical human growth. The early or late onset of this last phenomenon probably has a considerable effect on behavior.

Many degenerative changes in the nervous system do not occur until relatively late in development. An outstanding example is the human hereditary disease Huntington's chorea, which does not appear until middle age.

Physiological factors affecting the differentiation of behavior. The primary action of genes is presumed to be an effect upon some sort of biochemical reaction. Such reactions may affect the physiological processes of growth, and they may also affect other physiological processes which go on throughout the lifetime of the animal. The possibility therefore exists that behavior may be affected by heredity in a very direct way, particularly through the physiology of the nervous system.

One of the best examples of this is presented by Ginsburg's (5) work on audiogenic seizures of mice. In the inbred DBA strain almost 100 per cent of all mice at 30 to 35 days of age are susceptible to seizures. Susceptibility gradually wears off as the animals get older. In the C57 Black strain a high proportion of animals are susceptible at 20 days of age, but this susceptibility disappears by 30 days. Extensive genetic crosses have been made measuring the response at 30 days, and the conclusion has been reached that there are two major genes involved in the differences between the two stocks.

In a long series of tests with substances affecting brain metabolism, Ginsburg and his co-workers have come to the conclusion that the DBA mice at 30 days of age are deficient in certain respects. This conclusion has been recently confirmed by Abood and Gerard (1), using biochemical methods which demonstrate that the DBA mice show a deficiency of two substances necessary for normal brain function, and that these deficiencies appear at the age of maximum seizure risk. Similar deficiencies occur in the C57 mice at the age when they are susceptible. It may be concluded that we have here an example of the fairly direct action of heredity upon the physiological function of the nervous system, and that this results in the brain's not being able to adapt to large amounts of auditory stimulation.

A genetic disturbance of metabolism in man results in the condition known as phenylpyruvic oligophrenia, and it is to be expected that in the future many other examples of direct genetic effects on physiology will be found, not only in the nervous system, but in both the function of effector organs and of organs controlled by the autonomic nervous system.

The differentiation of behavior by learning processes. In connection with our work on genetics and behavior in the dog, we have made a detailed study of behavioral development, including the process of learning (17). On the basis of descriptive data, it is possible to divide development into several periods based upon important changes in social relationships. (See Table 2.) During the *neonatal* period the behavior of the animals is stereotyped and appears to be largely reflex in nature. Behavior is chiefly governed by three types of stimuli: hunger, pain, and cold. Elimination is stimulated by the mother in a reflex fashion, and righting reflexes are also present. Puppies do not improve in their ability to locate the mother, and there is no indication of any change in behavior except improvement in coordination. The chief function of the period is adjustment to oral nutrition.

At approximately 10 days of age the *transition* period begins with the opening of the eyes, and from this point until 20 days of age there is a rapid metamorphosis of behavior involving sensory, motor, and psychological capacities. According to Fuller's results (3) with conditioned avoidance techniques, traces of unstable conditioning will

Table 2. Period of Development in Mammals,
Based on Changes in Social Relationships

Period	Nature of Change*	
	Major	Minor
Neonatal	Birth: beginning of mammary nutrition	
Transition		Changes in relationship to mother, caused by sensory, motor, or psychic development
Socialization	Capable of forming new relationships; partially independent of mother	
Juvenile		Change in relationship to mother; weaning
Pubertal	Capable of first complete sexual relationships (first estrus or first menstruation)	
Parental	Birth of first offspring	

*Whether these changes are major or minor depends in part on the species concerned.

appear in the transition period, but no stable conditioning is present until approximately 20 days. At this point there is a sharp change in behavior which occurs wthin 24 hours. James (7) has confirmed these results, and has also shown that the avoidance reaction, which has hitherto been general in nature, becomes specialized into withdrawal of the part stimulated at 28 days of age.

The results have also been confirmed by the anatomical studies of Harman (6), who finds that the puppy brain is almost totally un-myelinated at birth and that changes in myelination correspond to changes in behavior. Charles (2) has shown that the electroencephalo-gram of neonatal puppies is almost without differentiation and that there is a pronounced change at 20 days, when sleeping and waking states can be differentiated for the first time. The electroencephalo-gram shows the mature pattern for the first time at approximately 7 weeks of age.

This sort of study needs to be extended, both within this species and in other species, as it has very important theoretical implications. One major problem is whether learning represents a single physio-logical process, or whether it is composed of several processes. If differ-ent kinds of learning appear at different times in development, we should have some reason for assuming that there are several different processes. Judging from the results with the neonatal puppy, the first process to appear is one involving improvement of motor coordination. This may simply represent improvement in muscular strength, but it also may represent a kind of learning which psychologists have some-what neglected in human beings; namely, unconscious coordination of physical activities. Simple associative learning appears before special-ization of response, again indicating that we may be dealing with different processes.

These results indicate that the amount of differentiation of the nerv-ous system which is possible by learning is limited by the state of development of the organism, so that experiences which may have great effects in certain periods of development have very little in others. They also point the way to a more thorough study of the de-velopment of primary mental abilities in children. We have many de-tailed studies on the later phases of human intellectual development, but little more than a description of motor development in the early stages.

In summary, it may be seen that factors which result in the differentiation of behavior may act very early in embryonic development or very late in postnatal development. Morphological differentiation precedes physiological differentiation, but overlaps it in later life. However, behavior is very strictly limited in a prenatal mammal, both by the state of development and by the protecting maternal environment. In certain mammals such restrictions may last for a considerable period after birth. This means that the effects of early differentiating factors may not be apparent in behavior until quite late in development. It also means that functional differentiation of behavior does not occur until relatively late. Indeed there appears to be a tendency for the young organism to be protected from this type of differentiation until a relatively mature state is reached.

GENETIC DIFFERENTIATION OF BEHAVIOR

We have little evidence of genetic differentiation of behavior in the early periods of postnatal development in the dog. Behavioral reactions are so limited and so stereotyped in early life that there is little oppor-

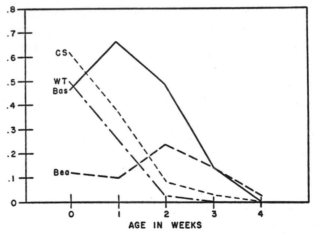

Figure 1. Strain differences in vocalization of young puppies. The lines indicate the proportion of puppies in each stock which made more than 60 noises in one minute while being weighed. At birth the mean (not illustrated) for the beagles is significantly lower than all other strains. At one week the basenjis diverge from the fox terriers and cockers. By four weeks the reaction has almost completely disappeared in all animals. (Bas = basenji, Bea = beagle, CS = cocker spaniel, WT = wirehaired fox terrier.)

tunity for any genetic differences to manifest themselves, and the most that we have been able to describe are differences in distress vocalization (Fig. 1) when the puppies are placed in a situation in which they may be cold; namely, while being weighed. Certain observations indicate that other differences could be found, as, for example, in the amount of oral activity.

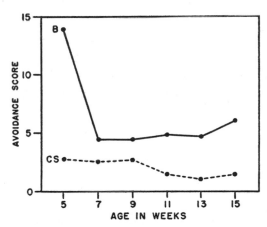

Figure 2. Strain differences in fearful reactions toward human handlers. The lines indicate average scores measuring avoidance and yelping. At 5 weeks of age basenjis are much more fearful than cocker spaniels. Under similar training these differences rapidly decrease, but there is some indication that the two strains again draw apart as they grow older.

We have also attempted to find genetic differences in behavior throughout later stages in development, and there appears to be very little that can be said in general except that differences may appear at all ages, and that they are manifested in various ways. For example, there are great differences in the avoidance responses which young puppies express toward human beings at 5 weeks of age (Fig. 2). With equal treatment and opportunity for association with human beings, these differences tend to disappear so that, after a few weeks of socialization, all the puppies respond in very much the same way (14).

On the other hand, certain kinds of responses appear to be very similar in all puppies at an early age, and to differentiate only as they grow older (15). When puppies are trained to stand quietly on the scales their behavior is slightly variable and shows few differences (Fig.

3). After a few weeks the differences become increasingly great, with certain puppies learning to stand quietly on the scales and others becoming constantly active. It would appear that the learning process can in certain cases result in a decrease of genetic differences in behavior and that in certain others it may actually magnify them, particularly where one type of learning is dependent upon a preceding type. Two individuals may be quite similar at the outset of training, and a very slight genetic difference may make it possible for one to learn where the other does not. From this point on, one individual is teachable and the other is not, and differences between them will tend to be magnified.

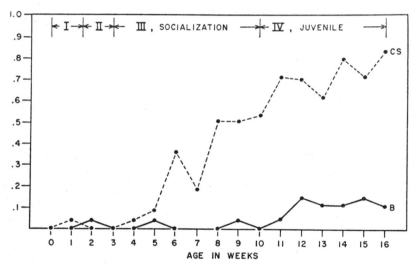

Figure 3. Proportion of cocker spaniel and basenji puppies (n = 34 and 27) which will stay quiet on the scales for a period of one minute. Note that there is no differentiation of behavior in the early stages, and that differences increase with similar training. This appears to be a genetic difference which is magnified by training and habit formation.

A behavioral measure may give different results when applied at different stages in development. The heart rate is particularly interesting because it can be ascertained at every stage in development and because, although it is a direct measure of physiological activity, it is very closely related to behavior, reflecting both emotional reactions and the general activity of the individual. In Figure 4 are shown the average heart rates of puppies from two breeds of dogs as taken at weekly intervals throughout the early stage of development. It will be noticed that in both breeds there is a considerable lowering of the heart rate during the early weeks of the period of socialization, probably reflecting a fearful reaction to handling. As the puppies become

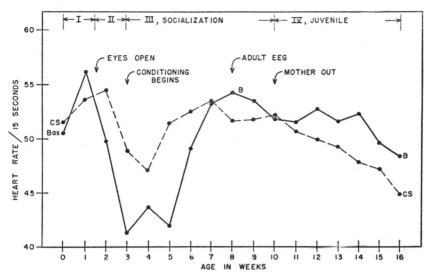

Figure 4. Average heart rates of basenji and cocker spaniel puppies taken at weekly intervals. Heart rates reflect behavioral stimulation. Note how heart rates correspond to periods of development. Note also the more extreme reaction of the basenjis during the early part of period III, probably reflecting a fear reaction. The strain differences in the latter part of the curves are statistically significant, and adult cockers tend to show a lower heart rate than basenjis.

used to handling, and develop positive social relationships with the handlers, the rate comes back up nearly to the same height and thereafter shows a gradual decline toward the adult level.

With regard to genetic differences, the basenjis show a greater depression of the heart rate during the early period of socialization, whereas in the juvenile period the cocker spaniel breed shows a consistently lower heart rate. It is obvious that this particular measure is one which is affected strongly by the stage of development, and that genetic differences may disappear at certain ages and at others may be opposite in nature.

One of the problems which this information brings up is the practical one of early recognition of basic genetic traits. If certain behavior traits appear only late in development there is no hope of trying to find them at an earlier point. On the other hand, it may be possible that there are really only a small number of important hereditary traits and that these are expressed in different ways at different ages. By correlation studies it should be possible to find out if the early behavior traits are related to later ones, and then identify them when they first occur. In a preliminary factor analysis, Royce (13) found that the distress vocalization in the neonatal period was correlated with measures of timidity at later ages.

THE SOCIAL DIFFERENTIATION OF BEHAVIOR

The dominance order as an example of social differentiation. Beginning with studies of the peck order in chickens, the study of dominance orders has been extended to all classes of vertebrates. As we see it developing in young puppies (10), the members of a litter at first show no aggressive behavior whatever. At the age of 4 or 5 weeks they may begin to show signs of playful fighting, biting and pawing each other. At the same time they may begin to growl at one another over the possession of bones. By 7 or 8 weeks there may be active fights and even group aggression toward certain individuals. At this age little physical damage is done in the fights, since the teeth are largely undeveloped. By 11 weeks of age some definite dominance relationships can be found, and a fairly stable dominance order is in existence by 15 weeks.

The behavior of individual puppies starts out by being similar, and in any given pair the two puppies will both be aggressive. As a result of a fight in early life, one pup wins and the other loses, and thereafter one learns to attack and threaten, and the other learns to run away and submit. As this is repeated day after day, the result is to develop a strong social relationship and a pronounced differentiation of behavior between individuals. The dominance order may not be the only type of social organization nor the most important type, but it does give a clear-cut picture of the process of behavioral differentiation that leads to social organization.

The effect of heredity on social differentiation. Different breeds of dogs have been selected for the presence or absence of aggressiveness.

All of the terrier breeds have been selected for the tendency to attack either each other or some form of game. On the other hand, the hounds and sporting dogs which are used to find game are often used in packs and have been selected for their ability to avoid fights. When the dominance orders of different breeds of puppies are examined, it is found that a terrier breed forms a very tight and definite dominance hierarchy, whereas breeds like beagles and cocker spaniels show rather indefinite examples of dominance. In the aggressive strains the differentiation between dominant and subordinate individuals is much greater than it is within nonaggressive strains. It may therefore be concluded that heredity has an important effect upon the social differentiation of behavior. This effect is even more obvious in studies of different breeds of chickens (11). When different kinds of hens are matched against each other, the more aggressive ones have an enormous advantage in any fight, and consequently tend to be dominant.

Socialization. In every social species of animal it is found that there is a relatively short period in life, usually fairly early, in which primary social bonds are formed, after which similar bonds are formed with increasing difficulty. Lorenz (8) has observed this phenomenon in his experiments of raising birds apart from their own species, and similar but not so rigid responses can be obtained with social mammals. In the case of the dog (14), this period of socialization begins at approximately 20 days of age, when associative learning is first possible, and continues for a few weeks thereafter. If the primary social relationships have not been formed within this time, it becomes increasingly difficult to do so later. There is obviously a critical period which tends to determine the nature of the primary social relationship.

The process of primary socialization is a special case of the differentiation of behavior in regard to a social relationship. It also forms one of the most important periods in the development of an individual animal because it effects the formation and differentiation of future social relationships.If the primary relationship is formed with a different species, social relationships may never be formed with the proper species to which an animal belongs. In the case of a dog exposed to both other dogs and human beings, social relationships may be formed with both. In Figure 2 are shown the scores of avoidance and fear which are given to a human handler during the process of primary socialization with human beings. It is obvious that the initial reactions

are affected by heredity, and that this relationship like others is subject to important hereditary modification.

The development of behavior has been considered in connection
with the concept of differentiation. This may be thought of as a process
which is affected by both genetic and environmental factors. The early
embryonic differentiation of an individual is largely dependent upon
growth processes, but differentiation becomes increasingly affected by
function in the later stages. Functional differentiation has great importance in the later development of the nervous system, and when
the available evidence on these points is reviewed certain important
conclusions can be made as follows:

Two opposing tendencies are seen in the behavior of higher organisms, one toward variability and the other toward consistency. Habit
formation is the chief factor that produces consistent behavior. Hereditary factors can reduce or magnify either tendency.

Changes in form that affect behavior can occur very early in development or relatively late. Modification of physiological processes
tends to occur somewhat later and to extend throughout life. The
special physiological processes of learning tend to be postponed until
postnatal life, or even after, but extend throughout later life. Since
hereditary factors act upon growth or any physiological processes, this
means that genetic factors may produce their effects upon behavior at
any time in life. Since most differentiation of growth processes takes
place prior to the onset of behavior, this means that the behavioral
effects may appear long after the original gene action of this type has
taken place. On the other hand, a genetic action may also produce an
immediate effect upon behavior.

The amount of functional differentiation of the nervous system is
limited by the stage of development of the organism. Functional differentiation of this type may either magnify, keep constant, or diminish
original genetic differences in behavior.

The development of a social relationship may be considered a
process of differentiation of behavior between two individuals. Genetic
as well as environmental factors may affect the outcome. The concept
of functional differentiation is therefore of considerable use in explaining both the changes in behavior of a developing individual and

the differences in behavior exhibited by individuals in social situations.

In the study of any natural phenomenon there is a tendency to start with a single unitary concept of a crude descriptive nature. When this has been found unsatisfactory, it is abandoned in favor of more precise and specific ideas that may still be included under the older and less meaningful term. Thus, the original crude idea of development as an unfolding process gave way to the ideas of maturation and learning. It has been the thesis of this paper that maturation in the sense of growing old and ripe is also an inadequate concept, and to suggest instead the ideas of organization and differentiation.

Viewed in this light, maturation and learning are no longer distinct and unrelated phenomena. Instead we have various processes of differentiation: growth, physiological processes, and learning processes. Some of these are very largely under the control of biological and physiological factors, while others are much more strongly affected by function and external stimulation. It should be possible to identify these different factors and separate them by experimental techniques.

The differentiation of the nervous system, and hence of behavior, can be modified by external factors at any stage in development. Differentiation by growth is important early in development, and becomes less so with age; while differentiation by function becomes increasingly important and is almost the sole remaining process in advanced age.

Function not only is an important factor in the differentiation of the behavior of an individual, but it also helps to differentiate and organize behavior *between* individuals in social relationships.

What is the role of heredity in relation to these various processes? Heredity can modify and differentiate a process at any stage in development in which it occurs. The general heredity of a species determines the kinds of differentiating processes which may take place, but it does not predetermine the behavior of an individual, which is affected by many other factors as well. In fact, as we accumulate more knowledge about the effects of heredity upon behavior, it would appear that it plays a dual but consistent role. On the one hand, it tends to promote the potential variability of behavior of an individual, although this can be modified in either direction. The most important factor in reducing the variability of behavior of an individual and rendering his behavior consistent is habit formation. On the other hand, heredity also tends to increase the variability of behavior between individuals, to differentiate the behavior which arises between them, and thus in part determine the nature of social relationships.

To summarize, heredity is one of the many determinants of behavior that Dr. Anderson has so admirably outlined in his chapter entitled "Dynamics of Development." As we see its role in relation to other determinants, heredity tends to promote variability of behavior, both within an individual, where adaptability is dependent upon variability, and between individuals, where it increases the variety of social relations and thus contributes to the complexity of social organization. All modern knowledge of heredity tends to emphasize the inevitability of variation, and hence of individuality. The conclusion which any citizen is entitled to draw is that we should in our culture respect and understand individuality and place a high value upon it rather than try to fight it or obliterate it.

REFERENCES

1. Abood, L. G., and R. W. Gerard. "A Phosphorylation Defect in the Brains of Mice Susceptible to Audiogenic Seizure," in *Biochemistry of the Developing Nervous System*. New York: Academic Press, 1954.
2. Charles, M. S. "A Developmental Study of the Electroencephalogram of the Puppy." Unpublished M.A. thesis, University of Maine, 1954.
3. Fuller, J. L., C. A. Easler, and E. M. Banks. "Formation of Conditioned Avoidance Responses in Young Puppies," *Amer. J. Physiol.*, Vol. 160 (1950), pp. 462–66.
4. ———, and J. P. Scott. "Heredity and Learning Ability in Infrahuman Mammals," *Eugenics Quart.*, Vol. 1 (1954), pp. 28–43.
5. Ginsburg, B. "Genetics and the Physiology of the Nervous System," *Proc. Assn. Res. Nerv. and Ment. Disease*, Vol. 33 (1954), pp. 39–56.
6. Harman, P. J. Private communication, 1952.
7. James, W. T., and D. J. Cannon. "Conditioned Avoiding Responses in Puppies," *Amer. J. Physiol.*, Vol. 168 (1952), pp. 251–53.
8. Lorenz, K. "Der Kumpan in der Umwelt des Vogels," *J. für Ornithologie*, Vol. 83 (1935), pp. 137–213; 289–413.
9. Oppenheimer, Jane M. "Functional Regulation in *Fundulus heteroclitus* Embryos with Abnormal Central Nervous Systems," *J. Exper. Zool.*, Vol. 115 (1950), pp. 461–92.
10. Pawlowski, A., and J. P. Scott. "The Development of Dominance in Different Breeds of Puppies," *J. Comp. Physiol. Psychol.*, Vol. 49 (1956), pp. 353–58.
11. Potter, J. H. "Dominance Relations between Different Breeds of Domestic Hens," *Physiol. Zool.*, Vol. 22 (1949), pp. 261–80.
12. Riesen, A. H. "Vision," *Ann. Rev. Psychol.*, Vol. 5 (1954), pp. 57–88.
13. Royce, J. R. "A Factorial Study of Emotionality in the Dog," *Psychol. Monogr.*, Vol. 69 (1955), pp. 1–27.
14. Scott, J. P. "The Process of Socialization in Higher Animals," in *Interrelations between the Social Environment and Psychiatric Disorders*. New York: Milbank Memorial Fund, 1953.
15. ———, and M. S. Charles. "Genetic Differences in the Behavior of Dogs: A Case

of Magnification by Thresholds and Habit Formation," *J. Genet. Psychol.*, Vol. 84 (1954), pp. 175–88.

16. _____, and M. M. Gault. "Genetic Differences in the Reactions of Dogs to a Maze Problem," (abstract). *Anat. Rec.*, Vol. 117 (1953), p. 565.

17. _____, and M. V. Marston. "Critical Periods Affecting the Development of Normal and Maladjustive Social Behavior of Puppies," *J. Genet. Psychol.*, Vol. 77 (1950), pp. 25–60.

18. Thompson, D'Arcy W. *On Growth and Form*, 2nd ed. Cambridge: Cambridge University Press, 1948.

T. C. Schneirla

THE CONCEPT OF DEVELOPMENT IN COMPARATIVE PSYCHOLOGY

THE concept of development, connoting a pattern of changes occurring in a system through time, is fundamental to the psychological study of animals. But a comparative psychology as a scientific discipline does not arise merely through the general recognition that some kind of relationship exists between the phenomena of phylogenetic and ontogenetic change (90). Nor is it to be established by the same methods as a comparative anatomy or a comparative embryology.

Although, as investigation progresses, the molecular basis of behavior and of psychological capacities is revealed with increasing clarity in organic processes, it is becoming evident that the principles holding for the molecular and molar levels of organic reality cannot be the same (76, 89). Although the principles for the *molecular* are basic to the molar level, the molar requires operations in investigation and theory beyond the specific terms of the molecular. No matter how thoroughgoing the studies of the embryologist and his colleagues in cognate biological fields may be, in themselves they cannot be expected to give an inclusive, comprehensive basis for dealing adequately with questions concerning the behavior and psychology of animals (76, 102).

It may not be altogether clear why a science of behavioral development should be responsible for deriving its own theories and validating its own principles, rather than accepting them fully formed from other fields in biology. But the probability exists that in all types of organisms, in ways depending on the characteristics of each respective phyletic level, behavior has differing degrees of indirectness in its relation to structure (91). The issue is often complicated by a confusion of

78

abstractions, or preliminary working attempts to represent phenomena, with a positivistic or finalistic view of reality itself. To emphasize these considerations, a conceptual distinction which is both empirically grounded and heuristically recommended is suggested here, to differentiate what is connoted by the terms *growth, differentiation,* and *development.* In *growth,* the emphasis is on change by tissue accretion; in *differentiation,* on variation in the changing of structural aspects with age in an organism. In *development* the emphasis is on progressive changes in the organization of an individual considered as a functional, adaptive system throughout its life history. Growth processes, as well as those of tissue differentiation, are subsumed by the term development, which further stresses the occurrence of progressive changes in the inclusive, organized function of the individual.

This distinction has great theoretical importance for the study of behavioral and psychological capacities in the animal series. For it stresses the fact — increasingly apparent with the advance of morphology on the one hand and of psychology on the other — that although tissue and organ, local movement and inclusive behavior are closely and inseparably related in functions, the represented phenomena are not fully describable in the same terms.

The problem of behavioral development. For an adequate perspective in the methodology of research and theory, we cannot accept an a priori definition of behavioral development either as an unfolding of the innate, with gains through learning presumably superimposed in superior phyla, or as a continuum expanding mainly through the pressure of environmental forces, with the genes merely contributing an initial push to the process. Rather, a defensible generalization is that species' genetic constitution contributes in some manner to the development of *all* behavior in *all* organisms, as does milieu, developmental context, or environment. The "instinct" question, then, is regarded as merely a traditionally favored way of posing the question of behavioral development in a general, preliminary way, with emphasis upon the role of genetic constitution (91).

The question of behavioral development is posed from the above standpoint not to be eclectic, but first of all to encourage behavioral analysis, an emphasis badly needed in all developmental psychology. In the history of this subject, studies of psychological development have been too predominantly descriptive, too discontinuous as to stages investigated, and too preoccupied with certain stages, particularly the adult, to promote the rise and use of adequate analytical methods.

The critical problem of behavioral development should be stated as follows: (1) to study the organization of behavior in terms of its properties at each stage, from the time of egg formation and fertilization through individual life history; and (2) to work out the changing relationships of the organic mechanisms underlying behavior, (3) always in terms of the contributions of earlier stages in the developmental sequence, (4) and in consideration of the properties of the prevailing developmental context at each stage. In attacking this problem, an adequate programmatic combination of cross-sectional and longitudinal studies must be carried out through an analytical methodology suited to the phyletic level under study, with the results then synthesized to the end of valid phyletic comparisons.

DEVELOPMENT CONSIDERED PHYLETICALLY

Behavioral relationships in the animal series. The phyletic study of development naturally presupposes some kind of series or order among contemporary animals as to their respective evolutionary backgrounds. However, no clear and supportable series, except in the broadest terms, has been established with respect to the behavioral properties of the respective animal phyla (44, 71). The phyletic tree has numerous long branches, with large sections now extinct, and present-day animals fall into a very irregular pattern on it. Although the order of evolutionary antiquity and recency is usually paralleled by the degree of specialization in the sense of behavioral plasticity, exceptions are numerous. For instance, the horse, which as a specific form of organism has had about the same evolutionary time as man to reach its present adaptive status, compares favorably with man only in specializations other than psychological. Our comparative behavioral study therefore must include all principal existing animal forms, and not just those that form some type of series (87, 90).

It is sometimes argued that a comparative psychology can be founded directly on comparative anatomy (67). This may presuppose or favor a preformistic answer to the instinct problem (64). But the concept of homology, connoting a significant evolutionary relationship between comparable mechanisms among species has not been validated as yet for behavior and its organization. To the extent that this may be possible in the future, what homologies may exist in the behavioral properties of different animals must be worked out essentially by psychological and behavioral methods; always, of course, in view of evidence from comparative anatomy and other biological sciences. For the chief difficulty, as we shall see, is that behavior seems to have very different relations to structure in different types of animals.

Psychological levels. For this task of phyletic comparisons, a theory of psychological levels promises to be useful, in which the capacities and organizations in behavior are compared as *high* or *low* in respect to psychological status (76, 89). If one knew only the reactive repertoire of the sea anemone's tentacle, the insect's antenna, and the cat's forepaw in their normal situations of use by the respective organisms, one would conclude without much doubt that among these three, the tentacle indicates by far the lowest psychological status in total behavior, the paw the highest. What we know about the respective owner organisms would not change this judgment.

Psychological level cannot depend upon adaptive success, for by hypothesis, all existing animal forms must be ranked more or less on a par in this respect. The principle of homeostasis, which concerns the physiological readjustment of an organism to biologically nonoptimal conditions, applies well to all animals considered against their respective environments. But at the same time, the mechanisms underlying homeostasis, along with other capacities crucial for behavioral organization, show progressive changes in their internal organization and in their relation to other individual functions, from psychologically low-status to high-status animals.

Complexity is often advanced as a criterion for distinguishing psychological standing. This, however, is a doubtful procedure until we know *what* it is that is complex. For instance, the compound eye is very complex in many insects, but in action it lacks associated perceptual capacities present in a mammal through experience. Insect visual discriminations through the compound eye are based on flicker vision rather than on pattern perception in the mammalian sense (89). The significant feature of behavior for psychological appraisal is not specifically dependent upon a multiplicity of molecular units, many sensory endings, and the like; it is rather a difference in *kind*, depending upon the qualitative aspects of behavioral organization and capacities.

From what might be termed the additive point of view, the capacity for lasting neural trace effects gained through experience often is regarded as crucial for the psychological appraisal of an animal. But it is probable that higher mammals do not necessarily retain behavioral modifications better than do many birds, or even insects; it is in the versatile use of the traces under new conditions of emergency that mammals typically excel (87). Also, on higher levels, the nature of variability in behavior becomes much more than the capacity for some kind of change. To say that higher levels are characterized by plasticity means that capacities and organizations appear which admit the possibility of systematic variations appropriate to new environmental conditions. Adjustments to changing conditions are no longer made merely through the random shifting of items in a fixed repertoire, but through the appearance of opportune new patterns.

The developmental process characterized as behavioral evolution, therefore, cannot be viewed as a process of accretion, by the addition of further mechanisms similar to the old. If it were such a process, phyletic comparison would be easier than it seems to be. Rather, development evidently has taken place in evolution through the progressive transformation of old mechanisms (e.g., homeostasis, 82) as well as through the appearance of new mechanisms (e.g., neural patterns underlying reasoning). Through organic evolution higher functional levels appear, which, as individual adaptive systems and as behaving wholes, may be considered qualitatively new.

ONTOGENY AND PHYLETIC COMPARISONS

Phyletic differences in behavioral attainments. Accordingly, on each further psychological level, the contribution of individual ontogeny is a characteristically different total behavior pattern arising in a different total context. This fact cannot be appreciated unless the comparison of different animal types is made in terms of their entire ontogenetic ranges, and not confined to certain stages such as the adult. This is a principle to which Orton (79) recently has called attention from the standpoint of biological procedures in systematics. The "waggle dance" as described for the honey bee by von Frisch (27) is an efficient communicative device and an impressive event, but when considered in the light of its stereoptyed ontogenetic basis, it must be viewed — contrary to a frequent conclusion from general similarity — as fundamentally inferior in its qualitative organization to symbolic processes in higher mammals and language in man. The appearance of behavioral stereotypy through ontogeny, if found characteristic of a species, indicates a lower psychological level, whereas a systematic plasticity in the organization of behavioral cues made broadly representative through experience indicates a high level.

Homologous mechanisms are transformed functionally in a new setting on each higher level, as through ontogeny a characteristically different total behavior pattern arises in a different total context. Consider, for example, how differently the vertebrate forelimb is involved in the feeding operations of a toad, an adult monkey, and a five-year-old human child. The same principle may hold roughly for analogous adaptive mechanisms in very different phyletic settings. For instance, the group unity and organization of an insect colony is held (88) as an extension of Wheeler's (107) concept of trophallaxis, to derive from reciprocal stimulative processes reinforced by a variety of sensitive zones and special secretory effects. In different but comparative ways, parallel intragroup processes of this type may be held basic to social behavior on *all* levels from invertebrates to man. The fundamental mechanisms are similar, in that specialized sensitivity and responses affecting the formation of individual affiliations and reactivities in the group situations are always involved; however, the various resulting patterns of collective behavior are distinctively different. I have characterized that of social insects as *biosocial*, in that it is evidently dominated by specific mechanisms of sensitivity, physiological processes and response; that of mammals as *psychosocial*, in that although trophallactic mechanisms are still basic and indispensable to them, group behavior is now characterized by plastic processes arising through learning, anticipation, and the like (88, 89). The principle is: that similar biological processes can lead to very different behavior patterns through ontogeny, depending upon what developmental capacities in species and what limitations are effective in the prevailing context.

Within each level there is a range of behavioral capacities differing in underlying organization — as in carnivores, from random emotionalized escape to a roundabout food-getting response. The different patterns in the behavioral repertoire of any level may be termed *functional orders,* and ranked high or low in organizational status. In a chimpanzee, for example, casually flicking away a fly represents a pattern of low functional order, gesturing to another chimpanzee a pattern of high functional order, although the actual movements are similar. The highest functional orders characterizing any psychological level are those utilizing its maximal possible gains through ontogeny. With respect to behavior and its organization, the ontogeny of any level is not so much a retracing through the stages and functional orders of successive ancestral forms as a new composite leading to a new total pattern characteristic of the level. Functional orders characteristically attained through ontogeny on any phyletic level are not replicas of those appearing through ontogeny at other levels, either with respect to their order of appearance, their individual make-up, or their properties of organization as part-processes in the inclusive behavior pattern.

Genes and behavior. It would be misleading to say that the behavioral patterns of lower psychological levels are inherited or innate, and those of higher levels learned. The traditional heredity-environment dilemma stands out more and more clearly as a pseudoproblem, as further evidence indicates that in all animals intrinsic and extrinsic factors are closely related throughout ontogeny (91). As a guide to investigation, it is no wiser to regard development as a natively determined unfolding of characters and integrations than as the result of the molding effect of extrinsic forces. We may therefore hold that genetic constitution contributes to *all* behavioral development at *all* phyletic levels, just as modern geneticists hold that without a participating environmental context at all stages there could be no development in any animal (95, 102). The question is *how* development occurs in the particular animal under prevailing conditions, not *what* heredity or environment specifically contributes, or how much either contributes proportionally to the process. Genes are complex biochemical systems, integrated from the beginning of ontogeny into processes of increasing complexity and scope, the ensuing progressive processes always intimately influenced by forces acting from the developmental context (102, 105).

In each species genetic factors contribute indirectly to advances in stabilizing organismic functions, and impose characteristic limits at which they tend to resist change. But as Dobzhansky (19) has emphasized, it is undesirable to confuse this natural state of affairs with the impression of heredity *directly* determining development. Nor does a correspondence of the theoretical genotype with strain-specific behavioral characteristics, appearing in any animal in the standard environment, demonstrate a *more direct* relationship of genetic constitution and behavior in highly selected than in relatively unselected strains (36, 91).

The fact that in all phyletic types modified or even radically different phenotypic alternatives may arise through ontogeny, according to variations in the context of development, militates against a doctrine of genic *Anlagen* directly determining the rise of behavior. Gesell's (30) conception of a human ontogeny, in which early behavior expands through "the innate processes of growth called maturation," seems more adequate for insects, although not really suitable in their case (91). Harnly (40) found, in experiments with the fruit fly, *Drosophila melanogaster*, that the same gene may influence the development of different wing size and structure according to what temperature prevails during the development of the phenotype. The types produced from the same genotypic strain were capable of full normal flight, erratic flight, or no flight, depending upon conditions of development. Not only wing size, but also wing articulation and neuromuscular control were believed differently affected according to what temperature prevailed during specific early stages of ontogeny. It is impossible to account adequately for such facts in terms of a preformistic theory of behavioral development.

Intervening variables in development. The nervous system is often represented as the carrier of an innate determination for behavior patterns presumed to arise solely through its passive development. For this type of conclusion, Coghill's investigation (16) of larval salamanders is often cited as evidence. However, it cannot be presumed that the full significance of this research is understood as yet, even for amphibian development (28). On any phyletic level, the nervous system develops as *one* part of the organism, closely interrelated with other mechanisms throughout, and like them, it is indirectly influenced by the genes (64, 91). Nativistic views of behavioral development (51) may often seem to furnish the sole available theoretical resolution of a problem in the appearance of individual behavior, but only when the developmental system is so incompletely understood that the burden can be placed upon neural growth alone. To carry weight, investigations on the ontogenetic causation of species behavior patterns must involve a thoroughgoing analysis of behavioral development as related to other processes at successive stages. Conclusions not based on such analyses are premature.

The problem of ontogeny is not one of instinctive patterns directly determined by the genes, but one of understanding what changing integrations of development underlie successive functional stages characteristic of the species. Two concepts may be used to represent the factorial complexes essential to the entire flow of events in development. The first is *maturation*, which connotes growth and differentiation together with all their influence upon development. Maturation is neither the direct, specific representative of genic determination in development, nor is it synonymous with structural growth. Much as an environmental context is now recognized as indispensable to any development (19, 95, 102, 105), students of behavioral development (59, 73) emphasize the roles of structure and function as inseparable in development. The second of these two fundamental concepts is *experience*, which connotes *all* stimulative influences upon the organism through its life history.

As an abstract operation, for heuristic purposes, these factorial complexes may be conceptualized disjunctively in their effects upon development, and there are indications that this logical procedure may be carried further as experimental methodology advances. But realistically, the two concepts must be considered as standing for complex systems of intervening variables closely integrated at all stages of development.

Circular functions and self-stimulation in ontogeny. An indispensable feature of development is that of circular relationships of self-stimulation in the organism (91). The individual seems to be interactive with itself throughout development, as the processes of each given stage open the way for further stimulus — reaction relationships depending on the scope of the intrinsic and extrinsic conditions then prevalent. At early embryonic stages, circular biochemical effects of expanding range, in a sense *spiral*, may be invoked in these terms; somewhat later, proprioceptive processes capable of integrating neurally with the early cutaneous stimulative effects (10, 62). From the time of fertilization, development is continuous and progressive (32, 108), its processes and stages being closely interrelated in their intrinsic and extrinsic aspects (91).

The potentialities of redundant stimulative processes for development have been incompletely investigated. For instance, Fromme (28) found, in replicating Carmichael's test (9) with early amphibian embryos immobilized by chloretone, that specimens held inactive during stages 17 and 20, in particular, in later tests swam more slowly than normal specimens and with deficient coordination. The need of further work along the lines of the Carmichael experiment is indicated, with reference to its bearing on the interpretation of Coghill's findings (16). The effects, particularly in the earliest stages, may not be those of obvious action or readily recorded impulses, so much as electromotive changes and action twitches of minute magnitude, slight afferent pulses, or other subtle energy releases capable of contributing in some way to the changing of patterns in development. Kuo (61, 62, 63) demonstrated for the chick embryo ways in which stimulative effects from early functions, such as heartbeat and rhythmical pulsations of the amnion membrane, could influence the development of a head-lunge response. Early self-stimulative relationships, influencing the rise of a basic generalized response, contribute (with the entrance of extrinsic, differentiated conditions) to the specialization of this act into pre-hatching responses such as egg-chipping or into post-hatching patterns such as preening, drinking, and food-pecking (63).

Hatching or birth represents only one of the stages at which the young individual influences a notable change in its own environment made possible by stimulative gains through its own prior develoment. Although opening the way for a wider scope of action in a more heterogeneous environment, neither involves an absolute change for the stimulus-response progressions of development.

At all stages, the individual possesses the maturational properties of its species, which inevitably exert species-typical feedback effects upon its development. That the relationship of such effects to the rise of behavior at later stages may be elusive is suggested by Nissen's statement (78): "Among animals at all levels in the phyletic scale there can be observed highly motivated, almost compulsive forms of behavior which have no relation to homeostasis in the usual sense of the term." He cites the nest-building and brooding behavior of birds as examples of activities that "have no obvious effect on maintaining the physiological equilibrium of the individual engaging in these activities." But actually, in many birds maturational processes affecting temperature change and causing irritability of the skin at the hypersensitive brood patches, lead to active, variable readjustments and appear to be key functions in the appearance of nesting and incubation. The outcome may be physiological adaptations of the homeostatic type. For mammals, Kinder's research (58) indicated that temperature conditions at the skin must somehow provide a basis for nest-building in rats. But such factors are likely to influence behavioral development only as part processes in a complex of interrelated organic events. Lehrman (65) found that feeding of the young by the parent ring dove did not occur except through the development of a behavior-influencing integration of (a) hormonal factors; (b) afferent effects, in particular, processes centering in the delicately sensitive brood patches; (c) neural factors, including certain processes bearing on a generalized "drive" excitation; (d) closely related circular processes in individual behavior; and (e) parent-young reciprocal stimulative processes occurring in a complex sequence. Without the last — an involved succession of stimulative exchanges between the two participants — there could be no feeding response by the parent to the perceived squab. Such findings suggest that the developmental pattern underlying behavior is a global one, including a range of circular stimulative and reactive processes based upon the gains of earlier stages.

Early self-stimulative relationships may provide a significant basis for later adjustments to new conditions involving members of the same species. Birch (5) found that female rats, provided from early youth with wide collars which prevented stimulative access to the posterior body and genital zones, in a later test at primiparous parturition lost their young through neglect or cannibalism. Controls indicated that it was not the weight or general disturbing effect of the collar but the effect of the wide flange in preventing stimulative relations with the posterior body that accounted for the abnormal outcome in experimental animals. Thus, self-stimulative experiences normally inevitable in everyday behavior during youth seem essential to efficient delivery and care of the young in this animal. One normal gain denied to the experimental rats may have been a general perceptual orientation to the posterior bodily areas as familiar objects; another, the capacity of responding to the genital zones — and to objects such as neonate young, bearing equivalent olfactory properties of attraction — by licking and not biting.

This point of view, of the maturation and experience complexes always intimately related in behavioral development, may be adapted to the study of turning points and intervening stages in mammalian development. The term *stage* has been extrapolated from embryology to the study of behavioral ontogeny and we must accept embryological evidence as integral, but we must advance beyond this to higher functional orders in development to which organic maturation is *one* contributor. The accomplishment of given maturational events often seems to influence behavioral changes rather promptly, particularly at lower phyletic levels, as when an amphibian larva metamorphoses into an adult with rather different properties of sensitivity and response. Higher in the psychological scale, the relation of one stage to following stages seems to be more involved. But the principle is much the same for all. Investigations of domestic cats in our laboratory (84) indicate how behavioral advances centering in birth, eye-opening, and weaning occur through complex intrinsic-extrinsic integrations. For a time after eye-opening, the kitten's approach to the mother evidently proceeds much as before, on a proximal sensory basis. Within a few days changes appear which seem attributable both to new gains through maturation (e.g., an increasing visual acuity [104]) and to an integration of previously established, nonvisual perceptual processes with new visual cues, which control a somewhat different adjustment to the mother. Transfer to solid food involves nutritive and behavioral adjustments that are accomplished by degrees and through the participation of various factors. Stages in behavioral development at higher psychological levels thus may be regarded as overlapping; their turning points occur in a more gradual manner than may be true of the events in maturation that contribute to them.

Ontogenetic progress and the role of experience. Under normal conditions, *experience* — the effect of stimulation on the organism, including especially stimulative effects characteristic of the species' ontogenetic milieu — is indispensable to development at all stages. The growing organism takes more from its environment than the energy essential for nutrition; it is affected from the first by energy changes in its environs and responds according to its developmental stage. *Trace effects*, organismic changes affecting further development, result.

Experience may contribute to ontogeny in subtle ways. From insects to man, not only the general developmental progression, but also events critical for the pattern changes of later stages, may involve factors of experience. We may expect to find that many physiological and behavioral rhythms, now often considered purely endogenous and innate, may result from an interrelation between intrinsic and *essential* extrinsic factors. For insects Harker (38) has found that the normal day-night activity rhythm of the adult mayfly does not appear unless the egg has been subjected to at least one 24-hour light-dark cycle. In some manner the organic effect of a specific physical condition, acting for a limited time at a very early stage, becomes deeply ingrained and influences complex daily behavioral variations in the adult stage. Comparable results were obtained by Brett (8) for the rhythm of pupal emergence in *Drosophila*.

In birds and mammals, organic periodicities basic to the development of adult drives may be stimulatively influenced by periodic experiences, as through changes in the behavior of the incubating mother. Comparably, tidal, diurnal, and other rhythms in the physical environment, as well as nonrhythmic changes, may affect the developing stages of animals from lower invertebrates to mammals, influencing the basis for both periodic and aperiodic processes underlying adult behavior. A striking case has been demonstrated by Hasler and Wisby (41) in Pacific salmon. When adult salmon ascend a river system to spawn, turns at stream branches are made toward the tributary carrying the chemical essence of the headwaters in which the individual developed from the egg before descending to the ocean.

The effects of early experience may influence the later stages of development in a nonparticulate manner. Moore (75) found that neonate rats, raised in an environment of 95° F. temperature, as adults had longer, more slender bodies and tails, and performed less well in maze-learning tests than did others kept at an environmental temperature of 55° F. It is not surprising that such extrinsic-intrinsic relationships are often overlooked or their effects misinterpreted in behavior studies.

The nature of gains through experience is both canalized and limited by the relative maturity of species-typical afferent, neural, and efferent mechanisms, in dependence upon the developmental stage attained.A definite conditioned response to a combination of contact and shock stimuli could not be demonstrated in the chick embryo before about 16 days (33); in the neonate dog, before about 20 days (29). According to phyletic capacities, the influence of experiential effects upon later behavior depends critically upon the stage at which they act. Thus in ungulates the mother is a prominent feature of the environment for the neonate, who, susceptible to specific exteroceptive effects such as odors, and with the eyes open, soon establishes a strong bond with the parent (6). In the phenomenon first described for birds by Lorenz (66) as "imprinting," the primacy of some available and conspicuous attractive object after hatching seems crucial, for the normal bond with the parent first of all and, secondly, with species mates. Newly hatched goslings first exposed to stimulation from a person are later unresponsive to stimuli from species mates as against the human object. In normal hatching, parent and species mates of course have the advantage of primacy (22). The prepotent stimulus for eliciting the approach seems to be highly generalized and definable in quantitative terms such as size and rate of movement. Stimuli specific to the initially adequate object soon become prepotent and canalize later response tendencies rather fundamentally. Such early adjustments are often virtually irreversible.

The trace effects of early experience seem to be characteristically generalized, diffuse, and variable, their influence at later stages non-particulate and difficult to identify. Even so, they must be reckoned with as important influences in the later behavior pattern. In tests of conditioning in chick embryos, Gos (33) found that specific conditioned responses to a touch-shock pairing could not be accomplished before approximately 16 days. But subjects stimulated repeatedly, after about the 10-day stage changed in their general responsiveness to the extrinsic stimuli used, indicating some trace effect. Hypothetically, the extent to which a vertebrate embryo is mechanically disturbed in the egg or uterus might be expected to affect the later levels of emotional excitability. Experiences common to the usual species environment, such as knocking about of the eggs as they are turned by the incubating parent or as the parent leaves the nest and returns to it, might have trace effects influencing similarly the development of all normally raised young. Therefore, from early biochemical effects to later experiences promoting learning, the characteristic properties of the species-standard environment are never to be taken for granted or minimized, but always admitted to the field of possible indispensable factors in normal development.

Relative maturity at birth differs widely among the mammals, and is to be considered a cardinal factor in development, determining which environmental effects will be influential. In ungulates such as goats, from a time shortly after birth the social bond seems to advance with acceleration to the stage of visual perception, greatly facilitated by a precocious quadrupedal motility as well as by specific olfactory, auditory, and tactual effects (6). In contrast, the advance of the neonate in carnivores such as cats and dogs seems to be much slower, against stricter early postnatal limitations along afferent, neural, and motor lines. Reciprocal stimulative relationships of the neonate with species mates seem based upon strong organic gratification from such stimulative processes, and must be considered fundamental to the wider social integration of the individual (88). Differences during and subsequent to the establishment of the primary bond with the mother, as well as in other group experiences bearing upon the litter period, may contribute basically to certain striking contrasts in group behavior tendencies characteristic of the various lower vertebrate orders. In carnivores, the typical disruption of such associations at the time of weaning would seem to be significantly related to organic and behavioral changes in the participants (e.g., maternal hormone effects) not common in ungulates, in which group associations typically persist with only secondary changes in the pattern of intragroup relationships.

The receptivity of the sexually mature mammal to a species mate may represent the rearousal of a perceptual responsiveness established earlier in life, as during the litter period. The appearance of this typical susceptibility, even in relatively nonsocial animals, would seem also to involve the lowering (through a hormonal priming of certain organic mechanisms) of afferent and other functional thresholds which serve as key items underlying the mating reaction. But the adjustments are perceptual, and for them, early experiences may well be critical. Thus, individual carnivores raised apart from their species mates are likely to display disturbance reactions upon encountering them for the first time in adult tests, and mate only after long delays and much disturbance, if at all.

In each species, the specificity and the nature of the effects of early experience upon later behavioral development seems to differ more or less characteristically according to developmental stage. Such trace effects may be major factors in ontogeny, but thus far have been difficult to identify as originating in the embryonic and early neonate stage of carnivores and other mammals with a protracted period of early development. One striking contrast is opened by the experiment of Fuller *et al.* (29), who found that puppies, presented with a combination of electric shock and a visual, auditory, or other exteroceptive stimulus, exhibited no specific signs of conditioning before the twentieth postnatal day. This result was confirmed by James and Cannon (54). It seems probable, however, that a less specific type of conditioning may occur at earlier postnatal stages in young carnivores, evidently mainly on a somesthetic and chemoceptive basis, and in terms of lower functional orders of neural integration. Studies in our laboratory (109) on the behavior of neonate kittens show that specialized feeding adjustments to the mother begin soon after birth and have taken on an individually characteristic pattern within the first day or two. The adaptations concern both a direct approach to the mother and the attachment of a given kitten to a particular nipple with increasing frequency, posted at the front, center, or rear in the nipple series. These adjustments, which usually are individually stabilized within the first four days after birth, clearly involve learning, and form a basis for wider social adaptations in the litter situation.

Species behavior patterns depend not only on characteristic maturation but also upon experiences normal to the species (59, 71). Kuo (60) manipulated the early experiential context of kittens to control their later reactions to rodents; and Patrick and Laughlin (80), by raising young rats in open areas as on table tops, obtained adults inclined to range more and to follow walls less than is usual for the species. Through tests with an isolated rhesus monkey, Foley (24) emphasized early associations with species mates as a factor in normal grooming reactions. Such results prepare us for Hebb's proposition (42, 43) that through early experience basic perceptual organizations are built up, and that the gains from experience are likely to be greater at opportune early phases in ontogeny than at later stages. With rats (25, 26) and with dogs (98) early environments of greater scope and heterogeneity provide a more adequate basis for perceptual adjustment to new situations than do more restricted, simpler environments, and a more adequate basis for performance in maze and problem-solving tests at later stages (3, 52). In mammals (1, 14) a wide variety of conditions in early postnatal experiences, from trauma (37) and deprivation (47, 50) to litter conditions (93) and maternal behavior (56) can influence behavioral development. Age normally brings a variety of accretions, substitutions and changes, attributable to progressive conditions in the organism and in its experience. For example, Seitz (92) found that young foxes, although they had been well tamed from an early age, from the age of about 36 days began to defend themselves against handling. Taming evidently serves to raise the excitation threshold for certain familiar perceptual patterns, but its inhibitive potency suffers at sexual maturity. Species properties like learning capacity, excitation threshold, tension adjustment, and a host of other characteristics must be considered among potential determinants of what experience may contribute at any stage.

Early generalized training often is basic to later more specialized adjustments. In Maier's tests (69) of reasoning in rodents, which required the combination of previously separate perceptual experiences, chance scores were made by rats younger than six months, scores of 80 per cent or more by adults. Young chimpanzees given early experience in handling of sticks in play later proved superior to chimpanzees lacking such experiences, when given reasoning tests requiring the combination of sticks into tools for reaching food (4).

The range and nature of developmental gains through early experience naturally depend first of all upon species capacities for learning. In insects and lower vertebrates gains through experience are less pervasive in later life than is typical for mammals (87). But for any species capable of learning, what is acquired must depend in part upon the conditions of exposure. Whether or not a mammal's response to an attractive or disturbing situation serves to change its motivational adjustment to that situation may determine whether a simple conditioned reaction or a selective-learning pattern is acquired (71, 72). Also, the tension level of the animal at the time of an experimentally introduced experience may determine the functional order of what is learned.

Finally, any generalization about stereotypy or variability in behavior through development must depend upon the phyletic level as well as on the conditions of individual experience and individual background. For instance, shock or punishment, as one well-studied condition, may promote variability (96) or stereotypy (70) in habit formation, according to the intensity of the shock and the manner in which it is administered. Many other conditions may determine whether experience in a mammalian species contributes to the individual repertoire a stereotyped habit of restricted scope or a more versatile pattern useful in new situations (71, 77).

Original nature and development. Rather than assume an "original nature," more or less modifiable secondarily, it seems preferable to regard behavior patterns on all levels as results of a developmental process representative of the species. In this process, genetic constitution is regarded as indirectly influential in the rise of structural-functional mechanisms through progressive intrinsic-extrinsic relationships characteristic of the level. In higher animals, developmental processes are progressively more labile in relation to capacities for profiting by experience and for behavioral plasticity. In the higher mammals, early behavior, although not formless, is most generalized of all, and the individual is most radically influenced by experience in the course of later development. But in no case can experience be considered a latecomer in development, limited to learning at later stages, for its earliest influences seem indispensable in the ontogeny of all animals. This is the case despite the fact that the trace effects of embryonic experiences seem qualitatively inferior and limited in comparison with higher functional orders of learning entering later on.

The concept of an original nature has found its main support in the widely used isolation method, purported to separate innate behavior from acquired (99). Typically, in an animal separated at birth and raised apart from its species mates, the principal responses appearing are considered innate or inborn (85, 92, 111). As a rule, this assumption places far too much weight on the experimenter's knowledge of the typical developmental setting and its effect in ontogeny (83). Actually, isolation tests unaccompanied by an appropriate analytical methodology show only what behavior can or cannot develop in either of the two situations — usual and unusual — through causes not demonstrated. For one thing, the contexts may be equivalent in certain important but unidentified respects, as, for example, when the animal through its *own* organic and behavioral properties has introduced a sequence of stimulative effects normal to the species (91).

LEVELS OF ATTAINMENT THROUGH ONTOGENY

Perception. Adaptive behavior may be achieved at different phyletic levels through capacities low or high in functional order, in relation to the species niche. Through ontogeny, irritability or sensitivity arises in all animals in very different manifestations which are basic to a variety of adaptive patterns. This fact does not justify generalizing the capacity of *perception* through all phyletic levels, as is often done by reducing it to any stimulative reaction whatever (77). It is imperative to investigate whether a given species really can progress, through development, beyond the lowest functional order of mere reaction to stimulation. Actually, critical phyletic differences in capacities for organizing sensory data seem evident, not as differences in degree but as differences in kind (42, 89). Stimulative irritability, in its simpler forms, need entail no more than simple sensory effects, far inferior to and qualitatively very different from the specialized perceptual processes of which higher mammals are capable.

Experimental psychologists have been unable to analyze out the raw-sensory effect element from other components in a perceptual adjustment (35), possibly because adequate investigations have yet to be made at early ontogenetic stages and with different phyla. Protozoa assuredly possess stimulative irritability, but it remains to be demonstrated that they perceive, i.e., *sense with meaning.* Recognizable perceptual adjustments of a low organizational order appear in lower vertebrates in a form which resists later ontogenetic modification. Ehrenhardt (20) could train lizards only to a limited extent to snap at the member of a stimulus pair with the more irregular outline, in opposition to the characteristic naïve response of this animal, i.e., the response most easily established early in ontogeny. In mammals, specialized and more plastic perceptual adjustments are mastered more slowly in ontogeny, but are modifiable to far greater extents as a rule than is possible in lower vertebrates.

Perceptual habits seem very different on lower and higher vertebrate levels. Within a few trials after hatching, the chick begins to discriminate grains from small, bright, inedible objects, improving on the nonparticulate stimuli which initially evoked the embryonic head-lunge (71). In contrast, young carnivores require more time to integrate visual cues with nonvisual perceptual adjustments established to mother and litter mates earlier in the neonate period (84). Methods must be devised adequate to the task of tracing ontogenetic progress from sensory naïvete to perceptual adequacy in animals at different phyletic levels.

Claims for "innate perceptual schemata" have not been validated in adequate experimental investigations. Presumed innate "sign stimuli" (99, 100) seem to resolve themselves, not into initially meaningful patterns, but into very generalized stimulus effects (31, 89). For example, the "hawk reaction" of nestling birds in certain species, which had been attributed to an innate meaning content, seems due rather to a diffuse stimulative shock effect than to an inborn pattern significance (31, 74). For perceptual meaning and organization, experience seems necessary, although its gains are much more restricted in lower vertebrates than in mammals. Through experiments in which, by means of translucent hoods, ring doves were deprived of early experience in visual definition, Siegel (94) found that even in this psychologically inferior bird, such experience normally must contribute an essential perceptual basis for learning pattern discriminations in adulthood. In a similar study of the chimpanzee, Chow and Nissen (13) found that experience is very essential for adult interocular equivalence in pattern discrimination. Experiments with the rat led Teas and Bitterman (97) to conclude that initial visual adjustments are "loosely organized wholes out of which the perception of objects and relations is subsequently differentiated."

The sensing of the new and strange is increasingly striking in ontogeny, from rodents to primates (42), and invites further study as indicating the integration of a wider scope of environmental cues. Correspondingly, from the fact that the chimpanzee's curiosity seems dominantly destructive in its motor outlets, and man's on the whole constructive, Nissen (78) refers to the greater command of object and situation relationships in the latter. In a comparative study of early development in the chimpanzee and the human infant, Jacobsen *et al.* (53) found the chimpanzee well ahead in all aspects of sensitivity and reactivity during the first nine months. However, as the infant began to accelerate in perceptual accomplishments and in early concept formation, as indicated by the mastery of his first words, his superiority in psychological development became increasingly apparent.

Motivation. The manner in which differentiated drives appear through ontogeny is still unclear for any animal. Comparative investigations are needed as to the ontogeny of motivation, and I wish here to offer some theoretical considerations with respect to this problem.

It is probable that homeostasis affords a comparable basis for adaptive behavior in all vertebrates: a generalized excitation set up by some marked deviation from the theoretical "steady state" forces a readjustment to the pattern of metabolic processes normal to the species. But, as Pick (82) has pointed out, homeostatic mechanisms elaborate and change from fishes to man. It is not only in the organic mechanisms of homeostasis themselves that the evolutionary elaboration occurs, but also in their potentialities for widened behavioral relationships through ontogeny. A primary question is, How do these reactions become differentiated appropriately as adjustments of approach or of withdrawal?

Theoretically, in all organisms, evolution has involved the selection of mechanisms favoring approach to *mild* stimulative effects and avoidance of *intense* stimulative effects (86, 89). This set of relationships between individual and environment may be proposed as a primary condition in the ontogeny of all animals, accounting for basic tendencies of the types traditionally contrasted as "appetite" and "aversion" (17, 48). Species violating this condition as basic in ontogeny would risk extinction. Other things equal, the pseudopod of an amoeba shrinks with intense local stimulation and extends with weak stimulation; correspondingly, the forelimb of a neonate mammal flexes or adducts, extends or abducts, according to the energy of local stimulation (11, 12).

The selective process postulated as operative in these terms throughout the phyletic series presumably has included all types of functional thresholds, from afferent and neural to those of visceral and motor systems. Fundamentally, before ontogeny advances very far, these mechanisms are specifically dominated by the intensity of stimulative energy presented in any given experience. The response here depends critically upon the intensity of the neurophysiological energy discharge produced, and not upon what *kind* of object or situation produced it, nor upon its potentialities for eventual benefit or harm to the organism. In the earthworm (46, 71) the response is typically a wholebody approach or withdrawal, stereotyped and appearing early in ontogeny, a forced type of reaction not much changed throughout life in its typical relationship to the intensity range of stimulation (other things — e.g., temporary sensory adaptations — being equal). Once onto-genetically established, as with the typical lunge reaction of lower vertebrates to small moving objects and withdrawal from larger mov-ing objects (21, 49), the stereotyped patterns resist modification (20). On higher levels, motivation must be thought of as having an increas-ingly complex ontogeny. New rules are possible; the primary naïve relation of response to objective stimulus intensity may then be modi-fied and, indeed, reversed, according to species capacities and the ex-ternal circumstances encountered in individual experience.

In mammals, a more generalized condition of drive is postulated in early ontogeny, although still paralleling the described biphasic basis for response according to stimulus energy effect, viewed as a central feature of development in all animals. Theoretically, the ontogeny of mammalian *withdrawal* adjustments is primarily centered in high-threshold mechanisms in afferent, neural, flexor-adductor muscles and in the sympathetic autonomic and related visceral systems; that of *approach* adjustments is centered in low-threshold, afferent, neural, extensor-abductor muscles and the parasympathetic and related viscer-al systems. It is presumed that the neural changes underlying learning are maximally affected through conditions activating either one of these systems in a synergic manner, as when intense stimulation is reduced or the source evaded through withdrawal, weak stimulation held or the source gained through approach. The ontogenetic basis of individual learning is thus viewed as essentially biphasic in these terms.

In contrast to the stereotypy characteristic of lower levels, higher mammals attain increasingly plastic and individually specialized drive, incentive, and consummatory relationships. "Searching for . . . ," as a term applied to lower animals, is a loose generalization usually in-dicating random behavior under drive impulsion; but through on-togeny in a mammal with advanced capacities for learning, the ex-pression can mean the specific, drive-impelled anticipation of an incen-tive. Infant rats, subjected to regular experiences of food and water deprivation, as adults learn to locate these objects with greater facility than do normal subjects (15). Such results would not be expected in reptiles; but in chimpanzees, capable of more involved differentiations in motivation, assemblage of appropriate symbolic tokens could occur under comparable conditions. Mammalian motivation is a superior attainment through higher functional orders in behavioral development than are possible in lower phyla.

Conditions widening ontogenetic attainment. The potentialities of ontogeny depend most significantly upon the extent to which the central nervous system has developed a basis for the processes underlying learning. Notwithstanding arguments for "learning" in the radially symmetrical invertebrates below flatworms (103), a general distinction of qualitative differences seems necessary here (71). The trace effects of experience in organisms such as protozoa and coelenterates seem to be diffuse or peripheral, and not a basis for more lasting changes in the individual behavior pattern. For example, in paramecia subject to the combined effects of light and temperature, temporary behavior changes may be produced which suggest conditioned responses (7, 103). However, these changes depend upon some evanescent condition in metabolism, due solely to thermal effects (2, 34) altering sensitivity to light for a limited time. In contrast, invertebrates such as worms and insects are capable of neural trace effects through experience (71), as a basis for more lasting changes in the individual behavior pattern.

In addition to neural trace effects, or *fixation*, there is the capacity of advanced neural systems for *correlation*, or the organization of trace effects. Phyletic differences in the capacity of the nervous system to correlate the effects of experience must account for the fact that although many insects are capable of forming rather complex habits, these patterns seem much more limited in plasticity (i.e., in properties for change and transfer) and far more situation-bound than is typically the case with mammals (71, 87).

Simple conditioned responses established when the animal's reaction alters the situation in some critically adaptive way have different properties from the simpler conditioned-reflex types of change learned by more passive subjects. The former pattern is more similar to selective learning in its properties (71, 72). The conditioned response of the flatworm, in its general make-up, vaguely resembles that typical of decerebrate carnivores (e.g., as generalized), but seems far inferior to the gains possible through learning in normal mammals. The cerebral cortex, evolving as a special modification of the vertebrate forebrain (45, 55, 57), introduces new properties and higher functional orders of attainment in species ontogeny, freeing the individual from the domination of specific afferent or motor mechanisms.

With the rapid acceleration of this correlative asset to predominance in the mammals, there appear striking advances in species attainments related to experience in ontogeny. Penfield (81) attributes man's superior intellectual attainments to the frontal and parietal lobes of the cerebral cortex, increasing through the mammals to man but without a specific counterpart in lower vertebrates. This superiority is also, although less obviously, due to evolutionary advances in the lower-center neural mechanisms (82) which specifically favor the acquisition of more extensive organizations of central and peripheral processes (as in motivation [91]). Improved neural correlation promotes the attainment of a wider, more intricate set of environmental adjustments, and of new behavioral patterns as individual accomplishments, provided that such acquisitions are favored by the circumstances of ontogeny.

From these considerations, one would anticipate significant improvements in animal intelligence tests through measuring plasticity in modifying learned habits, rather than through measuring acquisition or retention. This seems to be the case after equivalent experience. Rodents are on the whole less gifted in the roundabout type of adjustment than are dogs, but carnivores fall short of the primates in this respect. Accordingly, in a test requiring the selection of the alternative learned response appropriate to whichever of two experienced incentives was presented, Fischel (23) found that although turtles and birds failed and dogs succeeded, the latter were distinctly inferior to human subjects. In higher animals, responses to young, food, and other goal objects are not necessarily more intense in energy output, but are richer in meaning content and more versatile in their appropriateness to changing environmental situations than responses in lower forms. With increasing cortical correlation capacity influencing ontogeny, species attainments in behavior are marked increasingly by the characteristics of appropriate variation and newness.

The existence of qualitative differences between species in capacities for behavioral organization cannot be doubted, and more extensive comparative studies are overdue (87, 90). Learning clearly furnishes the ontogenetic basis for higher attainments such as reasoning; but reasoning does not therefore reduce to learning, any more than these capacities may be considered fully distinct from each other. Harlow

(39) has shown for the monkey how cumulative experience in "learn-ing to learn" object discriminations may progress to a high degree of complexity and skill. However, visual-discrimination methods may not be well suited for the analysis of higher mental functions based on learning (71). If systematic tests adequate for this purpose can be de-vised for a variety of animal forms, phyletic differences in potentiali-ties for psychological development may prove more striking than has been suspected.

The advantages of the comparative method have been scarcely ex-plored in the study of behavioral development (87, 106). A child's at-tainment of sentences marks a new advance from the stage of unitary verbal symbols, and contrasts sharply with a monkey's inability to master symbolic relationships beyond the simplest abstractions. In a far wider sense, man's capacity for repatterning verbal symbols serially, or for attaining such symbols at all, is qualitatively far above the functional order represented by the gestural symbolic processes to which the chimpanzee seems developmentally limited, although not altogether dissimilar in its ontogenetic basis.

SUMMARY AND CONCLUSIONS

As a recapitulation doctrine has not been validated for behavior, the concept of *psychological levels* is advanced to express the phyletic range of behavioral organization and psychological capacities, and the concept of *functional orders* is advanced to express the ontogenetic range on any one level.

The term *development* with respect to individual behavior stresses progressive changes in organized adaptive function through ontogeny. Behavioral development on any phyletic level is not so much a re-tracing through the stages and levels of successive ancestral forms as a new composite leading to a new pattern distinctive of the level.

Genetic constitution and developmental setting influence *all* be-havioral development in *all* organisms, operating jointly through a complex formula of intervening maturation-experience variables in a casual nexus typical of the level. *Maturation* connotes processes con-tributed through growth and differentiation, and *experience* connotes the effects of stimulation on the organism.

The nature and specificity of the developmental effects of early ex-perience depend upon species capacities, developmental stage, and setting. The trace effects of early experience, although mainly generalized and diffuse in comparison with those of later stages at which specific conditioning and learning enter, may be fundamental to behavioral development. At higher levels, simple conditioning must be considered a possible developmental factor even in prenatal stages.

Within the unusual developmental setting of the species, typical patterns of successive self-stimulative effects, as well as of other feedback effects and of inevitable experiences, offer key factors for the progression of stages characteristic of species ontogeny. In many species, ontogeny may also entail characteristic reciprocal stimulative ("trophallactic") processes between individuals, essential to the rise of group behavioral affiliations as well as of mating.

In lower phyla, behavior patterns are stereotyped within a relatively short ontogeny in terms of lesser functional orders, and thereafter resist change; in higher phyla, after generalized early stages, through a longer ontogeny they involve functional orders of increasing scope and plasticity. But for no species is ontogeny based upon an initial innate pattern ("original nature") modified to different extents at later stages.

Plasticity, a superior functional order in variable behavior, depends both upon the species capacities for the fixation and correlation of neural trace effects and upon the range and character of individual experience. From a simple sensory irritability prevalent in the lowest phyla, animals in higher phyla advance through ontogeny to higher orders of relationships and meaningful organization in perception. In mammals, early naïve sensory responses are basic in ontogeny to progressively higher perceptual orders attained according to species capacities and opportunity through experience.

A wide parallelism exists among phyla in the mechanisms underlying adaptive behavior, susceptible to specializations of approach and withdrawal adjustments according to ontogenetic capacities and opportunities on the respective levels. On this basis, increasingly elaborate drive processes underlie the attainment of successively higher orders of anticipative motivational adjustments.

Superior behavioral attainments at higher psychological levels depend not only upon capacities for neural correlation and systematic organization, but also upon advances in phyletically old mechanisms (e.g., those of homeostasis). Species attainments in behavioral plasticity broaden correspondingly, with greater situation-appropriate variation and newness, when extrinsic conditions are favorable in ontogeny.

REFERENCES

1. Beach, F., and J. Jaynes. "Effects of Early Experience upon the Behavior of Animals," *Psychol. Bull.,* Vol. 51 (1954), pp. 240–63.
2. Best, J. B. "The Photosensitization of *Paramecium aurelia* by Temperature Shock," *J. Exper. Zool.,* Vol. 126 (1954), pp. 87–99.
3. Bingham, W. E., and W. J. Griffiths, Jr. "The Effect of Different Environments during Infancy on Adult Behavior in the Rat," *J. Comp. Physiol. Psychol.,* Vol. 45 (1952), pp. 307–12.
4. Birch, H. B. "The Relation of Previous Experience to Insightful Problem-solving," *J. Comp. Psychol.,* Vol. 38 (1954), pp. 367–83.
5. ———. "Ontogenetic Sources for Order in the Maternal Behavior of the Rat." Unpublishd paper.
6. Blauvelt, Helen. "Dynamics of the Mother-Newborn Relationship in Goats," in *Group Processes,* 1st Conference, 1954, pp. 221–58. New York: Josiah Macy, Jr., 1955.
7. Bramstedt, F. "Dressurversuche mit *Paramecium caudatum* und *Stylonchia mytilus,*" *Z. vergl. Physiol.,* Vol. 22 (1935), pp. 490–516.
8. Brett, W. J. "Persistent Diurnal Rhythmicity in *Drosophila,*" *Ann. Ent. Soc. Amer.,* Vol. 48 (1955), pp. 119–31.
9. Carmichael, L. "The Development of Behavior in Vertebrates Experimentally Removed from the Influence of External Stimulation," *Psychol. Rev.,* Vol. 33 (1926), pp. 51–58.
10. ———. "A Re-evaluation of the Concepts of Maturation and Learning as Applied to the Early Development of Behavior," *Psychol. Rev.,* Vol. 43 (1936), pp. 450–70.
11. ———. "The Onset and Early Development of Behavior," in L. Carmichael, ed., *Manual of Child Psychology,* pp. 43–166. New York: Wiley, 1946.
12. ———, and M. F. Smith. "Quantified Pressure Stimulation and the Specificity and Generality of Response in Fetal Life," *J. Genet. Psychol.,* Vol. 54 (1939), pp. 425–34.
13. Chow, K. L., and H. W. Nissen. "Interocular Transfer of Learning in Visually Naïve and Experienced Infant Chimpanzees," *J. Comp. Physiol.,* Vol. 48 (1955), pp. 229–32.
14. Christie, R. "Experimental Naïveté and Experiential Naïveté," *Psychol. Bull.,* Vol. 48 (1951), pp. 327–39.
15. ———. "The Effect of Some Early Experiences in the Latent Learning of Rats," *J. Exper. Psychol.,* Vol. 43 (1952), pp. 381–88.
16. Coghill, G. E. *Anatomy and the Problem of Behavior.* New York: Macmillan, 1929.
17. Craig, W. "Appetites and Aversions as Constituents of Instinct," *Biol. Bull.,* Vol. 34 (1911), pp. 91–107.
18. DeBeer, G. R. *Embryos and Ancestors.* Oxford: Clarendon Press, 1951.
19. Dobzhansky, T. "Heredity, Environment, and Evolution," *Science,* Vol. 111 (1950), No. 2877, pp. 161–66.
20. Ehrenhardt, H. "Formensehen und Sehscharfebestimmungen bei Eidechsen," *Z. vergl. Physiol.,* Vol. 24 (1937), pp. 258–304.
21. Eibl-Eibesfeldt, I. "Nahrungserwerb und Beuteschema der Erdkröte (*Bufo bufo l.*)," *Behav.,* Vol. 4 (1952), pp. 1–35.
22. Fabricus, E. "Zur Ethologie junger Anatiden," *Acta Zool. Fennica,* Vol. 68 (1951), pp. 1–177.

23. Fischel, G. *Die Seele des Hundes*. Berlin: Paul Parey, 1950.
24. Foley, J. P. "First Year Development of a Rhesus Monkey (*Macaca Mulatta*) Reared in Isolation," *J. Genet. Psychol.*, Vol. 44 (1934), pp. 390–413.
25. Forgays, D. G. and Janet W. "The Nature of the Effect of Free-environmental Experience in the Rat," *J. Comp. Physiol. Psychol.*, Vol. 45 (1952), pp. 322–28.
26. Forgus, R. H. "The Effect of Early Perceptual Learning on the Behavioral Organization of Adult Rats," *J. Comp. Physiol. Psychol.*, Vol. 47 (1954), pp. 331–36.
27. Frisch, K. von. *Bees: Their Vision, Chemical Senses, and Language*. Ithaca: Cornell University Press, 1950.
28. Fromme, A. "An Experimental Study of the Factors of Maturation and Practice in the Behavioral Development of the Embryo of the Frog, *Rana pipiens*," *Genet. Psychol. Monogr.*, Vol. 24 (1941), pp. 219–56.
29. Fuller, J., C. A. Easler, and E. M. Banks. "Formation of Conditioned Avoidance Responses in Young Puppies," *Amer. J. Physiol.*, Vol. 160 (1950), pp. 462–66.
30. Gesell, A. *The Embryology of Behavior: The Beginnings of the Human Mind*. New York: Harpers, 1945.
31. Ginsberg, A. "A Reconstructive Analysis of the Concept 'Instinct,'" *J. Psychol.*, Vol. 33 (1952), pp. 235–77.
32. Gluecksohn-Waelsch, Salome. "Some Genetic Aspects of Development," in *The Mammalian Fetus: Physiological Aspects of Development*. Cold. Spr. Harb. Sympos. Quant. Biol., (1954), XIX.
33. Gos, M. "Les reflexes conditionels chez l'embryon d'oiseau," *Bull. Soc. Sci.*, (Liège, 1935), 4me Année (4–5), pp. 194–99, (6–7), pp. 246–50.
34. Grabowski, U. "Experimentelle Untersuchungen über das angebliche Lernvermögen von Paramaecium," *Z. Tierpsychol.*, Vol. 2 (1939), pp. 265–81.
35. Graham, C. H. "Behavior, Perception, and the Psychophysical Methods," *Psychol. Rev.*, Vol. 57 (1950), pp. 108–20.
36. Hall, G. S. "The Genetics of Behavior," in S. S. Stevens, ed., *Handbook of Experimental Psychology*, pp. 304–29. New York, Wiley, 1951.
37. ———, and P. H. Whiteman. "The Effects of Infantile Stimulation upon Later Emotional Stability in the Mouse," *J. Comp. Physiol. Psychol.*, Vol. 44 (1951), pp. 61–66.
38. Harker, Janet E. "The Diurnal Rhythm of Activity of Mayfly Nymphs," *J. Exper. Biol.*, Vol. 30 (1953), pp. 525–33.
39. Harlow, H. "The Formation of Learning Sets," *Psychol. Rev.*, Vol. 56 (1949), pp. 51–65.
40. Harnly, M. H. "Flight Capacity in Relation to Phenotypic and Genotypic Variations in the Wings of *Drosophila melanogaster*," *J. Exper. Zool.*, Vol. 88 (1941), pp. 263–74.
41. Hasler, A. D., and W. J. Wisby. "Discrimination of Stream Odors by Fishes and its Relation to Parent Stream Behavior," *Amer. Nat.*, Vol. 85 (1951), pp. 223–38.
42. Hebb, D. O. *The Organization of Behavior*. New York: Wiley, 1949.
43. ———. "Heredity and Environment in Mammalian Behavior," *Brit. J. Anim. Behav.*, Vol. 1 (1953), pp. 43–47.
44. Hempelmann, F. *Tierpsychologie vom Standpunkte des Biologen*. Leipzig: Akad. Verlagsges., 1926.
45. Herrick, C. J. *Neurological Foundations of Animal Behavior*. New York: Holt, 1924.
46. Hess, W. "Reactions to Light in the Earthworm, *Lumbricus terrestris, L.*," *J. Morphol. Physiol.*, Vol. 39 (1924), pp. 515–42.
47. Holland, J. G. "The Influence of Previous Experience and Residual Effects of Deprivation on Hoarding in the Rat," *J. Comp. Physiol. Psychol.*, Vol. 47 (1954), pp. 244–47.
48. Holt, E. B. *Animal Drive and the Learning Process*. London: Williams and Norgate, 1931.

49. Honigmann, H. "The Visual Perception of Movements by Toads," *Proc. Roy. Zool. Soc.*, Series B, Vol. 132 (1945), pp. 291–307.

50. Hunt, J. McV. "The Effects of Infant Feeding-Frustration upon Adult Hoarding in the Albino Rat," *J. Abn. and Soc. Psychol.*, Vol. 36 (1941), pp. 338–60.

51. Hunter, W. S. "Summary Comments on the Heredity-Environment Symposium," *Psychol. Rev.*, Vol. 54 (1947), pp. 348–52.

52. Hymovitch, B. "The Effects of Experimental Variations on Problem-Solving in the Rat," *J. Comp. Physiol. Psychol.*, Vol. 45 (1952), pp. 313–20.

53. Jacobsen, C. F., M. M. Jacobsen, and J. G. Yoshioka. "Development of an Infant Chimpanzee during her First Year," *Comp. Psychol. Monogr.*, Vol. 9 (1932), No. 41, pp. 1–94.

54. James, W. T., and D. J. Cannon. "Conditioned Avoiding Responses in Puppies," *Amer. J. Physiol.*, Vol. 168 (1952), pp. 251–53.

55. Jerison, H. J. "Brain to Body Ratios and the Evolution of Intelligence," *Science*, Vol. 121 (1955), pp. 447–49.

56. Kahn, M. W. "Infantile Experience and Mature Aggressive Behavior of Mice: Some Maternal Influences," *J. Genet. Psychol.*, Vol. 84 (1954), pp. 65–75.

57. Kappers, C. U. A., G. C. Huber, and E. C. Crosby. *The Comparative Anatomy of the Nervous System of Vertebrates, Including Man.* New York: Macmillan, 1946.

58. Kinder, E. F. "A Study of the Nest-Building Activity of the Albino Rat," *J. Exper. Zool.*, Vol. 47 (1927), pp. 117–61.

59. Kuo, Z. Y. "A Psychology without Heredity," *Psychol. Rev.*, Vol. 31 (1924), pp. 427–48.

60. ———. "The Genesis of the Cat's Response to the Rat," *J. Comp. Psychol.*, Vol. 11 (1930), pp. 1–30.

61. ———. "Ontogeny of Embryonic Behavior in Aves. II. The Mechanical Factors in the Various Stages Leading to Hatching," *J. Exper. Zool.*, Vol. 61 (1932), pp. 395–430.

62. ———. "Ontogeny of Embryonic Behavior in Aves. III. The Structure and Environmental Factors in Embryonic Behavior," *J. Comp. Psychol.*, Vol. 13 (1932), pp. 245–72.

63. ———. "Ontogeny of Embryonic Behavior in Aves. IV. The Influence of Embryonic Movements upon the Behavior after Hatching," *J. Comp. Psychol.*, Vol. 14 (1932), pp. 109–12.

64. Lehrman, D. S. "A Critique of Lorenz's 'Objectivistic' Theory of Animal Behavior," *Quart. Rev. Biol.*, Vol. 28 (1953), pp. 337–63.

65. ———. "The Physiological Basis of Parental Feeding Behavior in the Ring Dove, *Streptopelia risoria*," *Behav.*, Vol. 7 (1955), pp. 241–86.

66. Lorenz, K. "Der Kumpan in der Umwelt des Vogels," *J. für Ornithologie*, Vol. 83 (1935), pp. 137–213.

67. ———. "The Comparative Method in Studying Innate Behavior Patterns," in *Physiological Mechanisms in Animal Behavior*, pp. 221–68. New York: Academic Press, 1950.

68. Lunchins, A. S., and R. H. Forgus. "The Effect of Differential Post-Weaning Environment on the Rigidity of an Animal's Behavior," *J. Genet. Psychol.*, Vol. 86 (1955), pp. 51–58.

69. Maier, N. R. F. "Age and Intelligence in Rats," *J. Comp. Psychol.*, Vol. 13 (1932), pp. 1–6.

70. ———, and J. B. Klee. "Studies of Abnormal Behavior in the Rat. XII. The Pattern of Punishment and its Relation to Abnormal Fixations," *J. Exper. Psychol.*, Vol. 32 (1943), pp. 377–98.

71. ———, and T. C. Schneirla. *Principles of Animal Psychology.* New York: McGraw, 1935.

72. ———. "Mechanisms in Conditioning," *Psychol. Rev.*, Vol. 49 (1942), pp. 117–34.

73. McGraw, Myrtle. "Maturation of Behavior," in L. Carmichael, ed., *Manual of Child Psychology*, pp. 332–69. New York: Wiley, 1946.

74. McNiven, M. A. "Responses of the Chicken, Duck, and Pheasant to a Hawk and Goose Silhouette: A Controlled Replication of Tinbergen's Study." Unpublished M.A. thesis, University of Pennsylvania, 1954.

75. Moore, K. "The Effect of Controlled Temperature Changes on the Behavior of the White Rat," *J. Exper. Psychol.*, Vol. 34 (1944), pp. 70–79.

76. Needham, J. *The Sceptical Biologist.* London: Chatto, 1929.

77. Nissen, H. W. "Phylogenetic Comparison," in S. S. Stevens, ed., *Handbook of Experimental Psychology*, pp. 347–86. New York: Wiley, 1951.

78. ———. "The Nature of the Drive as Innate Determinant of Behavioral Organization," in *Nebraska Symposium on Motivation.* Lincoln: University of Nebraska Press, 1954.

79. Orton, Grace. "The Role of Ontogeny in Systematics and Evolution," *Evol.*, Vol. 9 (1955), pp. 75–83.

80. Patrick, J. R., and R. M. Laughlin. "Is the Wall-Seeking Tendency in the White Rat an Instinct?" *J. Genet. Psychol.*, Vol. 44 (1934), pp. 378–89.

81. Penfield, W. "Some Observations on the Functional Organization of the Human Brain," *Proc. Amer. Phil. Soc.*, Vol. 98 (1954), pp. 293–97.

82. Pick, J. "The Evolution of Homeostasis," *Proc. Amer. Phil. Soc.*, Vol. 98 (1954), pp. 298–303.

83. Riess, B. "The Isolation of Factors of Learning and Native Behavior in Field and Laboratory Studies," *Ann. N. Y. Acad. Sci.*, Vol. 51 (1950), pp. 1093–1102.

84. Rosenblatt, J., J. Wodinsky, A. Frank, and T. C. Schneirla. "Analytical Studies on Maternal Behavior and Litter Relations in the Domestic Cat. II. From Birth to Weaning." Unpublished paper.

85. Schneider, K. M. "Aus der Jugendentwicklung einer künstlich aufgezogenen Schimpansin. III. Vom Verhalten," *Z. Tierpsychol.*, Vol. 7 (1950), pp. 485–558.

86. Schneirla, T. C. "A Theoretical Consideration of the Basis for Approach-Withdrawal Adjustments in Behavior," *Psychol. Bull.*, Vol. 37 (1939), pp. 501–02.

87. ———. "Ant Learning as a Problem in Comparative Psychology," in P. Harriman, ed., *Twentieth Century Psychology*, pp. 276–305. New York: Philosophical Library, 1945. See also "Contemporary American Animal Psychology" in the same volume, pp. 306–316.

88. ———. "Problems in the Biopsychology of Social Organization," *J. Abn. and Soc. Psychol.*, Vol. 41 (1946), pp. 385–402.

89. ———. "Levels in the Psychological Capacities of Animals," in R. W. Sellars, *et al.*, *Philosophy for the Future.* New York: Macmillan, 1949.

90. ———. "A Consideration of some Conceptional Trends in Comparative Psychology," *Psychol. Bull.*, Vol. 49 (1952), pp. 559–97.

91. ———. "Interrelationships of the 'Innate' and the 'Acquired' in Instinctive Behavior," in *Colloque Int. sur l'Instinct Animale*, pp. 387–432. Paris: Masson et Cie., 1956.

92. Seitz, A. "Untersuchungen über Verhaltensweisen bei Caniden," *Z. Tierpsychol.*, Vol. 7 (1950), pp. 1–46.

93. Seitz, P. F. D. "The Effects of Infantile Experience upon Adult Behavior in Animal Subjects: Effects of Litter Size during Infancy upon Adult Behavior in the Rat," *Amer. J. Psychiat.*, Vol. 110 (1954), pp. 916–27.

94. Siegel, A. I. "Deprivation of Visual Form Definition in the Ring Dove: Discriminatory Learning," *J. Comp. Physiol. Psychol.*, Vol. 46 (1953), pp. 115–19; "Perceptual Motor Transfer," *Ibid.*, pp. 250–52.

95. Snyder, L. H. *The Principles of Heredity.* Boston: Heath, 1950.

96. Stone, G. R. "The Effect of Negative Incentive on Serial Learning: The Spread

of Variability under Electric Shock," *J. Exper. Psychol.*, Vol. 36 (1946), pp. 137–42.

97. Teas, D. C., and M. E. Bitterman. "Perceptual Organization in the Rat," *Psychol. Rev.*, Vol. 59 (1952), pp. 130–40.

98. Thompson, W. R. "The Effects of Restricting Early Experience on the Problem-Solving Capacity of Dogs," *Canad. J. Psychol.*, Vol. 8 (1954), pp. 17–31.

99. Tinbergen, N. *The Study of Instinct.* New York: Oxford University Press, 1951.

100. ——, and D. J. Kuenen, Über die auslösenden und die richtunggebenden Reizsituationen der Sperrbewegung von jungen Drosseln (*Turdus m. mercula L. und T. e. ericetorum Turton*)," *Z. Tierpsychol.*, Vol. 3 (1939), pp. 37–60.

101. Van der Kloot, G., and C. M. Williams. "Cocoon Construction by the Cecropia Silkworm: The Role of the Internal Environment," *Behav.*, Vol. 5 (1953), pp. 157–74.

102. Waddington, C. H. *Organizers and Genes.* Cambridge: Cambridge University Press, 1940.

103. Warden, C. J., T. N. Jenkins, and L. Warner. *Plants and Invertebrates*, Vol. II of *Comparative Psychology*. New York: Ronald Press, 1940.

104. Warkentin, J., and K. U. Smith. "The Development of Visual Acuity in the Cat," *J. Genet. Psychol.*, Vol. 50 (1937), pp. 371–99.

105. Weiss, P. "Some Introductory Remarks on the Cellular Basis of Differentiation," *J. Embryol. Exper. Morphol.*, Vol. 1 (1954), pp. 181–211.

106. Werner, H. *Comparative Psychology of Mental Development.* New York: Harper, 1940.

107. Wheeler, W. M. *The Social Insects.* New York: Harcourt, 1928.

108. Willier, B. H. "Phases in Embryonic Development," *J. Cell. Comp. Physiol.*, Vol. 43 (1954), pp. 307–17.

109. Wodinsky, J., J. S. Rosenblatt, G. Turkewitz, and T. C. Schneirla. "The Establishment of Stable Individual Nursing Adjustments by Neonate Kittens." Unpublished paper.

110. Woodger, J. H. "What We Mean by 'Inborn,' " *Brit. J. Phil. Sci.*, Vol. 3 (1953), pp. 319–26.

111. Zippelius, Hanna-Maria, and F. Goethe. "Ethologische Beobachtungen an Haselmäusen (*Muscardinus a. avellanarius L.*)," *Z. Tierpsychol.*, Vol. 8 (1951), pp. 348–67.

Howard V. Meredith

A DESCRIPTIVE CONCEPT OF PHYSICAL DEVELOPMENT

P HYSICAL development is not "a scientific term with defined and constant meaning" (32). Consequently, the first obligation of one who discusses physical development is to make explicit the meaning the term will carry.

Biologic organisms are studied developmentally in two respects, phylogenetically and ontogenetically. Students of phylogenetic development investigate changes within phyla, species, and subspecies from generation to generation, from eon to eon. Students of ontogenetic development study sequential modifications of individual organisms, beginning with their earliest embryonic condition and continuing to the close of senility. Throughout this presentation the term physical development will be employed with delimited reference to ontogenesis.

Applied to the life span of the individual organism, physical development may denote anatomic and physiologic changes or it may denote anatomic changes alone. In the broader application physical development is synonymous with developmental somatology, encompassing the entire structural and functional ontogenesis of cells, tissues, organs, and organism. In the more restricted application there is "both physical and physiological development" (22), the dichotomy obtained by separating developmental anatomy from developmental physiology, and making the term physical development synonymous with anatomic ontogenesis.

With the foregoing as background, it is possible to place the key-

stone for communication on an unequivocal basis. The concept projected for discussion pertains to physical development *with the understanding* that this term has the sense or meaning of anatomic ontogenesis. In other words, physical development will carry the connotation of being identical with the gamut of structural change that occurs
during ontogeny. To borrow phraseology from Krogman (16), physical
development is equated with "the sequential sum total" of anatomic
modifications that an individual organism undergoes "throughout its
entire life span."

HISTORIC CONCEPTS OF PHYSICAL DEVELOPMENT

During the century 1650 to 1750, zoologic studies involving the
utilization of crude microscopes and the inference of "preformation"
fostered one of the early concepts of physical development. On the
interpretation that at fertilization "a fully formed animal exists in
miniature" (1), anatomic ontogenesis was conceptually described as
increase in size.

With the improvement and extension of both microscopic and
macroscopic observations, it became well demonstrated by 1900 that
the developing organism did far more than increase in size. The
zygote was proved not a miniature adult, but a structurally simple
organism without head or limbs, heart or brain, bones or teeth, muscles
or sense organs. Investigation at a number of postzygotic stages showed
replications at the cell level, differentiations at the tissue level, specializations at the organ level, and transformations at the organism
level. These discoveries necessitated revision of the concept of anatomic ontogenesis.

The reformulations of this time took the form of two-category concepts. One group of revisions (a) made physical development and anatomic ontogenesis equivalent terms, and (b) designated the components
of development as "growth" and "differentiation." Three representative statements of this concept may be cited. Hellman (14) observed
that "The processes designating *development* fall naturally into two
groups: one is concerned with increase in size, the other with increase
in complexity of structure and form. The name for the processes concerned with change in size is *growth;* that of the other, *differentiation.*"
Ashley-Montagu (2) agreed that "Development consists of growth or
increase in size, and differentiation or increase in complexity." Daven-

port (6) similarly remarked that "Growth . . . is increase in size. This, combined with differentiation, or the process of specialization of parts, constitutes development."

Other revisions gave no synonym for anatomic ontogenesis, but labeled its components "growth" and "development." From the standpoint of definition of the components, these revisions fall into two main groups: one in which growth is defined as cell multiplication, and development as cell specialization; another in which growth is defined as increase in size, and development as increase in complexity.

These bipartite concepts had value as transitory formulations in a rapidly expanding area of knowledge. It is unfortunate that from wide early use they tended to become firmly entrenched. Certainly the fact that research information long since has outgrown them should be recognized more decisively and more generally than is currently the case.

What has happened with reference to the posited "growth" component of anatomic ontogenesis? Conceptually it was obvious that increase in size and cell multiplication (increase in number) were different definitions. That these definitions could not be used interchangeably became clear when continuing research revealed instances of cell multiplication without increase in size (29), and of increase in size in the absence of cell multiplication. It also was found that anatomic ontogenesis involves numerous manifestations of cell resorption (decrease in number), and decrease in tissue and organ size.

Those concerned with concept reformulation faced the choice of retaining or discarding "growth" as the symbol for one portion or sector of anatomic ontogenesis. Some decided to discard, some to retain by redefinition, and some to retain with the aid of a third component. The last procedure considered decreases in size and number as expressions of a component variously termed anatomic aging, decline, involution, or senescence. Of the revised definitions for growth the following are indicative: change in size (33), change in number or size (3), and quantity increase by increase in size or number (20).

The impact of advancing knowledge also necessitated redefinition of the component labeled "development" or "differentiation." The definition "increase in complexity" became unsatisfactory for several reasons (3). On the one hand, it was found that there were sequential decreases as well as increases in complexity. A revision which took cognizance

of this equated "development" with "change in kind or type" of structure (33). Other sorts of accumulating information were not so easily
handled. It was found, for instance, that in the absence of any change
in complexity there were changes in the position of parts, i.e., migra-
tions from one site or location to another (4). This, in conjunction
with expanding nodes of fact on ontogenetic changes in tissue composition and the shape of structural units, had the insalutary effect of
prompting more amorphous definitions of development rather than
precise ones of greater scope. Illustrative of this trend are statements
describing development as structural "rearrangement" (8), as anatomic
changes apart from changes in size (19), and as "progress toward maturity" other than "dimensional growth" (17).

It is timely at this point to make reference to the term *maturation*.
In its early anatomic service this word was not a key term in concept
formulation. Regarding an integrative function, the most that can be
held is that in its varied specific applications it carried an implied
connotation of structural "ripening" (19). Under this notion fall its
otherwise unrelated uses in describing the chromosome reduction of
germ cells, the enucleation of blood cells, the myelination of nerve
fibers, and the union of skeletal epiphyses with diaphyses.

By 1940 *maturation* had been employed as a major term in at least
one concept of anatomic ontogenesis (31). Gradually it has been placed
in several conceptual roles. It has been regarded as a composite symbol
for growth and development (19), a synonym for development, a "component" of development (10), and as a component "that may be distinguished from both growth and development" (9). Its most frequent
use has been as an alternative symbol for the second term of a growth-
development dichotomy. Characteristically, these definitions of "development or maturation" have been worded vaguely, except with respect to what they exclude. Condensed samples are: change in structure other than dimensional change (5); anatomic stages through which
an organism passes excluding change in magnitude (3); and structural
modification other than augmentation in size (8).

In general, the history of two-category descriptive concepts of anatomic ontogenesis may be epitomized as follows: At an early stage one
category was defined as increase in size, the other as increase in complexity; at an intermediate stage one category was defined as increase
in size or number, the other as "progress in specialization, organization,

or differentiation" (18); and at a late date one category was defined as change in size or number, the other as the remainder of structural change.

Not all conceptual thinking since 1900 has adhered to a schema of interposing a set of second-order terms of reference between the general topic under study (anatomic ontogenesis) and what is studied (changes in size, number, shape, composition, and so forth). During the period from 1925 to 1940, several scholars began registering the view that no fruitful purpose is served by utilizing such terms as *growth* and *development* differentially. In a paper written in 1926 Jackson (15) employed the words *growth* and *development* as synonyms for anatomic ontogenesis and presented a description of cell changes under the captions "number, form, position, size, and structure." Todd (30) in 1932, after noting that anatomic ontogenesis involves "increase in dimensions, change in proportions and adjustment of parts," pointed out that "to restrict the term growth to the first of these, and reserve the term development for the other two . . . would be pedantic." He proposed the compound "developmental growth" as an alternative for anatomic ontogenesis. In 1937 Hammett (11) spearheaded an effort to establish the use of *growth* and *anatomic ontogenesis* as equivalent terms when he wrote: "Increase in cell number is as much growth as is increase in cell size. Increase in cellular specialization is as much growth as is increase in cellular segregation." Meredith (24) in 1938 examined the ways in which the terms *growth* and *development* were being utilized both in formal definitions and in the reporting of investigations. His findings on definition included the observation that two attempts to distinguish between growth and development used precisely the same information on cell cleavage, one to illustrate growth and the other to illustrate development. With respect to the publication of research it was noted that phrases such as *trend of growth, pattern of growth*, and *growth stage* served the same discourse functions as *course of development, sequence of development*, and *developmental level*. He concluded: "The position that there is a useful and significant distinction between physical growth and physical development is . . . unsupported."

In more recent years this historic thread has been extended. Additional writers have called attention to the ambiguity (7), discordance (32), and major exclusions (21) of different concepts in current use, and there have been several publications (12, 13, 26, 27) concerned with formulating a revised concept that is sufficiently explicit and inclusive to have contemporary adequacy in research and teaching.

In turning to the constructive portion of this presentation, it is pertinent to repeat a statement made in the introduction: The concept projected for discussion pertains to physical development with the understanding that this term has the sense or meaning of anatomic ontogenesis.

The study of physical development is far from complete. It cannot be claimed that the *total series* of ontogenetic structural changes has been investigated, that *every variety* of anatomic change has been studied, or that *all possible approaches* to this area of knowledge are known. Consequently, it must be expected that concept revision will be an ongoing process. A contemporary concept will have value if it orders what is known, encompasses what is under investigation, and stimulates conceptual and investigative thinking in the years immediately ahead.

What does the investigator of anatomic ontogenesis do with reference to structural units? He classifies them by kind, observes their position, measures their size, describes their shape, counts their number, and studies their composition. This work, carried out under explicitly stated procedures (28), yields "definite, unambiguous" data (23). And these data, obtained at successive ontogenetic points and analyzed sequentially, depict physical development systematized as ontogenetic change in the kind, position, size, shape, number and composition of anatomic structures. Such a set of research-given subdivisions constitutes, as of a particular time, a descriptive definition of what physical development is known to comprise.

Having delimited and specified a descriptive concept of physical development, there remains the task of vitalizing it with illustrative material. This task will be discharged with particular reference to human ontogenesis.

Change in kind. The life span of the human individual commences with the formation of a new kind of cell called a zygote. This is the initial manifestation of a continuing series of such changes. Many kinds of structural unit are acquired and replaced, derived and obliterated, added and shed. The head region of the organism acquires a brain and tongue, a nose and ears, eyes and eyelids, lips and teeth, head hair and eyelashes. The trunk region acquires heart and lungs, liver and stomach, shoulders and hips, arms and legs, digits and nails. Embryonic ectoderm is replaced by nerve tissue, epidermis, the lens of the eye, and tooth enamel. Mesenchyme is replaced by muscle tissue, cartilage, bone, and tooth dentin.

Some kinds of anatomic structures are found at most stages of ontogeny. Nerve cells are present from the first month of life, bone cells from the second month, and nail cells from the third month. Again, the heart is present from the first month, the limbs from the second month, and body hair from the fourth month.

Other kinds of structure are transitory. The exocoelomic membrane is present for less than a week, the pronephros for about two weeks, and the branchial arches for no more than three weeks. Between the second and fourth months of life an external tail emerges and is submerged, between the third and fifth month touch pads are acquired and lost. In early infancy the umbilical cord is discarded, in late childhood the haploid germ cell appears, in early adulthood the cartilaginous metaphysis is obliterated, in middle adulthood the female ovum disappears, and in senility both sexes are "sans teeth."

Clearly, ontogenesis involves the appearance and disappearance of different kinds of cell, tissue, and organ. The investigator of physical development discovers and describes the kinds, determines the segment of ontogeny during which each kind is present, and explores sequential associations among changes in kind. Between the time when a particular kind of structure appears and the time when it is no longer found, the investigator studies the structure with respect to its size, shape, composition, location, and numerical representation.

Change in number. In its earliest ontogenetic state the human being is a unicellular organism; two decades later it has become an organism of more than twenty trillion cells. During the first few days of life there is simple geometric increase in cell number. This is succeeded by a gradual transition to diversified patterns of change in number.

The numerical pattern differs with kind of cell. In the case of nerve cells there is rapid increase in number during early prenatal life, no change in number throughout childhood and early adulthood, and slow decrease in number during late adulthood and senility. In the case of blood cells, from the first month of prenatal life until death, changes in absolute count are the product of simultaneous cell production and dissolution. Between these stable and labile extremes lie many intergrades. The pattern for striated muscle cells is a close variant of that for nerve cells, and the pattern for epidermal cells is similar to that for blood cells.

Of particular relevance are examples of decrease in cell number. Marked reductions occur in the tubules of the mesonephron during early prenatal life, in the chamber of the middle ear during late prenatal life, in the reticular layer of the adrenal gland during the first postnatal year, and in the root portions of the deciduous teeth during childhood. During adolescence the number of cartilege cells absorbed greatly surpass the number produced.

Turning from cells to other structural units, brief reference will be made to developmental changes in number of taste buds, number of teeth, and number of bones. During the middle third of the prenatal period taste receptors increase in number on the tongue, tonsils, palate, and parts of the esophagus. In late prenatal life and early childhood there is numerical decrease to the extent that usually none remain except on the tongue. There is an increase in the number of teeth from the embryonic period into childhood; around five years of age the child's dentition consists of 48 to 52 teeth in varying stages of development. A decade later the number has been reduced by 20, and with the passing years there is further reduction. The number of bone masses in the body does not increase to some maximum, rather there is a staggered pattern of bone formation and coalescence which produces an over-all increase for the period from the second prenatal month to puberty and a decrease thereafter. At puberty the number of bone masses approximates 350 while in early adulthood it is near 200.

Change in position. During ontogeny there are many changes in the location of structural units. Outstanding examples at the cell level are the essentially migratory blood cells, and the nerve cells that travel out to the muscles and skin of the fingers and toes.

At the organ level there are movements in practically all directions. Initially the heart lies in the vicinity of the lower part of the face. Its positional changes include downward and backward migration, counterclockwise rotation, and oblique tilting from right to left. When the stomach first is identifiable, it is situated high in the trunk. Its repositionings include movement to a lower level, rotation clockwise, and oblique tipping from left to right. In early prenatal life the stomach has a vertical orientation, in early childhood it lies almost transversely, and in late childhood it returns to a predominantly vertical orientation.

The teeth first travel deeply into the jaws, and then reverse themselves and erupt into the oral cavity. Combined with this vertical migration there are tooth rotation, horizontal movement, and travel in numerous oblique paths. The ribs are formed in a nearly horizontal plane and tilt downward at the front. The ovaries move from their original vertical orientation into a transverse position; they also revolve about the uterine tubes and come to rest below them. There is migration of the testes from the abdomen, through the pelvic cavity, into the scrotum. In the neonate the intestines and bladder are located almost entirely within the abdomen; during early childhood they move down into the pelvis. There is a progressive shift in the positional relation of the vertebral column and larynx; the cricoid cartilege approximates the top of the fourth cervical vertebra in the newborn, the top of the fifth cervical vertebra at six years of age, the bottom of this vertebra in early adulthood, the top of the seventh cervical vertebra in late adulthood, and the region of the second or third thoracic vertebra in late senility.

At the level of surface anatomy, examples will be restricted to the limbs. Both pairs of limbs undergo a torsion of 90 degrees. For the upper limbs there is turning at the shoulders so that the elbows are rotated from an outward position to a posterior position; for the lower limbs there is turning at the hips so that the knees are brought to the front. The feet first lie along the same axes as the shafts of the legs. During the last half of the second prenatal month they turn out of the leg planes and approach a right-angle relationship with the legs. When the great toes are individuated, each diverges from the four other toes and has its plantar surface turned toward them. Gradually each moves to a position parallel with the other toes and rotates sufficiently to bring the plantar surface into the sole plane.

Change in size. During the first few days after formation of the zygote no change occurs in the over-all size of the organism (29). Then follow size changes at varying rates, in diverse directions, and of differing durations. From the thousands of available studies on the length, breadth, depth, area, volume, and weight of anatomic structures, selections have been made to illustrate (a) decrease in size and (b) complex patterns of change in size.

The external tail becomes progressively smaller during the last half of the second prenatal month. A short time later there are decreases in the size of the Müllerian ducts in males and the mesonephric ducts in females. During the last third of the prenatal period, Hunter's gubernacula shorten by 75 per cent, pulling the testes down into the scrotum. Body weight decreases by about 6 per cent during the first few days after birth. There also are neonatal decreases in the size of the suprarenal glands and female genitalia. Thickness of the subcutaneous adipose tissue on the thorax and calf decreases between the middle of the first postnatal year and the sixth year. Deciduous teeth undergo reduction in length for many months prior to being shed. There are decreases in the size of the thymus gland from late childhood to early adulthood, and in the size of the pharyngeal tonsil in early adulthood. Later adulthood brings shrinkage of cerebellar fibers, and reduced cross-sectional area of head hairs. In senility there are decreases in the thickness of the skin, the volume of the striated muscles, the weight of the liver, and the size of the corpus callosum.

The size of the uterus and female mammary glands increases in the fetal period, decreases during the first month after birth, remains almost stationary throughout infancy and early childhood, increases in late childhood and adolescence, enters a moderately stable period except for fluctuations with pregnancies, then enters a second period of decrease following the menopause. The alveolar processes increase in height preceding and during the eruption of deciduous teeth, remain at a fairly stationary height over the period they are supporting these teeth, fluctuate in height with the transition from deciduous to "permanent" teeth, and decrease markedly with the loss of the latter. Stature increases at a declining rate between early prenatal life and late childhood, increases at an accelerating rate in early adolescence and a declining rate from middle adolescence to early adulthood, remains on a plateau during middle adulthood, then turns on a course of slow decrease.

Frequently when anatomic structures change in size there is increase in one region and decrease in another. The mandible changes in its breadth by deposition on the outer surface and absorption along its lingual wall. For the femur, the interplay of increase at the periphery and decrease within is such that its medullary cavity in adulthood is as large as the entire shaft at birth.

Change in shape. Two weeks after fertilization the human organism has the form of an ovoidal disc or plate, the widest part being toward one end. Three weeks later the organism has become cylindroid rather than plate-like, and its major form facets are a predominant head flexed far forward and a thorax that is 50 per cent greater in depth than in breadth. Characteristics of the body configuration at the close of the second prenatal month include the following: head breadth greater than shoulder breadth, broad nose and face, circular thorax, and limbs conspicuously short in relation to trunk length.

Lower limb length increases from 37 per cent of trunk length at the end of the second prenatal month to 87 per cent by the middle of the prenatal period. There is almost no change in this relation during the last half of the prenatal period, but during infancy and childhood the index rises again. In white children around twelve years of age, the lower limb length approaches 150 per cent of the trunk length (25). Between this time and early adulthood the index declines to below 145 per cent, i.e., the predominance of limb length decreases. The face length in relation to face breadth follows a similar course except that the face continues to elongate through adolescence, shows little change during adulthood, and returns to a squat form in senility upon the loss of teeth.

During infancy the cervical and lumbar curvatures of the back become more pronounced, the hands and feet less stubby, the nose more elongated and high-bridged. In childhood the abdomen attains a less protruding contour, and the limbs become progressively more slender. At adolescence the aperture of the male larynx becomes strongly elliptical, and the aperture of the female pelvis decreases in ellipticity.

Changes in shape are no less varied at the cell level, or for organs such as the brain, heart, and lungs. Cells flatten, elongate, invaginate and branch, thereby manifesting a wide variety of form modifications. Internal organs bend, bulge, loop, and convolute, many exhibiting a highly complex panorama of transformation. The stomach, which presents a comparatively simple shape sequence, begins as a swelling of one portion of the digestive tube, passes from this capsular form to a configuration approximating a cow's horn, and then changes to a "J" shape.

Change in composition. Human cells, tissues, and organs are studied with regard to texture, resilience, and color. On the chemical plane, these facets of developmental anatomy relate to variables such as calcium, pigment, protein, and water.

Numerous structures undergo changes in color with age. The iris of the eye is blue or violet in the neonate and, as a result of increasing density of pigment, darkens during the childhood years. In senility there is a decrease in the ratio of pigment-carrying cells to pigment-free cells, and eye color becomes lighter. During infancy and childhood there is a darkening in skin color; this holds for Negroid as well as Caucasoid people. Negro infants show a rapid increase in skin pigmentation during the first few months after birth, and a slower increase over the childhood years. The hair of the head shows a darkening over the childhood years, followed by graying in adulthood. Except for a difference in timing, the facial hair in males follows a similar cycle. In adulthood pigmentation occurs in the dentate nucleus of the cerebellum, and with advanced age the muscle fibers of the heart become densely pigmented.

Examples of change in tissue texture and resiliency are those resulting from alterations in the water content of muscle and the fat content of subcutaneous adipose tissue. Underlying the commonplace fact that subcutaneous adipose tissue is more resistant to compression in childhood than in infancy is the reduction in both extracellular water and proportion of oleic acid. Compositional changes in striated muscle between birth and early adulthood include declines in water and chloride content and a rise in nitrogen content.

At the level of the organism, the human body undergoes marked dehydration during the fetal and infancy periods. This decline in total body water is from around 90 per cent in the young fetus, through about 73 per cent at birth, to 60 per cent at the end of the first postnatal year. During the childhood and adolescent periods there is a moderate increase in total body calcium.

The inorganic iron content of the liver rises during the fetal and neonatal periods, drops precipitously during the last half of the first postnatal year, remains fairly constant during the second year, then gradually rises throughout childhood. During the adult years the kidneys show an increase in calcium and iron deposits. Changes with age in the composition of the skeleton include a decrease in water content, an increase in nitrogen content, and increases in calcium, phosphorus, and total ash. In old age the brittleness of many bones attests a decrease in the ratio of organic components to inorganic components. Aspects of compositional change at the forefront of contemporary interest relate to the lessening suppleness of the arteries and the declining resiliency of the heart valves during the later years of life.

SUMMARY

Physical development has been defined as anatomic ontogenesis. The physical development of the human organism has been shown to comprise changes in the kind, number, position, size, shape, and composition of its structural parts. It remains for tomorrow's students of physical development to determine whether anatomic ontogenesis includes sequential changes not provided for in the categories enumerated and illustrated, and/or whether anatomic ontogenesis can be described more meaningfully from a different perspective.

REFERENCES

1. Arey, L. B. *Developmental Anatomy*, 6th ed. Philadelphia: Saunders, 1954.
2. Ashley-Montagu, M. F. *Adolescent Sterility*. Springfield, Ill.: C. C. Thomas, 1946.
3. Bakwin, R. M., and H. Bakwin. *Psychological Care during Infancy and Childhood*. New York: Appleton-Century-Crofts, Inc., 1942. See also *Am. J. Dis. Child.*, Vol. 59 (1940).
4. Brash, J. C. "Growth of Alveolar Bone and its Relation to Movements of Teeth, including Eruption." *Internat. J. Orthod., Oral Surg., and Radiog.*, Vol. 14 (1928), pp. 196–223.
5. Breckenridge, M. E., and E. L. Vincent. *Child Development*, 1st ed. Philadelphia: Saunders, 1943.
6. Davenport, C. B., et al. "Growth," *Annual Review of Physiology*, Vol. 1 (1939), pp. 81–108.
7. Dillon, C. F. S. "Orthodontic Diagnostic Procedures," *Am. J. Orthod. and Oral Surg.*, Vol. 31 (1945), pp. 458–79.
8. Draper, G., C. W. Dupertius and J. L. Caughey, Jr. *The Human Constitution in Clinical Medicine*. New York: P. B. Hoeber (Harper), 1944.
9. Frank, L. K. "Concept of Maturity," *Child Develop.*, Vol. 21 (1950), pp. 21–24.
10. Gesell, A. "Maturation and the Patterning of Behavior," in C. A. Murchison, ed., *Handbook of Child Psychology*. London: Oxford University Press, 1933.
11. Hammett, F. S. "Introduction to Growth," *Growth*, Vol. 1 (1937), pp. 1–2.
12. ———. "The Role of Amino Acids and Nucleic Acid Components in Developmental Growth," *Growth*, Vol. 6 (1942), pp. 59–123, Vol. 7 (1943), pp. 331–99.
13. ———. "What is Growth?," *Scientia*, Vol. 79 (1946), pp. 93–98.
14. Hellman, M. "Changes in the Human Face brought about by Development," *Internat. J. Orthod., Oral Surg., and Radiog.*, Vol. 13 (1927), pp. 457–516.

15. Jackson, C. M. "Some Aspects of Form and Growth," in W. J. Robbins, *et al.*, *Growth.* New Haven: Yale University Press, 1928.
16. Krogman, W. M. "Growth of the 'Whole Child' in Relation to Dental Problems," *Oral Surg., Oral Med., and Oral Pathol.*, Vol. 3 (1950), pp. 427–45.
17. Lussier, E. F. "Growth Plateau in Orthodontics as it applies to Children's Dentistry," *Am. J. Orthod. and Oral Surg.*, Vol. 29 (1943), pp. 403–13.
18. Macy, I. G. *Nutrition and Chemical Growth in Childhood*, Vol. 1. Springfield, Ill.: C. C. Thomas, 1942.
19. Mainland, D. *Anatomy as a Basis for Medical and Dental Practice.* New York: P. B. Hoeber, 1945.
20. Marriott, W. M., and P. C. Jeans. *Infant Nutrition*, 3rd ed. St. Louis: C. V. Mosby Co., 1941.
21. Massler, M., and I. Schour. "Studies in Tooth Development: Theories of Eruption," *Am. J. Orthod. and Oral Surg.*, Vol. 27 (1941), pp. 572–76.
22. McKee, J. P., and D. H. Eichorn. "Relation between Metabolism and Height and Weight during Adolescence," *Child Develop.*, Vol. 26 (1955), pp. 205–11.
23. Medawar, P. B. "Transformation of Shape," *Proc. Royal Soc. of London*, Series B, 889 (1950), p. 474.
24. Meredith, H. V. "An Empirical Concept of Physical Growth," *Child Develop.*, Vol. 9 (1938), pp. 161–67.
25. ———. "Growth of Components of Stature," *Child Develop.*, Vol. 10 (1939), pp. 129–44.
26. ———. "Toward a Working Concept of Physical Growth," *Am. J. Orthod. and Oral Surg.*, Vol. 31 (1945), pp. 440–58.
27. ———. "Physical Growth," in Vol. 13, pp. 499–502, *Encyclopedia Americana*, 1952. (Also Vol. 16, pp. 34–36, *Collier's Encyclopedia*, 1952.)
28. ———. "Longitudinal Anthropometric Data in the Study of Individual Growth," *Annals, New York Acad. Sci.*, Vol. 63 (1955), pp. 510–27.
29. Streeter, G. L. "Prenatal Growth of the Child," *Carnegie Instit. Wash. News Service Bulletin*, Vol. 4 (1937), No. 14, pp. 127–32.
30. Todd, T. W. "Hereditary and Environmental Factors in Facial Development," *Internat. J. Orthod., Oral Surg., and Radiog.*, Vol. 18 (1932), pp. 799–808.
31. ———. *Atlas of Skeletal Maturation.* St. Louis: C. V. Mosby Co., 1937.
32. Weiss, P. "Differential Growth," in A. K. Parpart, *ed., The Chemistry and Physiology of Growth.* Princeton University Press, 1949.
33. Wetzel, N. C. "Growth," in O. Glasser, ed., *Medical Physics.* Chicago: The Yearbook Publishers, 1944.

The Development of Human Behavior

Heinz Werner

THE CONCEPT OF DEVELOPMENT FROM A
COMPARATIVE AND ORGANISMIC POINT OF VIEW

T H E field of developmental psychology, as it is conceived here, transcends the boundaries within which the concept of development is frequently applied: development is here apprehended as a concept not merely applicable to delimited areas such as child growth or comparative behavior of animals, but as a concept that proposes a certain manner of viewing behavior in its manifold manifestations. Such a developmental approach to behavior rests on one basic assumption, namely, that wherever there is life there is growth and development, that is, formation in terms of systematic, orderly sequence. This basic assumption, then, entails the view that developmental conceptualization is applicable to the various areas of life science, and is potentially useful in interrelating the many fields of psychology.

The developmental approach has, of course, been clearly of tremendous heuristic value in systematizing certain aspects of biological phenomena in various fields of life science such as comparative anatomy, neurophysiology, and embryology. Analogously, developmental psychology aims at viewing the behavior of all organisms in terms of similar genetic principles. However, this aim of developmental psychology is perhaps even farther reaching than that of developmental biology. Developmental psychology does not restrict itself either to ontogenesis or phylogenesis, but seeks to coordinate within a single framework forms of behavior observed in comparative animal psychology, in child psychology, in psychopathology, in ethnopsychology, and in the general and differential psychology of man in our own culture. Eventually, in linking these variegated observations, it attempts to formulate and systematically examine experimentally testable hypotheses.

In order to clarify and evolve its conceptual framework, developmental psychology has to search for characteristics common to any kind of mental activity in the process of progression or regression. In this comparative venture one has to be wary of the error made by early evolutionists such as Haeckel and G. Stanley Hall, who sought to treat as materially identical various developmental sequences when the data warranted only the assertion of similarity or parallelism. The statement, for instance, that the individual recapitulates in his development the genesis of the species, and the attempt to identify childlike and abnormal forms of behavior, have, in their extreme formulation, aroused just criticism, but criticism which has spread more and more toward undermining comparative developmental psychology as a discipline.

Between the extremes, on the one hand, of viewing as identical various developmental sequences, and on the other, of denying completely any comparability among them, some beginnings toward a theory of development have been made. These beginnings take into account the formal similarities in these various developmental sequences as well as material and formal differences distinguishing each developmental sequence from another.

THE ORTHOGENETIC PRINCIPLE OF DEVELOPMENT

Developmental psychology postulates one regulative principle of development; it is an orthogenetic principle which states that wherever development occurs it proceeds from a state of relative globality and lack of differentiation to a state of increasing differentiation, articulation, and hierarchic integration.* This principle has the status of an heuristic definition. Though itself not subject to empirical test, it is valuable to developmental psychologists in leading to a determination of the actual range of applicability of developmental concepts to the behavior of organisms.†

We may offer several illustrations of how this orthogenetic principle

---

* This, of course, implies "directiveness." It seems to us, therefore, that one must on logical grounds agree with E. S. Russell (33) that organic development cannot be defined without the construct of "directiveness."

† In regard to the following discussion, see item 47 in the References.

is applied in the interpretation and ordering of psychological phenomena.

According to this principle, a state involving a relative lack of differentiation between subject and object is developmentally prior to one in which there is a polarity of subject and object. Thus the young child's acceptance of dreams as external to himself, the lack of differentiation between what one dreams and what one sees, as is found in psychosis, or in some nonliterate societies, the breakdown of boundaries of the self in mescaline intoxication and in states of depersonalization—all of these betoken a relative condition of genetic primordiality compared to the polarity between subject and object found in reflective thinking. This increasing subject-object differentiation involves the corollary that the organism becomes increasingly less dominated by the immediate concrete situation; the person is less stimulus-bound and less impelled by his own affective states. A consequence of this freedom is the clearer understanding of goals, the possibility of employing substitutive means and alternative ends. There is hence a greater capacity for delay and planned action. The person is better able to exercise choice and willfully rearrange a situation. In short, he can manipulate the environment rather than passively respond to the environment. This freedom from the domination of the immediate situation also permits a more accurate assessment of others. The adult is more able than the child to distinguish between the motivational dynamics and the overt behavior of personalities. At developmentally higher levels, therefore, there is less of a tendency for the world to be interpreted solely in terms of one's own needs and an increasing appreciation of the needs of others and of group goals.

Turning to another illustration, one pertaining to concept formation, we find that modes of classification that involve a relative lack of differentiation between concept and perceptual context are genetically prior to modes of classification of properties relatively independent of specific objects. Thus, a color classification that employs color terms such as "gall-like" for a combination of green and blue, or "young leaves" for a combination of yellow and green, is genetically prior to a conceptual color system independent of objects such as gall or young leaves.

It may be opportune to use this last example as an illustration of the comparative character of the developmental approach. That the color classification attached to specific objects involves a mode of cognition genetically prior to a classification independent of specific objects is, of course, consistent with the main theoretical principle of development. In regard to the comparative character of our discipline, however, it does not suffice for us merely to find this type of classification more typical of the man of lower civilization than of the man of higher. The anthropological data point up the necessity of determining whether there is a greater prevalence of such primitive color conceptualization in areas where cognition can be readily observed in terms of lower developmental levels, e.g., in the early phases of ontogenesis. Experimental studies on young children have demonstrated the greater prevalence of concrete (context-bound) conceptualization with regard not only to color but to many other phenomena as well. Again, to take organic neuropathology as an example, in brain-injured persons we find, as Goldstein, Head, and others have stressed, a concretization of color conceptualization symptomatic of their psychopathology; similar observations have been made on schizophrenics.

At this point we should like to state that a comprehensive comparative psychology of development cannot be achieved without the aid of a general experimental psychology broadened through the inclusion of developmental methodology and developmental constructs. There have appeared on the scene of general psychology beginnings of an extremely significant trend toward the studying of perception, learning, and thinking, not as final products but as developing processes, as temporal events divisible into successive stages. Such "event psychology," as one may call it, introduces the dimension of time as an intrinsic property into all experimental data. It stands thus in contrast to approaches, like that of classical psychophysics, in which the treating of successive trials as repetitive responses eliminates as far as possible sequential effects. European psychologists, particularly in Germany and Austria, have turned to the direct study of emergent and developing mental phenomena (34, 42, 46). For instance, using a tachistoscope, we may study the developmental changes in perception which occur when the time of exposure is increased from trial to trial. In studies of this sort, such developmental changes, or "microgenesis," of percepts are predictable from a developmental theory of the ontogenesis of perception. Some of the ensuing parallels between microgenesis and ontogenesis might be summarized as follows (5): In both microgenesis and ontogenesis the formation of percepts seems, in general, to go through an orderly sequence of stages. Perception is first global; whole-qualities are dominant. The next stage might be called analytic; perception is selectively directed toward parts. The final stage might be called synthetic; parts become integrated with respect to the whole. Initially perception is predominantly "physiognomic." * The physiognomic quality of an object is experienced prior to any details. At this level, feeling and perceiving are little differentiated. Again, in the early stages of development imaging and perceiving are not definitely separated.

There is another important technique of studying the emergence and formation of perception. This method was originally utilized in Stratton's well-known experiments in which a person wearing lenses had to adjust to a world visually perceived as upside down. More recently, Ivo Kohler of the Innsbruck Laboratory has utilized this method in extremely significant long-range experiments. He studies stages of perceptual adaptation to a world visually distorted in various ways by prisms or lenses (16, 17, 49). Again, these perceptual formation stages are found to conform to ontogenetic patterns. Ontogenetic studies have made it reasonably certain that the experience of space and spatial objects grows through stages which can be grossly defined. There appears to be an early sensorimotor stage of spatial orientation, succeeded by one in which objects emerge in terms of "things-of-action" (44), where perceptual qualities of things are determined by the specific way these things are handled. For instance, a chair is that object which has a "sitting tone" (Uexküll). A later stage is that of highly objectified or visualized space where the spatial phenomena are perceived in their rather "pure" visual form and form relations.

Keeping these ontogenetic states in mind, it is most enlightening to follow the reports of the subjects used in the Innsbruck Laboratory as they move from level to level in developmental order, adjusting themselves to a disarrayed world. First, they learn to master space on a sensorimotor level; that is, they are able to move about without error. But, though they may be able to ride a bicycle quite skillfully, the visual world as such may, at this stage, still be extremely confused, upside down, or crooked. The further development toward visual adaption shows some remarkable features: the objects seem to fall into

* In regard to this term, see item 44 (p. 69) and item 45 (p. 11) of the References.

two classes, things-of-action and purely visual things. The observer conquers first the things-of-action and only later purely visual things. For instance, observers wearing prisms which invert left and right can see an object already in correct position if it is part of their own actions, but incorrectly — that is, reversed — when purely visually grasped. In a fencing situation, a subject sees his own sword correctly pointing toward the opponent, but at a moment of rest it becomes visually inverted, pointing toward himself. By the same token, a little later in development any object-of-action, such as a chair or a screwdriver, whether it is actually handled or not, is correctly transformed, whereas purely visual objects, such as pictures or printed words, remain reversed. Only at a last stage the differences disappear, and complete transformation of the visual world is achieved.

Another area of general psychology where genetic methodology has been fruitfully applied is that of problem-solving behavior. Whereas Wertheimer's contribution to productive thinking, outstanding as it was, remains essentially agenetic, the signal importance of Duncker's work (7) lies in its genetic methodology. Duncker studied the problem-solving process in terms of genetic stages which follow each other according to developmental laws well established for ontogenesis.*

UNIFORMITY VERSUS MULTIFORMITY OF DEVELOPMENT

The orthogenetic law, being a formal regulative principle, is not designed to predict developmental courses in their specificity. To illustrate, it cannot decide the well-known controversy between Coghill's and Windle's conceptions (6, 50) concerning ontogenesis of motor behavior. According to Coghill, who studied the larval salamander, behavior develops through the progressive expansion of a perfectly integrated total pattern, and the individuation within of partial patterns that acquire varying degrees of discreteness. Windle's conception, derived from the study of placental mammals, is that the first responses of the embryo are circumscribed, stereotyped reflexes subsequently combined into complex patterns. It may be possible to reconcile, under

---

* Duncker has also clearly seen one aspect of creative thought processes, hitherto little recognized, namely, the fact that successful problem-solving depends not only on the ability to progress along new ways, but also on the ability to regress back to a point from which new development can take place. In other words, he has observed a most important genetic principle, that of oscillatory activity in terms of progression and regression. (See the last section of this paper.)

the general developmental law, both viewpoints as follows: The development of motor behavior may, depending on the species or on the type of activity, involve either the differentiation of partial patterns from a global whole and their integration within a developing locomotor activity (Coghill) or the integration of originally juxtaposed, relatively isolated global units which now become differentiated parts of a newly formed locomotor pattern (Windle). In both cases there are differentiation and hierarchic integration, although the specific manifestations differ.*

Now, it is precisely this polarity between the uniformity of a general regulative principle and the multiformity of specific developmental changes that makes the study of development necessarily a comparative discipline. If we were merely to seek the ordering of changes of behavior in terms of a universal developmental principle, developmental theory might still be of interest to the philosophy of science and theoretical psychology, but it would be of far lesser value to empirical psychology.

In order to get a clearer picture of what is involved here, it might be advantageous to refer to one of our studies, namely, that of the development of the acquisition of meaning, by the use of a word-context test (48).

In this experiment eight to thirteen-year-old children had the task of finding the meaning of an artificial word which was embedded successively in six verbal contexts. For instance, one such artificial word was "corplum." After each of these six sentences the child was interrogated concerning the meaning of the artificial word.

The six sentences in which "corplum" (correct translation: "stick" or "piece of wood") appears, are as follows: (1) A corplum may be used for support. (2) Corplums may be used to close off an open place. (3) A corplum may be long or short, thick or thin, strong or weak. (4) A wet corplum does not burn. (5) You can make a corplum smooth with sandpaper. (6) The painter used a corplum to mix his paints.

Now, the task confronting the subjects in the word-context test is essentially the synthesis of the cues from a set of six contexts for the purpose of forming a general meaning of the word, that is, a meaning applicable to all six sentences. The success of such an operation is re-

* Cf. the excellent discussion by Barron, presented at the Chicago Conference on Genetic Neurology (2).

flected in two kinds of results. The first shows a steady and continuous increase in the achievement of a correct solution with increasing age. The second reflects changes in the underlying patterns of operation. As to the first point, there is a developmental increase in achievement which signifies the increasing capacity for hierarchization, that is, for integrating the various cues within a common name. However, the finding concerning a steady rise in achievement of correctness was, for us, not the most important result. Our main aim was to study the processes underlying such achievement. We were far more concerned with detecting the fact that conceptual synthesis is not achieved by a unitary pattern of operations, but that there are various sorts of processes of synthesis which differ from each other developmentally. The lower forms were found to emerge, to increase, and then to decrease during intellectual growth, yielding finally to more advanced forms of generalization (48, p. 97).

Studies of this sort inform us that the workings of the orthogenetic law as a uniform, regulative principle have to be specified through the ordering and interpretation of the multiform operations. Such a view implies the rejection of a tacit assumption made by many child psychologists that the measured achievement always reflects unequivocally the underlying operations, or that overt achievement is necessarily a true gauge of the developmental stage. This assumption is untenable; the same achievement may be reached by operations genetically quite different (41). An analysis of types of operations rather than measurement merely in terms of accuracy of performance often reveals the truer developmental picture.* In fact, a greater accuracy in certain circum-

---

* It is not accidental that out of the immense field of potentially great significance for developmental psychology, the two main areas emphasized by psychologists in this country were the area of intelligence and the area of learning. They were chosen because they were clearly amenable to rigid quantification on a continuum in terms of more or less. The successes of workers in these fields obtained by statistical treatment of overt behavior and the successes in practical application have reinforced the conviction that outside the rather trivial notion of continuous increase in achievement with increase in age, developmental theory is not needed. In regard to intelligence testing the evaluation of G. Stanley Hall, the father of comparative genetic psychology, still seems to hold: Intelligence tests and measurements, he stated, have done a great work in applying psychology to life and industry but have added scarcely a scintilla to our knowledge of human development (11, p. 450). As to the situation in the area of learning, it seems significant that a man as deeply informed as Hilgard, in a well-balanced evaluation of this field of research, comes to the conclusion that undue stress on quantification may lead to a collapse when underlying processes are not understood (13, p. 328).

stances may even signify a lower developmental level, as in the case of a decorticate frog who shows greater accuracy in catching flies than the normal frog. Gottschaldt (10) presented normal and mentally deficient eight-year-old children with the task of constructing squares or rectangles from the irregular pieces into which these figures had been cut. The normal children had difficulties with the test because they tried to relate the figuratively unrelated pieces to the end form. Operating on a purely mechanical level, the mentally deficient children matched the edges of the same length and thus performed quicker and with fewer errors. Again, a thinker oriented toward and capable of highly abstract thought may be at a disadvantage in certain concrete tasks of concept formation, compared with a concretely thinking person.

CONTINUITY VERSUS DISCONTINUITY OF DEVELOPMENT

The orthogenetic principle of increase in differentiation and hierarchic integration is not meant to imply continuous progress as the exclusive characteristic of developmental change. A good deal of the controversy centering in the continuity-discontinuity problem appears to be due to a lack in clarification of these terms. In particular, there has been considerable confusion about two different aspects of change. One is the quantitative aspect of change. Here the problem of continuity versus discontinuity is related to the measurement — in terms of gradual or abrupt increase with time — of magnitude, of efficiency, of frequency of occurrence of a newly acquired operation in an individual or in a group. The other aspect concerns the qualitative nature of changes. Here the problem of continuity versus discontinuity centers in the question of the reducibility of later to earlier forms — emergence — and the transition between later and earlier forms — intermediacy.

It seems that discontinuity in terms of qualitative changes can be best defined by two characteristics: "emergence," i.e., the irreducibility of a later stage to an earlier; and "gappiness," i.e., the lack of intermediate stages between earlier and later forms. Quantitative discontinuity* on the other hand, appears to be sufficiently defined by the second characteristic.

* To facilitate distinction and alleviate confusion, I would suggest substituting "abruptness" for quantitative discontinuity, reserving the term "discontinuity" only for the qualitative aspect of change. It also appears feasible to distinguish between two types of emergence: (a) emergence of a single operation, e.g., abstract function, (b) emergence of a novel pattern of operation. A novel pattern may

Now it seems that in many discussions, particularly among psychologists, the quantitative and qualitative forms of continuity and discontinuity have not been clearly kept apart. Thus, a change may be discontinuous in terms of quality but may become distinguishable (e.g., measurable) only gradually; i.e., there may be a continuous quantitative increase, such as in frequency of occurrence or in magnitude. For instance, the attempt of the young child to walk on two legs is discontinuous with four-limb locomotion, though the successive actual attempts may show gradual progress toward precision and success.* In accordance with our definition given above, two-legged locomotion cannot be reduced to four-limbed locomotion, and, furthermore, there is limitation in regard to intermediate steps.

Another related mistake is that of accepting smallness of change, whether qualitative or quantitative, as an indicator of continuity. For instance, the genetic changes termed "mutation" may be very slight, but there has to be "discontinuity inasmuch as there are no intermediate forms between the unchanged and the changed."† This significant fact in mutation, namely, discontinuity, says Schroedinger, "reminds a physicist of quantum theory: no intermediate energies occurring between two neighboring energy levels. He would be inclined to call de Vries's mutation theory . . . the quantum theory of biology." Because of the smallness of change, in developmental psychology as well as in developmental biology, one often will find it possible to argue for discontinuity only on the basis of extensive data accumulated in extensive temporal sequences; discontinuity in change may then be con-

---

emerge as a consequence of new operations that enter the pattern, or it may also emerge through a reorganization of the existing characters within a certain pattern, through a changing dominance between these existing characters, etc. One may note here some analogies between psychological emergence and biogenetic emergence coming about (a) through mutant genes, and (b) through changes in local constellations of genes.

* Such paradoxical coexistence of qualitative discontinuity and gradualness of appearance (progression) seems to pertain to developmental changes of various kinds. For instance, regenerative development of transplanted tissue is either determined according to the domicile within which the transplant is embedded (place-wise) or according to the original extraction of the transplant (origin-wise). This determination is an all-or-none phenomenon; however, visible differentiation is not instantaneously evident but progressive (26, pp. 70f).

† Schroedinger, p. 34 (37). Schroedinger points out that Darwin was mistaken in regarding the small, continuous chance variations within a species as the basis of evolution by natural selection. These variations (e.g., length of awn in a pure-bred crop) cannot be formants of a new species because they are not inheritable.

cluded after a trait has become sufficiently distinct in terms of frequency, permanency, and magnitude.

Other factors that are often not clearly recognized for their importance in determining sequences as either continuous or discontinuous are (a) the handling of the data and (b) the nature of the universe of discourse.

Concerning the first factor, it should be realized that discontinuous process changes typical in individual development may be obscured by averaging developmental achievement scores of individuals to secure a composite curve for a group which then suggests continuous growth.*

Another fallacy in deriving continuity of behavioral development from group scores has been most recently discussed by Lashley (21) in regard to a particular feature of the usual mental tests, namely, the heterogeneity (discontinuity) of the items which the test patterns comprise. Lashley's criticism implies that discontinuity of processes may be obscured by interpreting developmental data on the assumption that variations in achievement can be based only on variations in a single underlying process. As noted before, the achievement of correctness on our word-context test shows a steady increase with age, whereas underlying processes give a picture of the rise and decline of more or less primitive operations and the abrupt rise of an adult type of generalization around ten or eleven years of age. Reference should be made here to the important study by Nancy Bayley (3) concerning mental delevopment during the first three years. She could show that in terms of accumulated scores there was a steady increase with age; however, a further analysis of the test items in terms of underlying operations revealed a shift from one type of function ("sensorimotor") to a qualitatively different type ("adaptive") occurring at approximately nine months of age.

Secondly, it should be recognized that it is the universe of discourse, the interpretational frame within which the material is grasped, that often determines the ordering in terms of continuity or discontinuity. To illustrate by an analogy, one may represent the relation between color hues in physical terms, i.e., wave length, that change continu-

---

* Lecomte DuNoüy (8) in his remarkable book, *Biological Time*, takes the extreme view that continuity always is "manufactured" by our treatment of the data: "one of the roles of consciousness is to manufacture continuity from discontinuity."

ously within the range of visibility. Within the psychological frame of reference, however, there is discontinuity. The gradual variation from blue to green is discontinuous with the gradual variation from green to yellow, which, in turn, is discontinuous with the gradual variation from yellow to red.

There is no logical necessity for a concordance in terms of continuity between the quantitative and qualitative aspects of any developmental series. A discontinuous (epigenetic) qualitative change may become distinct gradually; that is, it does not need to be "saltatory" in a quantitative sense, if by that word is meant that a new form or function becomes suddenly overt. Nor does unevenness — spurt versus depression — of any growth curve necessarily point to novel process formation. However, though we have to beware of confusing quantitative discontinuity-continuity with qualitative discontinuity-continuity, quantitative unevenness may, possibly more often than not, point to qualitative discontinuity or emergent evolution. We may illustrate this from Paul Weiss's discussion (40) on embryonic growth: "An obstacle to simple mathematical treatment of growth is its lack of continuity; for embryonic growth advances unevenly, in spurts and jumps, with intermittent depressions. These depressions correspond to phases of intensive histological differentiation" (p. 44). Furthermore, if embryonic growth curves in terms of weight are compared with progress in terms of differentiation and morphogenesis, one finds that both kinds of progressions advance unevenly, but, that "maxima of differentiation coincide with minima of growth." From this, Weiss concludes that "acceleration of differentiating activity is attended by retardation of growth activity, or in other words, that there is some antagonism between differentiation and growth" (p. 134).*

Weiss's observations point to an important instance where the saltations and depressions of "accumulating" activity (growth in terms of quantitave discontinuity) appear to be vicariously related to morphogenetic processes directed toward the production of "discrete discontinuous . . . cell types which are not connected by intergradation" — development in terms of qualitative discontinuity (p. 98).

Quite possibly there are analogies to this vicarious correspondence between quantitative growth and qualitative development on the

---

* One may note the possibility of discriminating between "growth" as a process of accumulation versus "development" defined by differentiation.

level of psychological behavior. To illustrate, one such analogy might be found in a frequent observation concerning certain phases of speech development. There appears to occur between the stage of babbling and that of naming, a period during which vocalizing is depressed (22, p. 82). It seems plausible to interpret this period as one during which the awareness of sound patterns as verbal symbols emerges. Once this novel operation has emerged, the child bursts forth with naming, increasing its vocabulary at a swiftly accelerating rate.

In conclusion, it seems to me, that development cannot be comprehended without the polar conceptualization of continuity and discontinuity. Within the "universe of discourse" in which the orthogenetic law is conceived, development, insofar as it is defined as increase in differentiation and hierarchization is, ideally, continuous. Underlying the increase in differentiation and integration are the forms and processes which undergo two main kinds of changes: (a) quantitative changes which are either gradual or abrupt, and (b) qualitative changes which, by their very nature, are discontinuous.*

UNILINEARITY VERSUS MULTILINEARITY OF DEVELOPMENT

The orthogenetic law, by its very nature, is an expression of unilinearity of development. But, as is true of the other polarities discussed here, the ideal unilinear sequence signified by the universal developmental law does not conflict with the multiplicity of actual developmental forms. As implied in the conclusion of the preceding section, coexistence of unilinearity and multiplicity of individual developments must be recognized for psychological just as it is for biological evolution. In regard to human behavior in particular, this polarity opens the way for a developmental study of behavior not only in terms of universal sequence, but also in terms of individual variations, that is, in terms of growth viewed as a branching-out process of specialization or aberration.

To illustrate, "physiognomic" perception appears to be a developmentally early form of viewing the world, based on the relative lack of distinction between properties of persons and properties of inanimate things (44, pp. 67f). But the fact that in our culture physiognomic

* For further discussion of the continuity-discontinuity problem, see Bertalanffy, ch. 12 (4); DuNoüy (8); Huxley, ch. 5 (14); Lillie (23); Novikoff (27); Simpson, ch. 14 (39); Schneirla (35, 36).

perception, developmentally, is superseded by logical, realistic, and technical conceptualization, poses some paradoxical problems, such as, What genetic standing has adult aesthetic experience? Is it to be considered a "primitive" experience left behind in a continuous process of advancing logification, and allowed to emerge only in sporadic hours of regressive relaxation? Such an inference seems unsound; it probably errs in conceiving human growth in terms of a simple developmental series rather than as a diversity of individual formations, all conforming to the abstract and general developmental conceptualization. Though physiognomic experience is a primordial manner of perceiving, it grows, in certain individuals such as artists, to a level not below but on a par with that of "geometric-technical" perception and logical discourse.

FIXITY VERSUS MOBILITY OF DEVELOPMENTAL LEVEL OF OPERATION

The assumption that all organisms normally operate upon a relatively fixed and rather sharply circumscribed developmental level appears to be tacitly accepted by many psychologists. A contrary view is that all higher organisms manifest a certain range of genetically different operations. This means, for instance, that a child of a certain age or an adult, depending on the task or on inner circumstances, may, qua normal, perform at genetically different levels. Furthermore, there is, so to speak, not only "horizontal" differentiation but also "vertical" differentiation; that is, the more mature compared with the less mature individual has at his disposal a greater number of developmentally different operations.

It should be recognized that these views are not necessarily antagonistic; i.e., fixity as well as mobility of levels of operation coexist as polar principles of development. The principle of fixity is implied in, or can be inferred from, the intrinsic trend of any evolution toward an end stage of maximum stability. Such maximum stability, as the end stage of a developmental sequence, implies the ceasing of growth; that is, implies the permanency, for instance, of specialized reaction patterns, or automatization of response. But the principle of fixity would finally lead to rigidity of behavior if not counterbalanced by the polar principle of mobility. As most generally conceived, mobility implies "becoming" in contrast to "being"; it implies that an organism, having attained highly stabilized structures and operations may or may not progress further, but if it does, this will be accomplished through partial return to a genetically earlier, less stable level. One has to regress in order to progress. The intimate relation of regression to progression appears succinctly expressed in the statement of one of the early evolutionists, Richard Owen (32). On interpreting the resemblance of the embryo to the phylogenetic ancestry, Owen said: "We perceive a return to the archetype in the early embryological phases of development of the highest existing species, or ought rather to say that development starts from the old point" (p. 108).

An impressive illustration of the relation between renewed development and regression on the biological level can be found in the processes of regeneration. Such regeneration, as extensively studied at the amphibian level, consists of two phases, regressive as well as progressive. The progressive phase — analogous to normal embryonic development — starts with the formation of the "blastema" or regenerative bud. But prior to progression there is regression. The regressive phase involves de-differentiation of already specialized cells (26, p. 3). Another probable source for blastema formation is reserve cells, that is, cells that have remained at a low state of differentiation (40, p. 466). It is noteworthy that power of regeneration, being associated with capacity to de-differentiate is, in general, inversely correlated with the organism's ontogenetic or phylogenetic status of differentiatedness (26, p. 62).

In speculating by analogy from biological events of this sort to human behavior one might argue that in creative reorganization, psychological regression involves two kinds of operations: one is the de-differentiation (dissolution) of existing, schematized or automatized behavior patterns; the other consists in the activation of primitive levels of behavior from which undifferentiated (little-formulated) phenomena emerge.

The polar conceptualization of normal levels of operation in terms of fixity-mobility appears thus closely linked to another polar distinction, namely, that involved in the relation between lower and higher levels of operation. In regard to this relation, one particular problem among many has aroused considerable interest. It concerns the degree of fixity or mobility of an operation emerging at a certain level, in relation to developmentally later forms of operation.

As mentioned before, development, whether it concerns single functions, complex performances, or the totality of personality, tends toward stabilization. Once a certain stable level of integration is reached, the possibility of further development must depend on whether or not the behavioral patterns have become so automatized that they cannot take part in reorganization. We may refer here to Rapaport's concept of "apparatus" (31, p. 76) or to Piaget's concept of "schema" (30). The individual, for instance, builds up sensorimotor schemata, such as grasping, opening a box, and linguistic patterns; these are the goal of early learning at first, but later on become instruments or apparatuses for handling the environment. Since no two situations in which an organism finds itself are alike, the usefulness of these schemata in adaptive behavior will depend on their stability as well as on their pliability (a paradoxical "stable flexibility").

Furthermore, if one assumes that the emergence of higher levels of operations involves hierarchic integration, it follows that lower-level operations will have to be reorganized in terms of their functional nature so that they become subservient to higher functioning. A clear example of this is the change of the functional nature of imagery from a stage where images serve only memory, fantasy, and concrete conceptualization, to a stage where images have been transformed to schematic symbols of abstract concepts and thought.

DIFFERENTIAL VERSUS GENERAL DEVELOPMENTAL PYSCHOLOGY: INDIVIDUALITY AS A PROBLEM OF DEVELOPMENTAL PSYCHOLOGY

At Clark University we are becoming increasingly impressed with the fruitfulness of the developmental frame of reference for the study of group and individual differences. We may illustrate this approach to the many problems which are in need of investigation by referring to a few studies on cognitive organization.

One problem concerns the over-all maturity status of the individual, that is, his cognitive level of operation under optimal conditions, and the stability of this level under varying internal and external conditions. Friedman, Phillips, and their co-workers at Worcester State Hospital and at Clark University have constructed a genetic scoring system of the Rorschach test founded on developmental theory, and standardized through an ontogenetic study of children. The scoring system is based essentially on the occurrence and frequency of "genetically low" and "genetically high" scores. Restricting ourselves here mainly to the various whole and detail responses, genetically low responses are those which indicate amorphous, diffuse, or confabulatory percepts where little attention is given to part relations and to perception of contours. The genetically high percepts are reflected in the responses whereby the percept is that of a precisely formed unit with integrated parts, where the whole is composed of relatively independent sub-wholes brought together in an integrated fashion. Applying this developmental scoring analysis to the responses of 160 children of from three to eleven years of age, Hemmendinger found the basic principle of development confirmed. That is, with age there is a decrease of the undifferentiated diffuse whole and detail responses along with an increase of the highly articulated, well-integrated whole and detail responses. There is further an interesting shift from the early whole responses toward small detail responses between the ages of about six and eight; later on there is a decline in favor of the integrated whole responses (12).

This genetic scoring method has been utilized for the gauging of developmental levels of cognitive organization in normal and deviant persons in studies carried out at Worcester State Hospital, Clark University, and Boston University.* According to the theory, the most severely impaired groups should here show the genetically lowest responses, and there should be a decrease of these responses and an increase in the genetically high responses with less impaired or unimpaired groups. The evidence is in good agreement with this expectation (see Figures 1 to 4). It was found that the genetic scores of the hebephrenic-catatonic schizophrenics resembled those of children three to five years of age. The paranoids were similar to children six to ten years of age; the psychoneurotics were intermediate between the ten-year-olds and normal adults (9, 28, 38).

We may add at this point that for the study of individual differences in their developmental aspects, experimental methods other than those based on ontogenesis have become available. Among these, probably the most promising method is that of "microgenesis." This method, already mentioned above, is based on the assumption that activity patterns, percepts, thoughts, are not merely products but processes

---

* The illustrations given here refer to perceptual organization. For some of our pertinent studies on language behavior, see items 1, 9, 15, 24, 45, and 47 of the References.

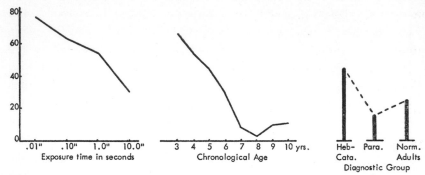

Figure 1. Median percentage of whole responses in normal adults at tachistoscopic exposures, and in children and diagnostic groups at full exposure, of the Rorschach.

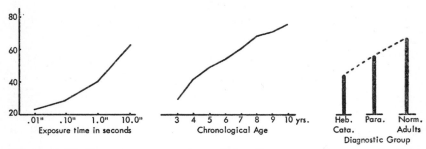

Figure 2. Median percentage of usual detail responses in normal adults at tachistoscopic exposures, and in children and diagnostic groups at full exposure, of the Rorschach.

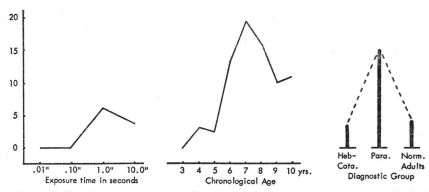

Figure 3. Median percentage of rare detail responses in normal adults at tachistoscopic exposures, and in children and diagnostic groups at full exposure, of the Rorschach.

142

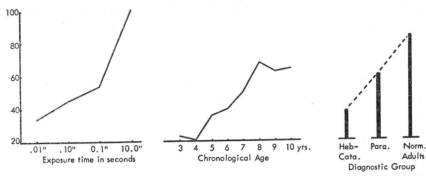

Figure 4. Percentage of developmentally-mature whole responses of all whole responses in normal adults at tachistoscopic exposures, and in children and diagnostic groups at full exposure, of the Rorschach.

that, whether they take seconds, or hours, or days, unfold in terms of developmental sequence.

To study microgenesis of perception, Framo presented the Rorschach cards to 80 normals. Twenty subjects in each of four groups viewed the cards at exposures of 0.01 second, 0.1 second, 1 second, and 10 seconds, respectively. A comparison of the responses in this study with the ontogenetic data obtained by Hemmendinger show striking agreements (29).*

The over-all conclusion is that the responses of the clinical groups represent various, more or less immature levels of perceptual development as compared to those of normals.

This evidence is supplemented by a study which E. Freed carried out under the direction of Leslie Phillips (29). Freed hypothesized that hebephrenic and catatonic schizophrenics would fail to show increased differentiation with time. Using the same design as Framo, he exposed the Rorschach to a group of 60 hebephrenic-catatonic schizophrenics, 15 at each of four exposure times. At the shortest exposure time their performance was not grossly different from that of the normal adults, but as exposure time was increased these schizophrenics increasingly lagged behind in the development toward perceptually mature responses (see Figure 5). It can be concluded, therefore, that unlike the

* Figures 1 to 4 show the W. D. and Dd responses and the genetically high responses (Mature W%, Mature D%) for (a) microgenetic changes and (b) ontogenetic changes, and (c) the responses of hebephrenic-catatonic schizophrenics, paranoids, and normals under the usual Rorschach Test conditions.

normal subjects, these schizophrenic groups did not utilize the increases in exposure time to improve their perceptual adequacy and integration.*

If we combine the notions and the evidence in terms of ontogenesis, microgenesis, and regression, we may conclude that perceptual processes develop and come to a halt at different levels. At what level the processes stop depends on such conditions as age, experience, and complexity of stimuli, and on the normal or pathologic maturity status

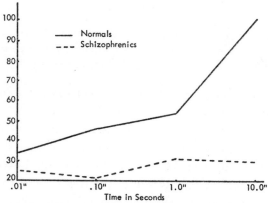

Figure 5. Median percentage of developmentally mature whole responses for normals and schizophrenics at four exposure times.

of a person. Thus, it might be said that by evaluating the Rorschach responses of a person through genetic scores, one tests the level of perceptual formation to which such a person under optimal time conditions progresses.

Not only has degree of psychiatric intactness been found to correspond to levels of development, but preliminary work at Worcester suggests that forms of symptom expression can also be ordered to the developmental sequence, as indicated by the genetic Rorschach scores. Thus, a number of studies have shown that persons whose symptoms are characterized by immediacy of overt reaction function at developmentally lower levels than those whose symptomatology represents dis-

---

* Another area of abnormal behavior to which the microgenetic methodology has been applied is that of speech pathology. Experiments on apprehension of tachistoscopically presented words by normal subjects suggest that paraphrasic naming is related to microgenetically early stages of name formation (46).

placement to more mediated forms of behavior. This has been shown by Misch, who found that a directly assaultive group is developmentally lower than a group of individuals who only threaten to assault (25). Similar findings have been obtained by Kruger (19) for subjects who demonstrate overt sexual perversion in contrast to those who only fear that they may act in a sexually perverse fashion. In addition, Kruger found that those patients who made a serious suicidal attempt were developmentally lower than those who only threatened to commit suicide.

Another developmental aspect of individuality that is in need of experimental and clinical study concerns what one might call the genetic stratification or the developmental heterogeneity of a person. Developmental stratification means that a person is structured into spheres of operations which differ in regard to developmental level. Still another aspect concerns the flexibility of a person to operate at different levels depending on the requirements of a situation.

In a particular way, it seems to us, this aspect of flexibility is connected with a further problem of individuality, namely, that of creativity. Now creativity, in its most general meaning, is an essential feature of emergent evolution, and this, in turn, implies progression through reorganization. Since we assume that such progress through reorganization cannot be achieved without "starting anew," that is, without regression, it follows that a person's capacity for creativity presupposes mobility in terms of regression and progression. The hypothesis would then be that the more creative the person, the wider his range of operations in terms of developmental level, or in other words, the greater his capacity to utilize primitive as well as advanced operations. This hypothesis is currently being tested at Worcester State Hospital and Clark University by means of the genetic Rorschach scores of relatively creative versus relatively noncreative adults.*

It might also be possible to study persons at the other extreme end of mobility, that is, those who, because of their excessive yearning for security, are coping with the environment in terms of rigidly formalized behavior. In this regard the work by the Swedish psychologist Ulf Krogh (18) seems very suggestive. He studied the microgenesis of complex pictures with various groups of people. Among other results he

* The study, well advanced, is being carried out by C. Hersch.

found that persons such as the compulsion-neurotics, whose reaction patterns to the environment are inordinately formalized, are lacking in microgenetic mobility, that is, they are lacking the intermediate steps that are normally present during the unfolding of percepts.

We should like, then, to conclude with this observation: The original aim of developmental theory, directed toward the study of universal genetic changes, is still one of its main concerns; but side by side with this concern, the conviction has been growing in recent years that developmental conceptualization, in order to reaffirm its truly organismic character, has to expand its orbit of interest to include as a central problem the study of individuality.

REFERENCES

1. Baker, R. W. "The Acquisition of Verbal Concepts in Schizophrenia: A Developmental Approach to the Study of Disturbed Language Behavior." Unpublished Ph.D. thesis, Clark University, 1953.
2. Barron, D. H. "Genetic Neurology and the Behavior Problem," in P. Weiss, ed., *Genetic Neurology*, pp. 223–31. Chicago: University of Chicago Press, 1950.
3. Bayley, N. "Mental Growth during the First Three Years," *Genet. Psychol. Monogr.*, Vol. 14 (1933), No. 1, p. 92.
4. Bertalanffy, L. *Modern Theories of Development*. London: Oxford University Press, 1933.
5. Bruell, J. "Experimental Studies of Temporally Extended Perceptual Processes and the Concept of 'Aktualgenese,'" in symposium on *The Developmental Viewpoint in Perception*, A. P. A. Meetings, Washington, D. C., 1952. Mimeogr. copy, Clark University.
6. Coghill, G. E. *Anatomy and the Problem of Behavior*. New York: Macmillan, 1929.
7. Duncker, K. "On Problem-solving," *Psychol. Monogr.*, Vol. 58 (1945), No. 5, pp. ix + 113.
8. DuNoüy, P. Lecomte. *Biological Time*. New York: Macmillan, 1937.
9. Friedman, H. "Perceptual Regression in Schizophrenia: An Hypothesis Suggested by the Use of the Rorschach Test," *J. Genet. Psychol.*, Vol. 81 (1952), pp. 63–98.
10. Gottschaldt, K. "Aufbau des Kindlichen Handelns," *Schrift. Entwickl. Psychol.*, Vol. 1 (1954), p. 220. Leipzig: Barth.
11. Hall, G. S. *Life and Confessions of a Psychologist*. New York: Appleton, 1923.
12. Hemmendinger, L. "A Genetic Study of Structural Aspects of Perception as Reflected in Rorschach Responses." Unpublished Ph.D. thesis, Clark University, 1951.
13. Hilgard, E. R. *Theories of Learning*. New York: Appleton, 1948.
14. Huxley, J. *Evolution*. London: Allen & Unwin, 1944.
15. Kaplan, B. "A Comparative Study of Acquisition of Meanings in Low-Educated and High-Educated Adults." Unpublished M.A. thesis, Clark University, 1950.
16. Kohler, I. *Über Aufbau und Wandlungen der Wahrnehmungswelt*. Wien: Rudolph M. Rohrer, 1951.
17. ———. "Umgewöhnung im Wahrnehmungsbereich," *Die Pyramide*, Vol. 5 (1953), pp. 92–95, Vol. 6 (1953), pp. 109–13.
18. Krogh, U. "The Actual-Genetic Model of Perception-Personality," *Stud. Psychol. Paedag.*, Series altera, Vol. 7 (1955), p. 394. Lund: Gleerup.

19. Kruger, A. "Direct and Substitute Modes of Tension-Reduction in terms of Developmental Level: An Experimental Analysis by means of the Rorschach Test." Unpublished Ph.D. thesis, Clark University, 1955.

20. Lane, J. E. "Social Effectiveness and Developmental Level," *J. Personal.*, Vol. 23 (1955), pp. 274–84.

21. Lashley, K. S. "Persistent Problems in the Evolution of Mind," *Quart. Rev. Biol.*, Vol. 24 (1949), pp. 28–42.

22. Lewis, M. M. *Infant Speech.* New York: Harcourt, 1936.

23. Lillie, R. S. "Biology and Unitary Principle," *Philos. Sci.*, Vol. 18 (1951), pp. 193–207.

24. Mirin, B. "A Study of the Formal Aspects of Schizophrenic Verbal Communication," *Genet. Psychol. Monogr.*, Vol. 52 (1955), No. 2, pp. 149–90.

25. Misch, R. "The Relationship of Motoric Inhibition to Developmental Level and Ideational Functioning: An Analysis by means of the Rorschach Test." Unpublished Ph.D. thesis, Clark University, 1953.

26. Needham, A. E. *Regeneration and Wound Healing.* New York: Wiley, 1952.

27. Novikoff, A. B. "The Concept of Integrative Levels and Biology," *Science*, Vol. 101 (1945), pp. 209–15.

28. Peña, C. "A Genetic Evaluation of Perceptual Structurization in Cerebral Pathology," *J. Proj. Tech.*, Vol. 17 (1953), pp. 186–99.

29. Phillips, L., and J. Framo. "Developmental Theory Applied to Normal and Psychopathological Perception," *J. Personal.*, Vol. 22 (1954), pp. 464–74.

30. Piaget, J. *Play, Dreams, and Imitation in Childhood.* New York: Norton, 1951.

31. Rapaport, D. "The Conceptual Model of Psychoanalysis," *J. Personal.*, Vol. 20 (1951), pp. 56–81.

32. Russell, E. S. *Form and Function.* London: Murray, 1916.

33. ———. *The Directiveness of Organic Activities.* Cambridge: Cambridge University Press, 1945.

34. Sander, F. "Experimentelle Ergebenisse der Gestalt Psychologie," *Bar. ü.d. Kongr. f. Exper. Psychol.*, Vol. 10 (1928), pp. 23–87.

35. Schneirla, T. C. "A Consideration of some Conceptual Trends in Comparative Psychology." *Psychol. Bull.*, Vol. 6 (1952), pp. 559–97.

36. ———. "Problems in the Biopsychology of Social Organization," *J. Abn. and Soc. Psychol.*, Vol. 41 (1946), pp. 385–402.

37. Schroedinger, E. *What is Life?* Cambridge: Cambridge University Press, 1951.

38. Siegel, E. L. "Genetic Parallels of Perceptual Structurization in Paranoid Schizophrenia." Unpublished Ph.D. thesis, Clark University, 1950.

39. Simpson, G. G. *The Meaning of Evolution.* New Haven: Yale University Press, 1950.

40. Weiss, P. *Principles of Development.* New York: Holt, 1939.

41. Werner, H. "Process and Achievement," *Harvard Educ. Rev.*, Vol. 7 (1937), pp. 353–68.

42. ———. "Musical Microscales and Micromelodies," *J. Psychol.*, Vol. 10 (1940), pp. 149–56.

43. ———. "Experimental Genetic Psychology," in P. Harriman, ed., *Encyclopedia of Psychology*, pp. 219–35. New York: Philosophical Library, 1944.

44. ———. *Comparative Psychology of Mental Development*, rev. ed. Chicago: Follet, 1948.

45. ———, ed., *On Expressive Language.* Worcester: Clark University Press, 1955.

46. ———. "Microgenesis in Aphasia," *J. Abn. and Soc. Psychol.*, Vol. 52 (1956), pp. 347–53.

47. ———, and B. Kaplan. "The Developmental Approach to Cognition: Its Relevance to the Psychological Interpretation of Anthropological and Ethnolinguistic Data." Mimeogr. paper, Clark University, 1955.

48. ———. "The Acquisition of Word Meanings: A Developmental Study," *Monogr. Soc. Res. Child Developm.*, Vol. 15 (1952), No. 1, p. 120.
49. ———, and S. Wapner. "The Innsbruck Studies on Distorted Visual Fields in Relation to an Organismic Theory of Perception," *Psychol. Rev.*, Vol. 62 (1955), pp. 130–38.
50. Windle, W. F., and J. E. Fitzgerald. "Development of the Spinal Reflex Mechanism in Human Embryos," *J. Comp. Neurol.*, Vol. 67 (1937), pp. 493–509.

Robert R. Sears

IDENTIFICATION AS A FORM OF BEHAVIORAL DEVELOPMENT

AMONG the many ways in which living organisms exhibit systematic changes with time is the behavioral. The term *behavioral* is at least as broad as the term *physical structure*, and must be broken down into more manageable categories if we are to examine the mechanics by which various kinds of behavioral changes come about. Presumably here, as elsewhere in ontogenesis, the rules and principles of growth are most easily discovered, and most precisely applicable, if we limit our investigation to homogeneous categories of events.

There are a number of different ways in which behavior can be analyzed. Each of them involves the definition of a set of dimensions, or separable categories, that describe the various aspects of behavior. One type of analysis, rather popular among child psychologists at one time, distinguished between mental, motor, emotional, and social behaviors. Another made the separation according to the psychological functions involved, such as perception, motivation, thinking, and learning. Neither of these methods has proved very useful, and we do not at present have a set of descriptive dimensions soundly based either on theory or on descriptive observation. The chief objection to these older classifications is that they sliced behavior into meaningless and entirely arbitrary segments. Social and emotional behavior both involve intellection, certainly, and the prediction of emotional behavior cannot be accurate without consideration of the habits constructed through social interaction.

In what follows, I will indicate briefly what kinds of dimensions seem more useful for describing behavioral development, and what mechanisms appear to be responsible for the changes. Then I will give an example of a process that is responsible for one kind of change. This is the process of *identification*.

Any new system for describing and classifying developmental behavioral changes will have to deal with the actions of the person-as-a-whole, and will then differentiate between the various theoretically relevant attributes of those actions. Doubtless we shall discover effective ways of breaking the totality of such actions into subordinate systems, and certainly we shall have to discover what are their theoretically relevant attributes. But the basic requirement is that the actions or the systems be specified as those which the person-as-a-whole performs in the process of interacting with and manipulating the environment — both human and nonhuman — in which he lives and grows.

It would be premature to try to estimate how many useful dimensions of developmental change can be discriminated. There are four, however, that may be worth mentioning simply as illustrations of the type of definition I have suggested. First, there is a change in the degree of precision, the efficiency, and the speed with which manipulative, locomotor, and communicative acts are performed. In the early part of life these qualities of action increase rapidly, but different action systems appear to have different rates. In later life there are differential decreases.

A second attribute of action involves its instigators. Characteristically there is an increase throughout life in the complexity of the stimulus conditions that can evoke effective interaction with the environment. This kind of change is particularly noticeable in action systems that involve response to social stimuli; for example, the child becomes responsive to his mother's moods, to the atmosphere produced by mother-father interactions, and eventually to elaborate and subtle cues in such matters as social status.

Third, there is change in the length and complexity of action sequences that the person uses in relating himself to his environment and securing gratification for his desires. This is exemplified by such differences as that between the infant's simple sucking and the older child's sequence of eating activities, which includes his coming into the house, washing his hands, and asking for what he wants at the table.

Fourth, there is change in the quality and complexity of the environmental events that are the apparent objects (or incentives) of actions. The infant may seek, under certain conditions, to get a nipple in his mouth, a breast against his cheek, and arms holding his body. The older child seeks only the last, under any conditions, but adds reassurance, loving smiles, nearness of mother, affectionate conversation, and many other less tangible signs of nurture to the list of environmental events toward the securing of which his actions may be directed.

These four dimensions of behavioral development are purely descriptive, of course, but they do imply something about the mechanisms responsible for their occurrence. Since they refer to attributes of action sequences that relate the person to his environment, they assume mechanisms that can be described in terms of instigators, incentives, expectancies, rewards and punishments, environmental events, and other conceptual paraphernalia of a behavioral theory of learning and action.

DETERMINANTS OF CHANGE

There appear to be three main mechanisms by which these changes are brought about. The first of these is the *learning process* itself. The conditions under which the child learns determine the specific kinds of instigators to which he will respond, the environmental events he will come to expect, and the actions he will engage in to produce such events.

By the very nature of the child-rearing process, and the demands that society places on parents for the socialization of their child, a youngster must learn to discriminate new kinds of cues. Not only must he react to increasingly complex stimuli of a social character, but he must develop ways of behaving that involve responsibility and self-reliance. The cues that initiate such actions are gradually established *as* cues, for the child, through the rewarding and punishing that the parents do. The four dimensions of behavioral development mentioned earlier are all affected by learning and by the culturally determined conditions under which learning takes place.

A second mechanism that provides for these changes is the *physical maturation* of the child. This is so obvious as to require no discussion, at least so far as the influence of changing capacities is concerned. If one thinks of maturation in respect to its social implications, of course, he is at once led to an influence that has nothing to do directly with physical change but is a stimulus by-product of it. As the child takes on new characteristics, his parents expect new things of him.

The third mechanism rests on an action principle that behavior is in part a function of the *expectancies for action* expressed to the individual by others. The parents' expectancies obviously change not only because of physical changes in the child but also because of their realization that he is learning new things.

To speak of these three general sources of influence on behavioral development as *mechanisms* is perhaps a misnomer. Only in the logical sense are they mechanisms, for they are in fact whole fields of scientific investigation that provide the phenomena for the explanation of which developmental behavior theories must be constructed.

I want to turn now to a specific instance of such a theory, in order to show concretely how certain types of changes in child behavior can be accounted for by principles of learning and action.

IDENTIFICATION

Children of two years and older have a tendency to act in a number of ways like their parents. They adopt parental mannerisms, play parental roles, and in the later preschool years seem to incorporate in their own value-systems many of the values, restrictions, and ideals of the parents. That is to say, they develop a conscience. It is the apparent "absorption" of these characteristics without specific training, either by direct guidance or by reward and punishment, that leads to the hypothesis of a process (identification) that short-cuts the direct training process. It is as if the child had learned a general principle "to be like my father and mother." He then incorporates many of their psychological properties into his own repertory of properties without, in each instance, appearing to receive overt rewards for so doing.

The overt actions elicited by identification are numerous. Three types have been distinguished that appear to be products of the process: qualities, roles, and demands. *Qualities* refers to mannerisms, motives, and temperamental characteristics. *Roles* refers to the systematized pattern of duties, attitudes, and actions that characterize such sociologically defined persons as mother, father, woman, and man. *Demands* refers to the standards of conduct required of the self and of others. Identification behavior, then, is *acting like another person*.

From a systematic standpoint, there are two aspects of identification to be considered. One is genetic, the sequence of events in infancy that culminates in the establishment of the process. The other is systematic, that is, the formal theoretical properties of the process once it has been established.

A theoretical account of the development of identification must specify the way in which known principles of learning create the new behavior. There appear to be three main developmental steps. First, the child develops a dependency drive for which the mother's affectionate nurture is the appropriate environmental event. Second, he imitates (behaves like) the mother. Third, this imitation provides sufficient gratification so that it becomes habitual and takes on the characteristics of a secondary motivational system. Let us consider these steps in order.

Since an infant is unable to secure his main primary gratifications without help, his mother is at once introduced into an interpersonal action system with him. She is nearly always present when his primary needs are satisfied. Hence her helping actions become a necessary part of the sequence of behavior that leads to the child's satisfactions. Her actions are the environmental events that link with his actions in a frequently repeated reinforcement sequence. This gradually produces, in the infant, a secondary drive system of dependency-on-the-mother. The ultimate outcome is that the mother's presence, her gestures and attitudes as well as her more manipulative actions, become secondary rewards for the child.

The next step is the child's incorporation of these attributes of the mother into his own action system; he comes to imitate the mother. There are probably a number of ways in which this occurs, and for our present theoretical purposes it is necessary only to specify that it does happen. One possible mechanism is suggested by psychoanalytic theory. Assume that at birth the infant is unable to discriminate between himself and others, and simply perceives movement in his universe. Some of these universe-movements are accompanied by drive and other internal stimuli, and are followed by such goal responses as eating, defecation, relaxation, warming, and sleep.

By direct reinforcement, any actions that the child himself makes consistently in such a sequence will become established as habitual responses to the internal stimulus conditions. Some of the universe-movements are actions of this sort, while others are actions performed by the mother or some other agent external to the child. However, since it is being assumed that the child does not discriminate between himself and his mother, the perception of *her* actions becomes an integral part of *his* action sequences just as much as his own actions do.

If the mother is absent on some occasion when drive stimuli occur and start off one of the child's action sequences, he will attempt to perform those parts of the total sequences for which his mother is normally responsible. This effort will not always be sufficient to permit continuation of the sequence to its goal response, but on some occasions such actions as smiling or babbling will arouse the mother and bring her. It is mainly the overt manipulative actions he tries that will fail, while affective and gestural actions will more often succeed. In any case, when the mother is present, she will make the necessary manipulative movements, and his affective behavior that is like hers will not be extinguished, but will be reinforced.

The fact that the mother is not always present when the child's action sequences are evoked is responsible for his growing discrimination of himself as different from others. He conceptualizes *others* initially by virtue of the consistent occurrence of rewards or non-rewards in association with the presence or absence of those universe-movements performed by other persons. It follows from this that the generalized discrimination of "self-other" would be the first one made, and only later would different *others*, such as mother and father, be discriminated from one another. This appears to be borne out by studies of infants' social smiling; at first, any person evokes a smile, and only later does the mother alone become, for a period, the main elicitor of smiles.

In any case, whatever the mechanism for imitation, its occurrence in a child with a dependency drive for which the mother's actions are the appropriate rewards will permit the child to reward himself. That is, when he is motivated to secure the mother's nurturing responses, he can imitate her affectionate attitudes and gestures himself and hence secure at least partial gratification for his dependency drive.

The consequences of this procedure account for the third step in the developmental process, the production of (a) a stable habit of responding imitatively, and (b) a secondary motivational system for which "acting like the mother" is the goal response; "acting like the mother" is a part of the reinforced sequence of behavior. Many symbolic acts performed by the mother (smiling, hugging, talking) become secondary rewards for the child, and when he performs these acts himself, he rewards himself. Thus his own performance of some kinds of identification behavior is self-rewarding. So long as the mother does not actually punish him for such actions, and so long as she continues to use reasonably consistent symbols of love and approval, this process will continue.

One consequence suggested by this formulation is that the degree of identification of the child with his mother should bear a curvilinear relationship to the amount of affectionate nurture the mother gives. If she is universally present and always plays her part in the dyadic mother-child sequence, the child will never have occasion to perform mother-acts, i.e., to establish identification. On the other hand, if she is continuously punitive, and is rarely associated with the satisfying completion of the child's goal striving, her acts will have no part in his action sequence, and there would be no initial instigation to act like her.

Once the process of identification has been established, it has the formal status of a secondary motivational system. There is no contradiction in the application of the term *process* to such a system, for *identification* is used here to describe the psychological operations which produce certain kinds of behavior.

The original problem with which we start is that of describing the conditions that determine the child's adopting or failing to adopt parental attitudes and values, behavior appropriate to his sex role, and other qualities found in the parents. It would be safe to hazard a guess in advance that no single conceptualized process is responsible for all the habit structures that a child develops. Some behaviors are established by direct training through reward and punishment, others by the process of imitation, and still others seem to involve more elaborate conditions which result in such processes as projection, symbolization, and displacement. The present hypothesis is that a secondary drive of identification produces the behavior that is replicative of the parents' qualities, role behaviors, and demands. In this sense, it is a process or mechanism. It has the effect of transmitting the values of the culture from one generation to the next, and of providing for the continuity, in a society, of persons appropriately trained for the roles of which the society is composed.

If identification is a secondary motivational system, the various parts of the system must be described. *The goal response is acting as if one possessed the psychological properties of another person (originally, the parent).* In the course of development, the reinforcement of identification comes from the self-rewarding produced by imitation of the parts of the mother's behavior that form the reward for the dependency drive. Imitation of other aspects of maternal behavior presumably is automatic, and though not rewarding of the dependency drive, is at least not met by punishment. But when identification has become a secondary motivational system in its own right, *any* action that is like that of the parent is a goal response.

The *instigation* to identification behavior is of two main kinds. One is *absence of the normally rewarding parent*, the drive being most strongly aroused by any situation in which the parents are unable (or unwilling) to provide their customary nurture. The other is *any situation that has previously been associated with the elicitation of identification behavior.*

From a measurement standpoint, the existence of identification can be determined only by the occurrence in the child of actions representing the three classes of psychological properties previously described, qualities, roles, and demands. *The operational measure of strength of identification is the degree to which such properties characterize his actions.*

I have described the identificant rather interchangeably as "mother" and "parents." This usage rests on the assumption that the dependency drive, which governs the development of identification, is at first based mainly on the mother's interaction, but that by the time a child is two or three years old, other persons (particularly the father under usual circumstances) become *Betas* for dependency drives. Hence, it is appropriate to refer to "parents" at these later stages of development.

Not all the parental behavior copied by the child is specifically desired by the parents. There are probably many qualities of the mother's actions of which she is scarcely aware — for example, her speech and gestural mannerisms, rate and style of movement, and methods of scheduling her work. In such matters she may have no preferences as to how her child behaves, or she may even recognize and somewhat dislike her own characteristics in some respects. According to the present view, identification would cause the child to adopt these behaviors nonetheless, at least to whatever degree the strength of his identification drive permits.

In the area of demands or standards of conduct, however, the parental viewpoint is quite different. Many demands are quite explicitly verbalized, and the parents watch carefully to see whether the child is behaving in accord with them. The child may quickly learn that affection or other rewards (including avoidance of criticism) come to him when he is compliant. Whether identification has occurred or not, he will behave in accord with these demands. With casual observation it would be difficult to differentiate such behavior from that induced by true identification.

A distinction can be made, however, if the child is observed not only when the parents are present but when they are not. The child who is complying solely or mainly because of anticipated rewards or punishments will be noncompliant when none of the stimuli are present that evoke such anticipations. The child who has strong identification, on the other hand, provides the necessary stimuli for compliance within his own action system, and hence will behave according to demands even when direct parental control is absent. Obviously the comparison is not so simple as is implied by "presence *vs.* absence of parents"; there are many situations in which the parents are symbolically present or in which a noncompliant act may be discovered later and punished. The distinction is between situations in which *symbolic parental stimuli* to compliance are present or absent.

Since the child's identification behavior frequently, at least in the early preschool years, includes fairly overt representation of the approving or disapproving symbolic actions of the parents, there is the possibility of direct reward for such behavior. The child of four who is heard to say "Bad boy!" after he has deviated from demanded standards of conduct is often given sympathetic approval by his parents for this expression of self-judgment. Indeed, many parents pay close attention to what they describe as a development of "moral understanding" and conscience. They may be disturbed by a deviation in behavior, but pleased to see the child's own self-condemnation; even in instances of self-approval, many parents are more likely to show pleased amusement, in the early years, than disapproval for "conceit."

This discussion has been concerned solely with the strength of identification, and not at all with its content. Since identification is the adoption of the psychological properties of the parents, the child's behavior will correspond to that of the parents insofar as he is able to discover what those properties are. Obviously the parental properties that are most tangible, most immediately in evidence to the child, are those standards of conduct (demands) the parents require the child to live up to. These range from simple motor control in the first year or two, to elaborately conceptualized kinds of behavior, such as being clean or neat or friendly in the later years. These demands constitute the "absorbed" properties of the parents; the content of the child's identifying behavior is as extensive as the parental repertory of demands.

The terms *reward* and *punishment* have been used frequently in this discussion to describe the events that produce learning. Now their nature must be defined more exactly. The reward given by the mother is ordinarily affection coupled with nurture. The punishment for failure to comply with demands is either the withholding or withdrawal of love. Other types of reward and punishment, incentives or threats, can be used for the control of behavior, but it is doubtful whether they have any influence on identification except as they are incidentally symbolic of giving or taking away love.

Not all demands by the parents are rewarded and punished in the same ratio, nor are all equally important from the parental point of view. Success or failure in compliance, then, may elicit from the parents varying degrees of affection or withdrawal, depending on the importance of the demand. Some demands may be highly rewarded when complied with but not strongly punished if compliance is lacking, and vice versa. For example, once the toilet training process is near completion, most children get little affection for regular bowel movements, but they may be treated rather sternly for an accident. Similarly, nonmasturbatory activity gains no reward but masturbation may be punished. On the other hand, the mother may not punish her child for getting dirty at play, but she may express particular pleasure if he does not. It seems probable that reward for compliance is usually more pronounced in the early stages of demand-training, when success is less to be expected and therefore more satisfying to the mother, while punishment for deviation is the stronger in the late stages.

The conscience is composed of those demands that have been most strongly established in the identification system by withdrawal of love.

Since identification involves the performing of the parental acts, the child ultimately comes to perform the rewarding acts for his own compliance and the punishing acts for his deviations and failures. The parents almost inevitably point to the child himself as the blameworthy agent in a deviation, and hence the child comes to do the same. He attributes blame to himself when he deviates. This is the origin of guilt. The most anxious and conscience-ridden child should be the one who has developed deep affectional ties with his parents, who has experienced inconsistent reward for compliance but consistent punishment for deviations, and for whom demands have been high and pervasive of many areas of behavior.

This theoretical formulation of identification suggests several hypotheses. First, the strength of identification varies positively with the amount of affectionate nurture given the child. Presumably a preschool-aged child is away from the mother often enough that there is little danger of a failure to identify because of too continuous and universal nurture. This follows from the assumption that the mother's help creates dependency motivation in the child; dependency is considered to be a necessary precondition to identification.

There is some support for this hypothesis in a study recently completed by several of us at the Harvard Laboratory of Human Development (1, 2). The mothers of 379 kindergarten children were interviewed with respect to their child-training methods and their children's behavior. One measure of the latter derived from the interviews was an estimate of the extent to which each child had developed *conscience* at age five. This rating may be used as a measure of the strength of the identification process. The interviews were also examined for evidence of maternal coldness and rejection of the child. Those children whose mothers gave some evidence of such rejection were judged to show less complete conscience development than those who were not rejected.

Second, the strength of identification varies positively with the severity of the demands placed on the child by the mother. It is assumed that identification behavior develops in the first place as a device to help the child create the necessary environmental conditions for satisfying his dependency drive; i.e., since the mother was not always present, or perhaps not always willing, to do those acts required of her to satisfy the child, he had to do them himself. Therefore, the more the child is required to substitute for her, the stronger will be the habit of identifying, and the greater the probability that such acts will become secondary goal responses. The severity of demands is important in this respect because the greater the demands, the greater the frequency of instances in which the child will not have immediate help from the mother, but will have to wait upon his successful accomplishment of the acts demanded. As with affectionate nurture, there is probably an upper limit of severity beyond which severity is negatively related to identification; if the mother sets standards entirely beyond the child's capacity for accomplishment, he will either never get loved (if affection is contingent on success) or the demands will not be true demands (if affection is given anyway). We have no data, at present, with which to test this hypothesis.

Third, the strength of identification varies positively with the extent to which the mother uses withdrawal of love as a disciplinary technique. It is the mother's affectionate love and nurture that serve as the original reinforcers for identification, and when these are withheld the child's efforts to secure them are increased. In the study mentioned before, the mother interviews were rated for frequency of use of various types of disciplinary techniques. It was found that the children whose mothers relied on physical punishment, deprivation, and material rewards had lower conscience development than those whose mothers used withdrawal of love and isolation as punishment, together with verbal praise as reward.

Fourth, the strength of identification will vary positively with the amount of absence of the person with whom the child identifies. Since the identification behavior is required only in the absence of immediate nurture by the identificant, the child can practice more with greater degrees of absence. This presupposes (a) that adequate primary identification has been established in infancy, and (b) that the absence is not of too long duration. The actual constants in these relationships may be quite complex. A fairly high identification to start with, coupled with a shift to high but not complete absence (mother takes a time-consuming job away from home), would probably produce the highest continuing reinforcement of the identification drive. We have no data with which to test this hypothesis because there were almost no cases of extended absence by mothers in our group.

Finally, we can predict that by kindergarten age children will have developed a substantial degree of sex-typing; that is, boys will have become masculine in their interests, values, and role choices, and girls will have become distinctly feminine. Furthermore, the process will be more complete for girls than for boys, because the boys must first identify with the chief caretaker, who is normally the mother, and then later must shift to the socially approved masculine identification.

Each of the 379 children in the study was given two twenty-minute sessions of permissive doll play with a family of dolls and a five-room doll house. The experimenters recorded the frequency with which a child chose each doll as the agent of thematic actions. The girls characteristically used the mother doll most frequently, while the boys chose the father doll a little more often than the mother doll. The difference was more striking for the girls than for the boys, and this is in accord with the prediction.

CONCLUSION

In sum, then, what I have proposed is that behavior can be viewed as a subject matter for a set of principles concerned with development. As with other areas of investigation, we require descriptive dimensions on which developmental changes can be charted and measured; and I have suggested four possible useful ones in the first part of this paper. I have also indicated briefly the three main types of mechanism responsible for observed developmental changes in these dimensions: physical maturation, the learning process, and changes in dyadic expectancies.

In the last section of the paper I have described in some detail one process — identification — that accounts for two major developments in the child's personality, his inner control, or conscience, and his adoption of sex-typed role behavior. The data presently available for testing these hypotheses are minimal, of course, but they at least illustrate the possibility of constructing and testing a theory of developmental change mechanisms.

REFERENCES

1. Levin, H., and R. R. Sears. "Identification with Parents as a Determinant of Doll Play Aggression," *Child Devel.*, Vol. 27 (1956), No. 2, (in press).
2. Sears, R. R., Eleanor E. Maccoby and H. Levin. *Patterns of Child Rearing.* Evanston: Row, 1956 (in press).

Wallace A. Russell

AN EXPERIMENTAL PSYCHOLOGY OF DEVELOPMENT: PIPE DREAM OR POSSIBILITY?

Experimental methods represent but one weapon in the arsenal of the scientific investigator. Many scientific disciplines, such as astronomy, are not experimental sciences at all. Others find experimental studies of limited usefulness, and there are those who would argue that psychology is one of these. However this may be, there are experimental psychologists who greatly esteem this method and who have evolved a characteristic way of viewing both their method and their subject matter. The question of whether or not there can be an experimental psychology of development within the experimentalist's meaning of the term is so linked with this viewpoint that it may best be approached somewhat indirectly by taking a closer look at some of the views of a hypothetical experimental psychologist.

The experimental psychologist is, first of all, one who clings to an ideal in matters scientific. Although he recognizes that methods other than laboratory investigations make valuable and objective contributions to science, he nevertheless continues to harbor the notion that that knowledge is *best* established which has been tested under experimental conditions. By this he means that the test has been made in a situation where the experimenter has (a) produced controlled, quantified variation in one or more independent variables, and (b) observed the resultant, quantified variation in one or more dependent variables, (c) while having assiduously ruled out in the dependent variable or variables the possibility of systematic variation due to any other factor. The experimentalist stands fast in this methodological value judgment even though he realizes that only the roughest approximations to this ideal have been possible in psychology and even though recent evidence shows that in this respect he is an extreme nonconformist when compared to other psychologists (2).

In view of this deviant characteristic it is not surprising that the experimental psychologist is prone to show more concern than others about the strictly experimental underpinning of any domain of knowledge he surveys. In examining an area of psychology he is likely to look first at the most clearly experimental evidence that has been gathered to determine what kind of a systematic picture this evidence yields. He might review, say, the *experimental* psychology of learning, the *experimental* psychology of motivation, or the *experimental* psychology of perception. In these particular areas, the evaluation and organization of such evidence offers no unusual problems. They are fields that the experimentalist can consider without any change in his usual frame of reference. But when an analogous task is undertaken for the psychology of development, a number of problems arise. In the first place, there is no obvious parallel between such constructs as learning, motivation, and perception on the one hand and development on the other. The former are inferred states or processes viewed as immediate determinants of behavior. Development, at least at first glance, does not seem to be a construct of this sort. In the second place, learning, motivation, and perception have reference to relatively non-overlapping classes of observations, whereas the notion of development appears to cut across all behavior classes. It taps new dimensions, dimensions in which the experimentalist as such is not used to thinking. Indeed, it is difficult for him to state with precision what an experimental psychology of development might be. To understand this difficulty one must examine certain other aspects of the basic orientation of the experimentalist.

THE ORIENTATION OF THE EXPERIMENTALIST

It must be recognized, of course, that there is no accurate way of describing *the* orientation of experimental psychologists. Those psychologists who are partial to experimental techniques have a variety of orientations, and it is only with considerable inaccuracy to some that one can present characteristics that are supposed to apply to all. Furthermore, the *experimental* orientation of a particular psychologist may not be the only framework within which he personally is capable of working. He may be experimentally oriented part of the time and yet be quite capable of thinking within the framework of the clinician, or the psychometrician, or the developmental psychologist at other times. Nevertheless, I believe that the psychologist when he is thinking in experimental terms is at least likely to reveal certain tendencies — to be dominated by certain habitual modes of thought — which make it difficult for him easily to subsume the concept of development within the framework of his experimental orientation. In part or in whole, these difficulties may be mere matters of emphasis rather than clear incompatibilities with a developmental approach, but at any rate they are worth reviewing.

1. *The tendency to think in terms of a restricted time scale.* The very concept of development as a process of organization over time forces the experimentalist into his first difficulty, for with respect to time his orientation can more frequently be classified as "cross-sectional" than "longitudinal." That is, the experimental psychologist is most usually interested in events that take place over relatively short periods of time. Like a short story writer, he is concerned with a "slice of life" rather than the entire life span of an individual. There are many reasons why this has been a characteristic of the experimental approach. Experimental studies, for one thing, typically take place under conditions which cannot easily be maintained for long intervals. People cannot be held indefinitely in a laboratory. Complex behavior recording devices, elaborate control conditions, and the like all demand that the experimental session be kept as short as possible. These considerations no doubt bias the experimentalist toward exploring the variables most adaptable to short-term investigation. And, of course, once interest is focused on such factors, other variables, such as long-term developmental processes, are looked upon as confounding factors to be removed or controlled rather than directly investigated.

The acceptance of a restricted time scope has implications for most phases of the experimentalist's work. It has no doubt contributed to his characteristic concern for the immediate antecedents of behavior. Perhaps because of it he has come to prefer to work with many persons in a single restricted experimental situation rather than with a few persons in situations distributed through time. Attention to a restricted time scope in the study of behavior can only increase interest in short-range prediction rather than in prediction of behavior which will take place over a long period of time or in the distant future.

2. *The preference for precisely defined variables.* Of course, any investigator prefers to work with precisely defined variables. In the experimentalist, however, this demand is unusually strong. He typically studies variables, such as number of trials in a learning task, which are closely linked to direct observation. He is most at ease with those variables which can be quantified. This preference for precision may lead him to be concerned with what have been termed molecular as opposed to molar phenomena, since they seem to offer the greater possibility for precise definition. These molecular phenomena are not likely to lead to a consideration of processes of development which take place over a long period of time. Those phenomena that do lead to developmental thinking, on the other hand, are likely to involve variables of such a general nature that their linkage to direct observation is somewhat remote. For example, consider the problem of the development of aggressiveness in a child and its relation to parental disciplinary practices. The independent variable — parental disciplinary practice — is a complex of events defying precise description and not lending itself to straightforward quantification. The dependent variable, as well, does not refer to a particular defined set, but rather to a characteristic that might be manifested in a variety of ways. The generalized nature of some of the variables that are conducive to thinking in developmental terms, does not, of course, lead to the conclusion that they are forever unamenable to experimental study. The inherent difficulties of these variables merely represent one of the conditions that make it difficult for the experimentalist to deal with them in his own terms.

3. *Interest in the functional determinants of behavior.* Some changes in behavior seem to take place more or less regularly with the passage of time. When such is the case it is possible to focus attention almost exclusively on the behavior itself — that is, on the dependent variable, without too much concern for the relevant independent variables. The result may be a very useful description of behavior change. Experimental psychologists, however, have not tended to deal primarily with descriptions of behavior of this sort. They have, rather, been interested in behavior which may be modified by the direct manipulation of some environmental stimulus or some elicitable state of the organism. They

have seen it as their purpose to state as accurately as possible the relationships that can be found between *controlled* manipulations of antecedent conditions and concomitant changes in behavior. These relationships in generalized form become scientific laws, and are in many ways the desired fruit of experimental research. Experimentalists emphasize the explanatory value of such laws. As a matter of values, they prize more highly those findings which are in this sense explanatory rather than merely descriptive. While the possibility of time laws is recognized, there is the opinion that changes which take place over time are determined not intrinsically by the passage of time but by the operation of other potentially specifiable variables operating in time. The specification, manipulation, and experimental study of these determinants of behavior are a central concern of the experimentalist. This very concern leads him to think little of the time-bound changes that may be central issues in developmental psychology.

4. *Involvement in the formulation of general behavior theory.* It is quite true that there are a great many applications of the experimental method which have no immediate relevance for the formulation of the systems of laws and constructs that are called theories. Nevertheless, in the training of most experimental psychologists there is implanted a vision of a general behavior theory which is never quite lost. In the search for laws, it is the search for the most *general* laws. In the formulation of theory, the goal is to find that one which will apply to the widest range of phenomena. When psychologists are considering the possibilities for a general theory — and here, the possibilities must be sharply distinguished from the achievements to date — it is not unusual to set a general theory of human behavior as a goal. This would be a theory that would apply to all human beings at any age level. For an individual with such a goal, the choice of subjects within the target area of humanity is dictated by tactical rather than strategic considerations. College sophomores are human beings, and if they are more available for experimental purposes than others, then there is no obvious reason why a general theory of human behavior could not be built on observations of them as well as on some other sub-set of human beings. Eventually the general utility of any theory based on college sophomores would have to be tested on other populations, but, say some experimentalists, this can wait until a tentative theory, at least, has been formulated for the sophomore group. This line of reasoning

is similar to that of theorists who are more ambitiously striving for a general theory of mammalian behavior, or even of behavior in general in whatever organism it appears. They begin their work with white rats, or goldfish, or whatever organism is most available, formulate their tentative general theories, and then, presumably, test the adequacy of the general theories on other groups.

At this point the main thing to note is that if the objective is to establish a general theory, however tentatively, then the problem of the differential manifestation of that theory in the life span of the organism becomes secondary. Since experimentalists have even the tentative formulation of a general theory still before them, it is understandable that they have not undertaken a developmental analysis of their theories.

A summary of these aspects of the orientation of the experimental psychologist may suggest why, in the words of a recent reviewer (1), "child psychology tends not to be an experimental science." The child psychologist, a term often used synonymously with "developmental psychologist," would probably differ from the experimentalist at three and possibly all four of these points. Where the experimentalist takes a cross-sectional approach with respect to time, the developmental psychologist would be committed to the long-term, or longitudinal, approach. Where the experimentalist prefers simple, refined, precise, molecular variables, the developmentalist is frequently forced by the very nature of his approach to deal with complex, relatively rough, imprecise, molar variables. Where the experimentalist is concerned with the functional determinants of behavior and the explanatory character of his laws, the developmentalist may devote his primary effort to the task of describing the characteristic modifications of behavior in time. And, finally, while the developmentalist might confess to an interest in general theory, he would almost certainly not agree with the experimentalist as to the best way to go about formulating one.

THE EXPERIMENTALIST AND DEVELOPMENTAL PSYCHOLOGY

Certainly there are such marked differences in orientation between our particular experimentalist and a developmental psychologist that one might wonder whether it would be possible for the two to communicate, to say nothing of collaborating on something called an experimental psychology of development. Actually, however, psychologists in institutes of child welfare and experimental psychologists in psychology departments *do* communicate, and often with a fairly high level of mutual understanding. Over the country it is not at all unusual to find experimentalists who receive their salaries in institutes or departments devoted to research and teaching about developmental problems. Apparently, the preceding description of the experimentalist and his orientational differences from the developmentalist is seriously overdrawn, or else some way of bridging the gap has been found. A completely nonexperimental survey of my friends who have had experimental training and who are now employed in the area of developmental psychology leads me to the conclusion that the latter rather than the former is the case. The different orientation emphases, I think, are real, but at least two bridges are currently being used to allow a limited kind of communication. To leave the analogy, it is my belief that many experimentalists who are now working in the developmental area, do so with one of two lines of thinking about their work. Each of these, I feel, falls short of incorporating all that might be desired from the term "an experimental psychology of development." I should like to describe these two lines of thinking and show how each one, while legitimate as far as it goes, does not fully integrate the general orientation of the experimentalist with that of the developmentalist.

The first of these lines of thinking is found among experimentalists who fully accept those orientational emphases I have just described. Their work involves a limited time dimension; they fastidiously define and quantify their variables; they seek explanatory S-R laws; and they have a passion for general behavior theory. When asked how their work ties in with developmental study, they are likely to respond that this is not really a problem. Their work, it is held, has precisely the same goal as that of any other experimentalist — they are striving toward a general theory of behavior. The only difference, they say, is that their subjects happen to be children rather than white rats or college sophomores. Apart from this, it is held, there is no difference. Presumably, an experimental psychology of development for these workers involves no problems that are not already of concern to experimentalists. It is a line of thinking that emphasizes the mutual concern of developmentalists and experimentalists for a general behavior theory. It solves the problem of differences by denying, at least implicitly, that there *are* any peculiarly developmental problems. There are only problems in general behavior theory. As far as their orientational emphases are concerned, these experimentalists have never left home.

The other line of thinking is in many ways the opposite of the first. It is found among developmental psychologists who have become engrossed with a problem whose solution seems most readily obtainable by investigations using experimental techniques. Of the orientational points I have described — which go beyond purely methodological issues to more comprehensive "biases" common to many experimentalists — they subscribe heartily only to those most intimately linked to refined laboratory procedures. They may not, for example, be much concerned with general behavior theory, or even in the establishment of functional laws. They may be concerned with a description of a developmental sequence, and resort to experimental techniques only in order to observe this sequence the better. These experimentalists have left home. They solve the problem of integrating the experimental and developmental orientations by stripping the former of all but its methodological essentials, and using it as a tool in the service of their developmental interests.

Both of these lines of thought are, in their ways, justifiable. All psychologists, including developmentalists, have some stake in general behavior theory. Developmental specialists, on the other hand, are completely correct in looking upon the experimental method as primarily a tool. And yet both of these lines seem incomplete: the one, with its denial of special problems of development; the other, with its tendency to ignore those theoretical leanings common to many experimentalists. Either one, pushed to its limits, would not result in a satisfying "experimental" psychology of development. The first would contain no developmental content, as such, and the other would comprise a fragmented discussion of developmental issues which happened to be subject to experimental investigation.

If a more satisfactory integration is to be had, it must come, it would seem, from a point of view which would not begin with the denial of elements of either field, but which would undertake to make each meaningful in terms of the other. Is there a way in which developmental problems, as such, may be viewed from the general theoretical orientation that is characteristic of the experimentalist? Or, conversely, can the developmentalist find a place in his orientation for the kind of theoretical organization held by experimentalists? If so, the

task of integration does not seem impossible. For in spite of the acknowledged orientational differences, no one of them, as was suggested
earlier, leads inevitably to flat contradiction. This is in fact a large
area of common concern. Perhaps the greatest common ground lies in
the shared desire for an adequate behavior theory. And from this it
should be possible to delineate problems in development whose experimental study could comprise an orderly endeavor.

Typically, the experimentalist regards a theory or system as a more
or less rigorously stated set of postulates from which theorems with
testable behavioral implications may be derived. In its ideal form,
these derivations would be made mathematically, and it would be possible to write equations expressing the relation between a given bit of
behavior, its situational antecedents, and the states of the various constructs that appear in the system. Response is looked upon as some
function of, say, the motivational state, the habits relevant to a given
situation, and the organism's perception of the situation. A general behavior theory applicable to human subjects would undertake to generate theorems corresponding to any bit of human behavior from the
same postulate set, and with the use of common constructs. Even
though no such theory can be said to exist at the human level, many
experimentalists tend to think in these terms, and there are suggested
beginnings of such systems in the work of Hull, Tolman, and others.
The concepts that can be readily fitted into such a scheme, those that
might appear in such a behavioral equation, are the ones experimentalists tend to be most readily concerned with.

Now the concept of development does not lend itself to such treatment. It does not appear as a separate construct in any one of the
dominant, experimentally based theories-in-the-making at the present
time. Nevertheless, one may wonder what sorts of questions a developmentalist might ask in connection with such a formulation. It seems to
me that there are a number of very pertinent issues that he might raise
—issues that are truly "developmental" in nature and yet completely
relevant to the general theoretical frame.

Confronted with a proposed general behavior system, the developmentalist might first ask the obvious question concerning its generality
over different age levels. We have already seen that the experimental
behavior theorist is prone to formulate his "general" theory from observations of a single class of subjects — usually white rats or college

sophomores. He recognizes that if he is to achieve the generality he seeks, his theory must apply across all the individuals of the species he is studying, or across all the species he is considering if his aim is that high. The comparative psychologist would be interested in the across-species problem. The developmental psychologist could well be concerned with the within-species problem. Does a given theory produce relevant and confirmable theorems when the subjects are infants, children, or octogenarians? If not, is the failure due to intrinsic weaknesses in the theory? Are certain necessary constructs missing from the formulation? Or is the whole set of postulates so out of gear with observation that its proposed generality is convincingly not confirmed? These are important theoretical questions. They are also important from a strictly developmental point of view, since they are concerned with the question of the continuity of behavioral determination.

Suppose this first question concerning the generality of a behavior theory over age levels is answered affirmatively. Are there further questions the developmentalist might ask? Certainly there is a very real question whether the specific constants or parameters that appear in behavioral equations as modifiers of the general constructs remain unchanged over the life span of the organism. At least this developmental problem has been acknowledged by one general theorist, Hull, who states in the final postulate of his system that "the 'constant' numerical values appearing in equations representing . . . behavioral laws vary . . . in the same individual at *different times.*" As so stated — with no further elaboration, by the way — the problem sounds perhaps over-technical. Actually, it may hint at some of the most important problems in psychology. If the construct of reinforcement is found to have general application, for example, would it be possible to ascertain the relative strength of its influence at various age levels? Or in the case of learning itself, can regular changes in the parameters relating to the growth of habits or cognitions be traced through time? It seems to me that here is a possibility for the elaboration of uniquely developmental laws which would play a major role in general behavior theory. They would be laws dealing with the changes in time of the parameters occurring in a general behavior theory. It may be relevant to note that the precise determination of these changes would in all probability require extensive use of the best experimental techniques over the whole developmental range.

The developmentalist considering a general behavior theory would probably be moved to inquire about still another problem that would be not at all tangential, even though somewhat more remote from general theory than the previous issue. It might be described as the problem of the boundary conditions within which the theory would have to be applied. He knows, for example, that the possible responses of an individual vary considerably as a function of the stage of physical growth or maturation. The central nervous mediators of the behavior, the muscles, the skeleton, etc., must reach certain levels of growth before some behavior becomes physically possible. A psychological theory of behavior is bounded by such nonpsychological factors. The problem of explicating the significance for general theory of many of these boundary conditions could well concern the developmentalist. There is a danger here, of course. Unless this explication is carefully made there is a likelihood that the developmental account may lose its relevance for behavior theory. The account may easily become an end in itself for the developmental psychologist, and the theorist may tend simply to ignore the real restrictions placed upon his theory by such a boundary condition. This danger can be overcome only if each party turns resolutely to the explicit discussion of the significance of the boundary condition for the behavior theory in question.

AN EXPERIMENTAL PSYCHOLOGY OF DEVELOPMENT?

We have now examined certain oddities in the orientation of some experimentalists and indicated how they make it difficult for such experimentalists to subsume the area of developmental psychology within their usual framework. A tendency to work with a restricted time scale, the preference for simple variables, the interest in functional determinants of behavior, and involvement with general theory were all seen as inhibiting to some degree a concern for developmental processes occurring over long spans of time. We have noted how these orientational difficulties are frequently circumvented by the denial that there are any peculiarly developmental problems, or by the abandonment of the "theoretical" aspects of the experimental orientation. In order to achieve a solution which did not deny elements of the experimental or developmental orientation, an effort was made to view developmental problems as one aspect of general behavior theory. It was found that meaningful developmental questions organized around a general behavior theory could be formulated. These related (a) to the generality of the theory over age levels, (b) to the problem of systematic changes in the constants of the general theory in time, and (c) to the boundary conditions limiting the application of the theory.

By this circuitous path it is at last possible to return to the question with which this paper began. Our wanderings, however, should facilitate a brief and early answer to the question "An experimental psychology of development: pipe dream or possibility?"

There remain only a few arguments which, if sustained, could make hopes for such a psychology unrealistic. First, if there were any clear incompatability of purpose between experimentalists and developmentalists, an experimental psychology of development would be as illogical as any pipe dream. For example, if a real dichotomy were found between the descriptive leanings of developmentalists and the explanatory leanings of experimentalists, it would be impossible to combine the two. Second, if the term "developmental" necessarily implied a method other than experimental, a contradiction would be involved. Third, if the laws which would be the fruit of an experimental psychology of development were not formulable after all the evidence was in, the hope would prove, indeed, to have been a mere pipe dream.

Fortunately none of these three contentions seems valid. Regarding the possible conflict of purpose, we have indicated, and it has been well expounded elsewhere, that any scientific discipline is to some extent *both* descriptive and explanatory, and never exclusively one or the other. Concerning the second argument, it may be noted that the term *developmental* has basic reference to a subject matter rather than a method, so that there is likewise no intrinsic methodological problem. With regard to the third contention, whether or not there are formulable laws to be found for an experimental psychology of development cannot be determined until after the effort at such formulation has been made. This line of reasoning cannot then be used to establish the futility of the effort in advance.

One final circumstance must be considered: if there were reason to believe that no developmental problems were amenable to experimental investigation, there would be grounds to charge the whole affair a pipe dream. This position is also most palpably false, since it would not be difficult to point to a large number of methodologically acceptable experimental studies relating to developmental problems.

This fact, furthermore, allows us to make at least a first claim for the possibility of an experimental psychology of development. If we are willing to adopt the position that the methodological criterion is the only one, it can indeed be asserted that we already have the discipline in question. And there is every probability that the field will grow enormously in the future.

We have seen, however, that the methodological criterion alone may do violence to the over-all orientation of many experimentalists. To deal with a subject matter which can be investigated by a variety of techniques in terms of only one of them is to invite a fragmented and disorderly treatment. It is a poor way to define an area unless there is added some further criterion designed to unite the topic investigated The experimentalist, as has been noted, frequently uses relevance for general theory as this additional criterion.

It is in the application of this criterion of relevance for general theory that the experimentalist experiences his greatest difficulty in considering the developmental problems. This paper has tried to show that in spite of this difficulty there are systematically relevant questions that can be asked concerning the concept of development. These questions do not, to be sure, exhaust the domain with which the developmental psychologist has been, or may be, concerned. There is no need for this. But they do indicate that an organization of experimental material in terms of its relevance for general behavior theory may be undertaken for the topic of development and that an experimental psychology of development in the full sense is therefore a very definite possibility.

REFERENCES

1. Radke-Yarrow, Marion, and L. J. Yarrow. "Child Psychology," in C. P. Stone, ed., *Annual Review of Psychology*, Vol. 6. Stanford University Press, 1955.
2. Sims, V. M. "Concerning Nonconformity in the Psychological Value Systems of the several Divisions of A.P.A.," *Amer. Psychologist*, Vol. 10 (1955), pp. 573–74.

The Concept of Development in the Humanities and Social Sciences

Norman J. DeWitt

ORGANISM AND HUMANISM: AN EMPIRICAL VIEW

SINCE the concept of growth and development, like other organic concepts, is concerned primarily with living organisms, it therefore has an exact empirical reference in the general field of biology.

The applications of organic concepts in other fields, such as language and literature, have proved to be very fruitful; so fruitful, indeed, that to view such applications critically may seem to be either ungenerous or unnecessary. Organic concepts have been the basic tools of our academic succession since the fourth century B.C., or, in biological terms, they have been and still are implicit in the *structure* and *function* of our *body* of *organized* knowledge.

However, when organic concepts are transferred from the field of biology to another field, the transfer may involve a sacrifice of empiricism. For this reason, organic concepts should be transferred with caution, and, equally important, with full awareness of their limitations as instruments of inquiry in fields which are not concerned with biological organisms.

Such, in brief, is my thesis.

I should now say that I am encouraged by the common theme of this collection of papers. It suggests the confirmation of a new direction of inquiry. That is, it suggests that we are moving on from an uncritical faith in scientific methods toward an awareness that the information produced by systematic inquiry may be true — that is, empirically verifiable — and at the same time predetermined in range and nature by its relation to our initial concepts.

This I take to be progress.

With this sense of movement and progress, therefore, I am offering a few comments on organic concepts, such as occur to me in relation to my own work in the fields of language and literature. I shall say something about organic concepts in general and about the general kind of thinking they represent. I shall call this kind of thinking "figurative." I shall be especially concerned with the limitations of figurative thinking. And then I shall review a case history in organic growth and development taken from the field of literature — concluding, if inspiration still supports me, with a flourish.

ORGANIC CONCEPTS IN GENERAL

I should like to preface my general remarks on organic concepts with a brief reconsideration of the statement that "information produced by systematic inquiry may be true — that is, empirically verifiable — and at the same time predetermined in range and nature by its relation to our initial concepts." This is a theme that is not generally stressed in the academic community; and it is so important that it may be well to ring a few changes on it.

The researcher, with his preliminary concepts, might be compared to a hunter and his weapons. The researcher and the hunter are both going to pursue something. It has been customary in the academic succession to say that the researcher is going to pursue the truth — I should prefer to substitute "information" for "truth." Be that as it may, the analogy is more important than the terminology; and we will agree that the hunter is going to pursue game of some kind.

Now, if we see the hunter loading a .22-caliber rifle into his car, we can state with some assurance that he is not going after moose. If we see him with a shotgun, we can make other valid predictions about the range and nature of his game. If we see him with a bamboo pole and a can of worms, we can make still other predictions, to say nothing of remarking his lack of finer sensibilities.

And so with organic concepts in systematic inquiry. They may very well predetermine the range and nature of our information, the kinds of truths — real truths, but *kinds* of truths — that we are likely to bring home. They may also predetermine the kinds of truths we are *not* going to bring home.

Now, if we are going to take a general view of organic concepts, we shall be well advised to go back to the master, Aristotle, founder of the biological sciences. Accordingly, in the remarks which follow immediately, I shall be basing my analysis, without further reference, upon Aristotle's little book on tragic drama, the *Poetics* (as it is usually called). Apart from its professional importance in the fields of criticism and aesthetics, the *Poetics* shows us how the master applies the standard academic methods: historical methods, analytical methods, comparative methods, definitions by function, definitions by structure, reduction to the unique, classification, taxonomy, and so on, all interrelated and all related in one way or another to organic concepts.

Since we are going back to Aristotle now, it will be helpful to recall that the Greek word *organon* had the everyday meaning of "instrument, tool for making or doing a thing," closely related to the word *ergon*, "work or task."

In Plato, the word begins to develop a specialized meaning, "an instrument of sense perception," which approaches our idea of "organ." In Aristotle, *organon* is becoming a general biological term, relating to a body and its parts. The adjective *organikos* in Aristotle frequently implies "used as an instrument or tool." This will remind us again of the strictly empirical relation of organic concepts to biology, and to the kind of thinking of which Aristotle is the acknowledged master.

In listing the general characteristics of organic concepts, we may say, first of all, that an organic concept requires us to regard our object of study as a finite sum or whole, an organized *body* with parts, so to speak, which can be referred to by one term, either linguistic or mathematical. By "mathematical" I mean to imply not only the result of simple addition, but also the use of statistical techniques which, however modern, do not necessarily involve an abandonment of organic concepts.

The second characteristic is a logical sequel to the first, although perhaps not so obvious. We assume that the body or sum we are studying is empirically finite, which is another way of saying, with Aristotle, that the object may be apprehended in one view and in a moment of time. Here we come, I think, to a point that is not too subtle, namely, that there is a close relation between organic concepts and visual images. If we cannot actually see the object we are studying, we try to *see* it figuratively, in the mind's eye — that is, "visualize" it. We can see the growth and development of a child; we can only "visualize" the growth and development of an historical institution — and that is obviously a different kind of empiricism.

The third characteristic elaborates the dependence of organic concepts upon visual imagery. The conceptualized or visualized object must have a certain mean magnitude, which Aristotle associates with a kind of beauty or immediate aesthetic appeal. That is to say, an object which is so small as to be invisible in detail without a microscope has no immediate appeal and can hardly be said to be beautiful in terms of ordinary experience; and one so large as to have no immediately determinable limits is equally lacking in ordinary aesthetic appeal. Beyond this, an object, actual or conceptual, which has no empirically determinable limits — not infinite, perhaps, but not empirically finite — is not only aesthetically deficient but also incomprehensible in terms of ordinary, immediate, visual experience. Organic concepts, therefore, tend both to subject our thinking to certain aesthetic controls and to limit it to the range of ordinary visual experience. (Plato was by no means the last intellectual to associate truth and beauty; he retains, however, the merit of having made clear what he was doing in this regard.)

Fourthly, organic concepts are neat and orderly, the result of a tidying-up process, as it were. Here, too, are points of aesthetic appeal. When we "organize" a large number of individual items into one general body, or when we classify them, we are bringing order out of chaos, making sure that there is a place for everything and that everything is in that place. Aristotle says that this sense of order, this ability to determine forms and classes, is "natural" or "innate," or, as I suppose we might say, "instinctive." Perhaps Aristotle is right, although I am not sure that the term "instinctive" would be accepted by the present company, and as a parent I tend to conclude that neatness is an acquired characteristic. At any rate, a youngster who has learned how to tidy up his room or put the screwdriver back where it belongs has taken a good forward step toward being an Aristotelian.

What I have been saying so far about organic concepts is both abstract and general; and it is time now to cite two specific examples out of many in our academic thinking, namely, the organic concepts of knowledge and language.

We have already noted that organic concepts have been the basic tools of our academic succession since the time of Plato and Aristotle;

and, of course, the over-all concept has been that of organized knowledge. The curriculum committee and the college catalogue work in terms of a body with parts, and so does the administrative structure: groups, like the trichotomy of natural sciences, social sciences, and humanities; departments, fields, divisions, subfields, subdivisions, and so on. This is a nice example of taxonomy, the anatomy of the body of knowledge; and let us remember that, as a concept, it predetermines our thinking about education.

However, if we take the long historical view of education, which I, as a classicist, recommend — a view that enables us to grasp the relative velocity of events — we may observe that the body of knowledge has expanded in the past century at a steadily accelerating velocity far beyond anything that can reasonably be associated with organic growth. I suggest, indeed, that an explosion is taking place; and we are in the middle of it. At any rate, we might do well to look at education in terms of information and then see if we can find anything that is empirically finite. By changing concepts, we shall at least get a new line of thought; and we may understand why the bibliography on general education, for example, is itself not empirically finite!

Let us move on now to consider language as an organic concept.

The instant we use the single term *language* we are almost certain to have committed ourselves to an organic concept. The classical grammarians, of course, took speech as a whole and defined its parts — a procedure which resulted in what we, rather loosely, call "traditional grammar." This simple taxonomy, or anatomy of language, at one time had such an appeal that schoolmasters took it to be an actual model of language as a whole. We are not so naive today. Yet we commonly hold that "language is a tool for communication," a view that not only takes us back to the Aristotelian term *organikos*, meaning "instrumental," but also implies that language is a whole, apprehensible in one view, to be included or excluded as such in a finite program of study, fairly close to a visual image, associated with a common object in ordinary experience — that is, a tool from the workshop — and, of course, empirically finite. In fairness, it must be admitted that the alternative to this proposition, a concept of language as *not* empirically finite, would be preposterous in terms of ordinary experience.

These remarks about the organic-instrumental concept of language lead me now to mention the fifth and last characteristic of such concepts, so far as our present interests are concerned. Emphasis on the instrumental aspect of organic concepts encourages us to derive information from a systematic exploitation of function in ordinary experience. As we shall see, this procedure severely limits the range of our information.

When we say that language is a tool for communication, we are really answering a question about the social function of language — and in the question itself we have predetermined the information we are going to get about language. That is, we have asked, "What *good* is language? What is it *for*?" We answer that it is a tool for communication; that is what *good* it is — and *that*, in terms of the philosophy to which these questions commit us, is its actual nature or essence. We need not examine this philosophy beyond the remark that these what's-it-for and what-good-is-it questions take us right back to Plato and Aristotle. They are very natural questions in ordinary experience, but not necessarily *good* questions in science. They tend to place a positive block in the way of acquiring a range of information outside of ordinary experience. Natural scientists have had to learn not to ask such questions. They had to learn the hard way and it took them a very long time. To be sure, you may ask, "What *good* is electricity? What is it *for*?" and you may get answers, but they will not be scientific answers and they will not get you very far in physics.

These, then, are characteristics of organic concepts that we may take as significant in a general review. In sum, they emphasize the relation of organic concepts to ordinary experience; that is, experience in a universe where straight parallel lines meet at infinity, where the sun visibly rises and sets, where the earth is flat (at least, its curvature is of no practical importance), where cause and effect have a direct sequential relationship, where action does not take place without an immediate objective as the motive of the actor, where objects are empirically (or visibly) finite. This is the universe which accounts for almost all our everyday experiences but represents a very limited range of experience — involving, if you will, the statistical fallacy that frequency of occurrence is an index of importance.

FIGURATIVE THINKING

Now, with these general remarks about organic concepts on record, I should like to discuss the kind of thinking we do when we use organic concepts outside the field of biology. I have called this kind of thinking "figurative," closely related to figurative language. You may have noticed that I have already spoken in figurative terms, as, for example, when I spoke of the "explosion" of knowledge in the past century. But now, for a more precise demonstration, I shall refer to an electric current, the elephant's trunk, Annie Laurie's throat, and the ship of state.

Let us look very closely at a very common problem-situation in human experience which we solve, for all practical purposes, by a linguistic device which, in turn, represents a way of thinking.

When we are confronted with a new and unfamiliar object, we like to associate it with something old and more familiar, and the easiest procedure is to give the new object the name of the old object. This mental and/or verbal procedure involves a transfer of information from the old to the new. It is a very helpful procedure, but it immediately raises the question of how much information we can safely transfer without making a false statement, or thinking falsely, about the new object — "false" and "falsely" meaning "not subject to strict empirical verification."

Early inquirers into electricity called that then unfamiliar physical phenomenon the "electric fluid." Later on the term "electric current" gained general acceptance. This is to say, we transfer information about common fluids, notably water, to electricity, and gain many practical insights therewith. But there is no likelihood that the Institute of Technology will merge hydraulics with electrical engineering. While we know that electricity does "flow," so to speak, and behaves in many ways like a common fluid, we also know that the term "current" applied to electrical phenomena in general is figurative rather than strictly empirical; and we shall also realize that our figurative terms fail to correspond to, and to account for, a very wide range of information about electricity — a range far beyond the limits of ordinary, everyday experience.

Let us, then, consider the elephant's trunk as a problem in the transfer of information. The elephant's trunk is really a preposterous gadget; and I say "preposterous" with full awareness of the derivation of the term in Latin. The Latin suggests that a thing is in front when it ought to be behind, or, as we say, "hind-end-to." Putting exact scholarship aside, however, we may note that the elephant's trunk has no satisfactory analogue in ordinary experience. There is nothing from which to transfer a satisfactory range of information — let us say, in the way we might transfer information about a pig's tail to an elephant's tail.

Lacking sources of information in ordinary experience, the European peoples have been hard put to it to give a satisfactory name to the elephant's gadget. Calling it a "trunk" in English is a neat, noncommittal solution of the problem, but it is also an evasion, since "trunk" gives us no information at all. We need either a picture or an elephant to go with it. Actually, we borrowed the word from the French, mispronouncing it as cheerfully as we mispronounce other borrowed French words. The French word is *trompe,* meaning "trumpet." That thing in front is the elephant's trumpet, figuratively speaking. This either shows a great deal of ingenuity, or very little, on the part of the French race, depending on how you want to look at it. It fails to transfer enough information; at the same time, it transfers too much. The Romans referred to the elephant's *manus,* his "hand." The classical Hindus also called it "hand" in Sanskrit. The Greek word *proboscis* sounds very learned and scientific in English, but all it really says is "front-feeder."

Now, as philosophers, let us face the problem courageously: what *is* that thing?

We are all agreed as to its location, namely, in front; but beyond that, what is its actual nature, or *essence* (as the medieval philosopher might put it)? Clearly, the elephant's trunk presents us with an epistemological problem of the first order.

The three terms we have examined, "trumpet," "hand," and "front-feeder" are all good tries at a functionally descriptive term, but they transfer a very narrow range of information. The elephant scratches himself with the thing, swats flies, breathes through it, whacks the young, holds the tail of the elephant ahead in circus parades, gives himself showers with it, and uses it for squirting in general. We owe to Aristotle, moreover, the acute observation that the elephant's trunk enables him to walk on the bottoms of lakes and rivers, since the thing works very nicely as a breathing tube, or *Schnörkel.*

What we are actually coming to, of course, is the realization that the elephant's trunk is functionally and existentially unique. The trunk *is* a trunk. We cannot adequately name it, conceptualize it, symbolize it, or generalize its functions by a figurative term transferred from any other field of experience. No term presently used or conceivable can be applied to the elephant's trunk that will correspond to, and account for, the actual range of information in nature. That information does not add up to or make a common arithmetical sum, any more than an orange, an overshoe, and a typewriter make three. We can *know* the elephant's trunk only by gross empiricism; that is, by a long series of discrete items of information without any massive generalizations. (The zoologist, of course, evades our problem completely by referring to an evolutionary process in which the elephant's upper lip was elongated to its present state. His nose, apparently, just went along for the experience and got lost.)

So much, then, for the problem of organizing the elephant's trunk in relation to the actual range of information in nature. The elephant's trunk is beyond ordinary experience or, in more technical language, it is non-Aristotelian.

We need to remark now that the transfer of information from one field of experience to another may be examined in the guise of simile and metaphor, which are, of course, well-known figures of speech in the realm of poetry and rhetoric. Fortunately, in the realm of letters, none of us is likely to take the comparison, or transfer of information, too literally. We are well aware that there are empirical limits to the transfer.

Thus, when Douglas sings of Annie Laurie that

> Her brow is like the snowdrift,
> Her throat is like the swan . . .

only a person with a disagreeably literal mind would observe that Annie would have an advantage over the rest of us in parallel parking situations. We who are of more artistic temperament know that the poet is using the simile of the swan's throat to symbolize certain information, not all qualities of throat but only certain ones which are appropriate to a lovely girl: the texture, the whiteness, the purity and grace, one assumes, rather than information about length, sinuosity, and feathers.

I should say at once, however, that in my own field Annie's throat would probably not be generally accepted as a good simile. At any rate, there are a great many better ones; and with this assurance, let us move on from simile to metaphor.

Back in the seventh century B.C., the Greek lyric poet Alcaeus addressed a fervent poem to his native city-state, viewing it as a ship engaged in a hazardous voyage through stormy seas. He thus confirmed, if he did not invent, the simile that is imbedded in our literary tradition — that the state is like a ship. And hence the metaphor, "the ship of state."

> Sail on, sail on, O Ship of State,
> Sail on, O Union strong and great . . .
>
> O Captain, O my Captain,
> Our fearful voyage is done . . .

And it is reasonable enough, in view of the universal acceptance of the metaphor, that our word *governor* should have been derived from Latin *gubernator,* "pilot," or "helmsman." Here again, as in simile, we accept the conventions of limited transfer quite naturally; and I need not emphasize the fact that our language and our thinking accept these conventions and are the richer for such figures. They present no dangers as long as the conventions of limited transfer prevail.

However, the dangers begin when we move on from simile and metaphor to analogy, which may be said to involve a much more rigorous, a much more extensive, transfer of information from the unfamiliar to the familiar. We readily recognize the "ship of state" for what it is; the conventions are firmly established. We would not argue against the election of a retired general to the helm of our ship of state on the grounds that the job calls for an admiral. We do not equate seamanship and statesmanship. Yet not every reader of Plato recognizes the easy shift from simile to metaphor to analogy to social action when Socrates argues that the passengers on a ship leave navigation to the captain, and do not hold public meetings to chart the course for him; therefore the passengers on the ship of state should leave navigation to the captain and not hold public meetings to chart the course. (Plato's analogies have to be watched rather carefully; he has a way of slipping more information over on us than we may want to accept.)

At this point, then, we can summarize our review of the kind of thinking which involves a transfer of information and which we have called figurative.

The use of organic concepts outside the field of biology represents a specific example of a general way of thinking. This general way of thinking involves the transfer of information about a better known object to a lesser known object for the sake of what we may loosely call "knowledge." This is a very useful procedure, but it is also a very dangerous procedure. The danger lies in the transfer of too much information — information that is empirically verifiable in relation to the better known object but not in relation to the lesser known object. The danger is particularly acute in a purely conceptual process when we transfer information about organic objects in ordinary experiences to aggregates of information, such as knowledge and language, that may be only figuratively and not empirically organic and finite.

We might observe, in passing, that the great classical philosophies are philosophies of ordinary experience, dealing with organic concepts and never able to relinquish the association with visual imagery. Plato, in particular, seduces the naive reader because his philosophy is so easy at first, but then his dialectic takes us into a realm where empirical verification is both impossible and rejected. The empiricist, on the other hand, is at a disadvantage because his philosophy is very hard at first; he may have to reject ordinary experience in a preposterous way at the outset, but later on he enters into a realm where empirical verification is possible, progressive, and acceptable.

We are now ready for a discussion of the application of figurative organic concepts in the field of language and literature.

A CASE HISTORY IN LITERATURE

For a number of years I have been teaching an advanced course entitled "Classical Literary Traditions," in which the various forms or *genres* of Greek and Roman literature are studied qua forms in anticipation of their survival and influence in later European literature. These forms are, of course, Epic, Lyric, Satire, Pastoral, the Novel, Drama, and so forth.

Now what we do, of course, is to take epic poetry (for example) as a whole under the general class and term Epic. We then observe that this organic whole has a durative or historical aspect; and when we do that, the organic whole takes on, figuratively, the aspect of a living organism. We have to be careful, however, from the standpoint of literary criticism, not to allow the organism to control our thinking beyond a certain point. If we go too far in transferring information from biology, we may be led to exclude other kinds of information which are useful in our business. (I might say, parenthetically, that my reference to Epic here is unfortunate; we know too little about its growth and development, since it appears already in perfected form with the *Iliad* and *Odyssey*.)

We shall find the clearest example of the problem of excluded information, along with an elegance of demonstration, in the concept of organic growth and development applied to drama.

In the case of drama, we should note that we have already committed ourselves to an organic concept by virtue of the basic linguistic procedure, namely, the term *drama*. We have generalized — that is, added — thousands of plays into one term, body, or sum. We could then take this body and divide it into its parts, namely, comedy and tragedy, as Aristotle does in his *Poetics*; and then take tragedy as a whole, or body, and examine its parts. This would involve, as it were, the anatomy of drama (as a part of the anatomy of art). But we are going to conceive of this body as having had an origin, a growth, and a development. That is, we are going to view it, figuratively, as an organism. And, of course, drama did have an origin, a growth, and a development; otherwise how could we have a history of drama? Or are we shifting very subtly from simile to metaphor to analogy?

Be that as it may, we really should be aware now that there are two main classes of historical concepts, the teleological and the evolutionary. The teleological variety is implicit in Aristotle's *Poetics*, where we read: "Tragedy advanced by slow degrees; each new element that showed itself was in turn developed. Having passed through many stages, it found its natural form and there it stopped." This sounds innocent enough, and plausible. It would have its strict empirical basis in what I suppose might be called "classical" embryology. One might take a chick embryo and trace its development into a newly hatched chick and then into a mature hen or rooster, emphasizing the fully developed form as *natural*, as the end or goal of the process, and implicit in it from the very beginning. The beginning, indeed, is for the sake of the end, and in that sense, the end or goal is the cause of the entire process. Thus speaks the philosopher of ordinary experience, the teleologist, the philosopher of ends as causes.

Still, this account of growth and development has its practical uses, although I gather that natural scientists are not entirely happy about causes in any conceptual framework. At any rate, the teleological organic concept leads us to suppose, with Aristotle, that tragic drama found its final or perfected form in fifth-century Athens, and there it stopped. This raises what, in my field, is regarded as a *good* question.

Moreover, if we have for reference a perfected form or type, we can describe it verbally — that is, produce a description for the permanent record, the way the botanist does when he describes a new plant — and Aristotle did just that for tragedy in his *Poetics*. The master's definition has all the qualities of neatness and finality that characterize organic systems, but it leads to extraordinary difficulties, not the least of which, in the field of literary criticism and aesthetics, is a phenomenal record of inconclusive "bibliography" — a sure sign of limited empiricism.

And if I may trespass briefly in the field of history, we may note that faith in the implicit goal as the cause of the process leads easily to a pseudoscientific analysis of human events, resulting in large laws and predictions — classical fate and destiny in modern dress. Even nineteenth-century liberalism maintained a vague faith in the inevitability of gradualism leading to a not-too-distant ideal state; that kind of liberalism appears to have come to an end in the 1930's. In his book *The Open Society and Its Enemies,* Karl Popper has shown how the application of the classical concept of growth and development to social institutions leads us via Hegel to Marx, suggesting that we might amend Aristotle to read: "Having passed through many stages it (society) found its natural form (with the help of the Party) and there it stopped." Although I do not agree with R. H. Tawney's comment that Karl Marx was the last of the schoolmen, I acknowledge reasonable grounds (other than those cited by Tawney) for such a statement.

The concept of *child* growth and development, on the other hand, as long as it is biological in its relationships and scientific in its applications, is strictly not teleological but evolutionary. And in general, the evolutionary concept makes no firm commitments as to ends or the finality of any form other than that, in botany and zoology, a species may become extinct. Thus, with the guidance of the evolutionary concept, we might summarize the figurative origin, growth, and development of the drama in the following terms.

Let us focus our imaginations on a small, isolated, agricultural community, a village in prehistoric Europe. The universal, absolute, controlling factor in individual or group survival is the seasons and their effect upon vegetation. A very wet year, or a very dry year, may mean a long, painful winter, with the prospect that the weaker members of the group may never greet the spring. In any event, winter can be quite disagreeable when you have only an open fire and a hole in the roof.

In this context, then, in the North Temperate Zone, the seasons and vegetation are dominant in the environment. Religion, which means the maintenance of the right relationship between the community and a personalized environment, leads to the development of various sympathetic, imitative, or symbolic enactments that, when repeated annually, are to be called ritual. One aspect of ritual is the dance and chorus in its various primitive forms, all designed to influence or control the natural environment: rain dances, harvest dances, fertility dances, totem dances, and the like. Another aspect of ritual directly related to the death of vegetation and its divine symbol is an enactment of defeat and death by a human actor — in very primitive times, or in times of stress and hysteria, involving, it may be, a human sacrifice. We have here, then, two basic components of tragic drama, the ritualistic dance and chorus and the defeat or death enactment, although none of this is as yet uniquely Greek or strictly dramatic. (We might also note that the procedure is what we have called figurative, involving the elements of simile, metaphor, symbolism, and analogy.)

True drama begins, according to one plausible suggestion, when a myth is added to the established rituals. The myth is historical, in the sense that it tells the story of some champion or hero of the community who fought a great fight in the past but met defeat or death. This is still symbolic of the death of vegetation, but the symbolism has been extended to include the historical self-awareness of the community in the person of one of its most distinguished members. In this way, then, the community figuratively "gets into the act" itself and increases the social significance of the ritual. It also symbolizes its own historical continuity, merging its own past with the present ritual and looking toward the future. At this point, too, the community engages in something that is recognizably dramatic — an enactment of *dramata*, "things done," as Aristotle puts it, with one main actor and a chorus.

But now we have to ask ourselves, How far do we carry on the life of this organism which has grown and developed in a sociocultural medium? Thus far, the history of the drama has been quite impersonal as it reaches the threshold of documentary history with one leading actor

and a chorus. But as soon as we reach the period of independent literary documentation we learn from Aristotle that Aeschylus added a
second actor and Sophocles a third. We then run the risk I have already mentioned, namely, of excluding information — of allowing the
organic concept to control our thinking to the exclusion of other kinds
of information; or, in broader terms, we face the problem of including
an impersonal organism and identifiable personal agents in one conceptual framework.

Another problem is that throughout the predocumentary period we
tend to restrict our attention to the function of drama as a religious
institution. It was also a social institution, and we may exclude the
information that an enduring social institution, like drama, or Christmas, or education, is likely to be multifunctional. In the historical
process, indeed, the secondary functions may actually outweigh the
primary function and ensure the survival of the institution after the
primary function has lost its meaning. Passing hastily over the possible
application of this principle to education, we can safely remark that
primitive ritual may be a good show. The dance may be religious in
origin, but it is also a lot of fun, even for those who may only watch
the purely secular performances of a Broadway show or a TV spec-
tacular. Moreover, in fifth-century Athens, the whole festival of which
drama was only a part had a decided chamber-of-commerce aspect. It
was the biggest annual show in the Greek world, including a grand
parade. And in spite of the solemn bibliography on the religious,
moral, and psychological aspects of tragedy, there is more than a sus-
picion (if one may trust a passing reference in Plato) that the Athenian
audiences turned out, not in reverence to Dionysus, but to have a
real good cry.

So much for tragedy. Now I should like to propose an interesting
objection to the organic-continuity treatment of comedy, the opposite
of tragedy. The prehistoric rituals of comedy can be identified with
the same nicety as those of tragedy; the earlier comedies of Aristophanes are full of material that is meaningful in anthropological and ritualistic terms. These earlier plays of Aristophanes are called "Old
Comedy" in the handbooks; the later plays of Aristophanes become less
anthropological, so to speak, less "old," and in terms of the organic
evolution of comedy, these later plays are said to anticipate "Middle
Comedy." The evidence for this stage, Middle Comedy, is scanty, and

no plays from it have survived. The continuous organic process then moves on to "New Comedy," ideally represented by the Greek playwright Menander in the late fourth century B.C. and by Plautus and Terence in Latin in the second century B. C.

This, again, is very neat, but it is possible that we have been transferring too much information from the biological field. Our account excludes another body of literature often referred to as the "Urban" or "City Tales," the popular fiction of the Greco-Roman world. The most popular theme is that of boy-meets-girl, then a series of complications, and finally . . . well, the complications are sometimes peculiar to ancient urban culture, but the basic formula is as modern, or as ancient, as TV. Now, the plots of the New Comedy are simply City Tales, formula fiction; and it is quite possible to suppose that comedy, in terms of the figurative evolutionary concept, became extinct as a species in the late fifth century, and that another species, the City Tale, moved into the physical home of the old species, namely the theater, and went through a process of adaptation to its environment that resulted in certain deceptive and secondary resemblances to the old species.

At this point it might be objected very reasonably that I am overworking the analogy of the drama to an evolutionary organism or species, and that my account has become transparently figurative. I think the answer is that the account has been figurative all along, and I have merely carried it to a point beyond the conventions of the field.

ALTERNATIVES TO ORGANISM

I should like now to recall the thesis that "organic concepts should be transferred (from the biological fields) with caution and with full awareness of their limitations as instruments of inquiry in fields which are not concerned with biological organisms."

I need hardly point out that an organized course in "Classical Literary Traditions" presents no hazards as long as we know what we are doing. This kind of organization does give us a working structure which, in practice, is no more than a mimeographed timetable telling us where we are and what we are supposed to be talking about each week. (The problem of keeping to this timetable need not be discussed here.) But, of course, figurative organic concepts are often used without awareness of the need for caution; and, by way of illustration, a few examples may be cited here. They need not be abstruse.

Any well-run organization, a successful business enterprise, let us say, needs a good system of taxonomy in dealing with documents. The organization, if it is to remain in business, needs to provide a place for everything — that is, it needs to set up a good filing system.

Accordingly, let us think of a business that is enterprising, active, and expanding, full of creative ideas. The girl in charge of the filing system is neat, orderly, systematic; and in this context, at any rate, has the aesthetic sense of order, balance, symmetry, and proportion. These are qualities of mind that also characterize good housewives, good library cataloguers, and college professors who hand out mimeographed outlines.

Now, the question in filing, as in any attempt to organize the numerous data of experience, or information, into a body is this: Does the product of organization — the taxonomy — the body and its anatomy, represent reality-in-nature or is it a projection of something that exists a priori in the human mind, a model either built or conditioned into it? In biology, we deal with objects-in-nature that come to us already organized; but is it empirically sound to assume that the body or object which we conceptualize corresponds to nature? Is information actually organized as we conceptualize it? Do we add information that is not in nature, but merely comes out of our heads? Do we tamper with our data, excluding information that perturbs our system? Or do we take things empirically, just the way they come?

In filing, three possibilities may be considered at once. First, the good filing clerk will take the system as she sets it up to be a model of reality, and throw all unclassifiable material into the wastebasket. This will be bad for business. (There are, incidentally, interesting examples of this procedure in the history of science.) Second, the girl will become mentally disturbed, and have to be put back in the general secretarial pool. Third, if she is smart, she will set up a Miscellaneous File.

But presently, in this enterprising, expanding business, the number of individual items in the Miscellaneous File will become very large. This may lead, in turn, to new possibilities. The girl may have to set up new categories and new folders; in time the folders may have to be reclassified and expanded into a Miscellaneous Section; and, if we project our creative, expanding business over a long enough period of time, the whole system may become Miscellaneous and break down, following the general principle that the sum of individual items, or categories, in the Miscellaneous File or Section may become greater than the number of categories in the original body or system, just as the secondary functions of an institution may, in time, outweigh the primary.

Or, to put this another way: Since the universe of information, being an enterprising, expanding business, full of creative ideas, is Miscellaneous itself and not empirically finite, the original organic unity or body imposed upon the universe of information by the human mind shrinks *in time* in proportion to the universe. The operation of this Law of the Miscellaneous File can be arrested only by arbitrary or authoritarian action — by throwing all the unclassifiable stuff into the wastebasket or, in less figurative terms, by limiting the range of one's own or others' experience and information — as may well prove to be the case in education.

But before the Law of the Miscellaneous File becomes unreasonably abstruse, we may do well to move on, or rather go back, to our earlier examples of neat but deceptive organic concepts, namely, knowledge and language.

As we have noticed, our concept of organized knowledge has a long and venerable history, taking us back to Plato and Aristotle. To discuss this history in detail would require more time than can be claimed here (a semester would be desirable), although it would be interesting to study the association of aesthetic qualities with organic concepts which is implicit in the aesthetic idealism of Plato. By aesthetic idealism I mean the belief that beauty is a quality of knowledge, and that beauty, indeed, is a test of truth. The further association of "the true, the beautiful, and the good," leads us into the realm of metaphysics where there is a semantic linkage between aesthetic and moral values. This complex of associations, having been fed into the general inheritance that we call "the humanities," makes an empirical humanism exceedingly difficult.

It would also be interesting to study the classical trichotomy of knowledge into the natural sciences, the social sciences, and the humanities. Or, I should say, the logic is classical; the system itself does not go back beyond the 1920's. But we can escape all of these historical studies quite simply, for our present purposes, by thinking in terms of information rather than knowledge. An empirical view of information in the modern university system should convince us that we are dealing with a number of items that is not empirically finite — and then off go the rules of classical taxonomy, no whole, no parts, no aesthetic qualities! Admittedly, this gets us into deep water; but, as a matter of intellectual honesty, we might also admit that our organic concept of knowledge has long since got us beyond our depth by way of the Law of the Miscellaneous File; and if it is a matter of sink or swim anyhow, the odds on survival are improved if we face facts.

As we move on to the organic concept of language, we may note, rather uneasily I hope, that education today is universally committed to the proposition that language *is* a tool for communication — and that is what *good* it is in terms of counseling and curriculum planning. I emphasize the *is* advisedly, to indicate that the proposition is put forward, and accepted, as representing the true nature of language, its essence, without any reservations as to the instrumental or figurative uses of the concept, and without any inkling that too much information may have been transferred from Aristotle's language workshop.

On the other hand, it ought to be clear that strict empirical considerations admit only one existential proposition; language *is* language (just as an elephant's trunk is a trunk), without analogues elsewhere in human experience. Language cannot be said to be empirically finite; it has no ascertainable beginning or end. It simply begins where you begin it; and it ends no one knows where. Its most important general physical characteristic is linearity; that is, the individual components of language, spoken or written, come one after another, in a series, and hence in the form of a line. I suppose that the communications engineer would say that language, being linear, is to be associated with a single-channel system, corresponding to the single-channel input and output circuits of the human communications system.

This linear concept of language is not figurative; it does not transfer information from one field of observation to another; it is subject to immediate and continued empirical verification, just like organic concepts in biology. Moreover, it is a concept that we can exploit quite elegantly in quantitative and mathematical terms. It opens up an interesting range of information, giving us many insights into the actual empirical difficulties of language, instead of conceptualizing it into something simpler than experience will support.

But that is another paper, and I am under obligation to bring this one to an end for the sake of both space and organic unity. As Aristotle puts it, with one of his great insights into the nature of things, an organic object must have a beginning, a middle, and an end. But for all the master's authority, the arbitrary nature of an organic concept in relation to this discourse must be obvious. The lines of discussion here have no determinable end; it is only this discourse that has to have a determinable end, not in nature, but by agreement and convention. (And it is always considerate of a contributor to leave something for others to discuss.)

Well, by way of a conclusion, then, and perhaps a flourish . . .

THE LIMITATIONS OF ORDINARY EXPERIENCE

I hope that I have made it clear that I am not *against* organic concepts. They give us much necessary and significant information. We need them in our business. What I am really against is ignorance of their nature and limitations. As a language teacher, I am not against traditional grammar, which is a product of the classical-organic concept of language; I am against the older view that grammar is somehow a model of language as a whole, so that when you teach the grammar, you teach the language. I am equally against the frantically modern teachers who are backing away from grammar without knowing what they are backing away from, much less backing into.

What I am really concerned about, however, is the limited range of the information derived from concepts based on ordinary experience. In looking at the history of the physical sciences, I notice that the great advances in information have been made when ordinary experience was rejected and, in fact, defied.

Our ordinary experience assures us, for example, and orthodox classical intellectuals accepted the assurance, that objects-in-nature are normally at rest — take your car — and do not move unless caused to move by some external agency. Motion must therefore be regarded as a special case in organic nature; and, indeed, many Greek intellectuals, dedicated to a static concept of nature, were led to consider motion as illogical, a perturbation of the natural organic symmetry of things, and even aesthetically and hence morally reprehensible.

Physics, as a science, had its beginnings in the late Middle Ages when inquirers began to conceive of things as naturally in motion, and rest as a special case in nature. The problem then is to explain theoretically how things stop, not how they start. This is a preposterous violation of common experience. When your car is stuck in a Minnesota snowdrift, you can hardly conceive of things as naturally in motion; you become a classical intellectual, badly in need of a Prime Mover who causes motion but does not move himself. And so, throughout the history of physics, there has been one conceptual violation of ordinary experience after another, until the science now leads us completely beyond the range of ordinary experience — into a universe of doubtful empirical finality in the direction of both the great and small. Our ordinary experience, in other words, is confined to a very narrow range between practical infinities.

Now we have it in our academic tradition, in the popular version, that modern science began with the development of scientific methods in the Renaissance, notably by Galileo, and their codification by Francis Bacon. This has been advertised as a revolution against medieval logic and the schoolmen, who took Aristotle as their authority in all things. But the revolution has been overpublicized.

We can say with assurance today that the Greeks — those neglected Greeks who were empiricists and not aesthetic idealists with Plato or logicians with Aristotle and the Stoics — were quite clever in the use of appropriate scientific methods, most notably in medicine. In the physical sciences they lacked apparatus and materials that had become available by the time of the Renaissance in Europe, such as good glass. But the important point is, of course, that the Renaissance failed to bring either awareness or rejection of figurative organic concepts; and in the absence of such awareness or rejection, even today, we are required to say that emphasis on scientific methods in many areas has simply perpetuated the classical and medieval preoccupation with methodology. Indeed, we can go beyond this and say that scientific methods, in the absence of any awareness of the conceptual basis of inquiry, simply succeeded medieval and classical formal logic as instruments for the exploitation of figurative organic concepts, and the compounding of ordinary experience.

But we have been making a beginning.

We may remind ourselves that the concept of child growth and development is strictly empirical; and we must keep it so, making sure that no commitments as to finality impair the consistency of our applications. This will not be easy. We cannot, as empiricists, say that human beings are infinite; that is a topic for theologians. But neither can we, as empiricists, say that human beings are finite other than in the most ordinary visual or three-dimensional sense, or that there is a determinable end to growth and development. We must always press beyond ordinary experience. True, it is very hard to escape the concept of organic finality which ordinary experience leads us to expect. But unless we escape from that narrow range we shall find ourselves, in one way or another, restricting free experience, limiting the range and nature of information, compounding the ordinary and commonplace, restraining human thought and action to less than their potential range in nature, reducing human beings to less than their actual status in nature, and, of course, denying the freedoms that are implicit in nature.

Herbert Heaton

CLIO PUTS THE QUESTION

THE word *development* is one well known to historians. Glancing casually over my European library, I find six books on one shelf with the word in their titles, ranging from *The Development of the Soviet Economic System* to a volume in an Oxford series on *European Civilization: Its Origin and Development.* Cheek by jowl on a shelf of Americana I notice five similar titles — development of the flour milling industry, of Federal Reserve policy, of two bank groups in the Central Northwest, of American industries, and of American business and banking thought. The current publishers' lists suggest that this tide of titles threatens to continue flowing wide and high. Meanwhile, my near neighbors, the economists, true to their traditional culture lag in learning the facts of life, have recently appropriated "economic development" as their latest hobby, and are producing a five-foot shelf of books on the nature and causes of economic development in the past or on the methods — including bulldozers and IBM machines — that are needed for the development of "underdeveloped" areas in the very near future — which means before the Communists beat us to the punch.

This widespread use of the word by our guild does not signify that we all know what it means or that we mean the same thing when we use it. In fact, it is one of those two score and ten words or terms frequently used by historians which the Social Science Research Council Committee on Historiography vainly tried to define ten years ago.* The Committee culled from the books numerous quotations in which

* *Theory and Practice in Historical Study: A Report of the Committee on Historiography*, Bulletin No. 54. New York: Social Science Research Council, 1946.

these fifty words had been used — with results that were described as "fearful and wonderful." It then dumped them into the lap of Sidney Hook, a professor of philosophy with a minor interest in history and the social sciences, and asked him to wring therefrom acceptable exact definitions of each term. When Hook failed to find any self-consistent definitions in the material, he was invited to formulate his own definitions as philosopher, albeit taking such account as he could of the quotations. The qualifying clause ruined that attempt, "for the varied and conflicting usages of the terms by historians could not be reconciled with one another or with those prevailing in general or in philosophy in particular." Thereupon the Committee threw up its hands in despair, and decided to publish Hook's definitions of twenty-one of the words as he had formulated them without any attention to how historians use or abuse the English language. Those definitions, with necessary explanations, filled twenty-two pages of print, of which two and a half were needed to define jointly the three words *change, development,* and *progress.*

If my reporting of this grim incident proves that confession is good for the soul, let him that is without sin among you cast the first stone. Before you throw it by demanding that history be evicted from the social sciences and the New Look Humanities, consider the burdens of age which historians bear on their arthritic shoulders. For History, Philosophy, and Classics are the old-timers in this symposium. By contrast, most of the others are newcomers and, thanks to the Foundations, some of them are *nouveaux riches.* The recorded human story is at least five or six thousand years long, yet during about half that time Clio, the historian's muse, has been asking, "What happened?" There have been a lot of answers, and the result has been, in the words of the two historians (3) who wrote the article on "History and Historiography" for the *Encyclopedia of the Social Sciences,* that "There is no branch of knowledge which in the course of intellectual evolution has exhibited more varied modalities and answered to more contradictory conceptions than has history. There is none which has and continues to have more difficulty in discovering its definitive status."

Two of those difficulties lie athwart the road this symposium is trying to tread. In the first place, what use can the historian make of concepts in general, and in the second place, what use, if any, has he made of the concept of development? Let me deal with the first question first. In the good old days he had an easy task: to write a pleasant readable tale, perhaps with rhetoric playing a more important part than veracity, as did Herodotus in the ancient world and many who came afterward; to record political or military happenings in forum, camp, battlefield, conspirator's den, and ruler's palace, as did Thucydides, the Roman scribes, and countless historians since their day; or to tell the story of the church triumphant, of its ideals, its leaders, saints, and martyrs, its victories over pagans, heretics, kings, and emperors, as did the medieval ecclesiastical chroniclers.

Most of these historians bothered little with concepts, except perhaps the concept of what history was: the biography of states, as Seeley called it; past politics, as Freeman defined it; the story, often highly biased, of one's city, state, party, or church; or just a bare chronological record of events and persons, a string of dates, such as made Dr. Johnson snort, "History is merely a kind of glorified almanack making."

Some of these men might wonder who made the wheels go round or handled the steering wheel or determined the outcome in the last chapter. They found their answer in Chance; in the Great Man (or the Great Woman, if that was not deemed a contradiction of terms), in the Hero or the Villain; or, on a higher plane, in Fate, Destiny, Nemesis, gods or God, and of course, Satan or lesser devils. Even the ancients did this, as Herodotus and the Old Testament make abundantly clear. The medieval scribes found God ever-busy in human affairs, taking sides, intervening, punishing, rewarding, and resorting to a miracle when His People were in a tight spot. In more recent centuries, when Providence lost favor among secular-minded European historians, He boarded the *Mayflower* and practised the Guiding Hand on His new Chosen People in New England; then, according to such historians as George Bancroft, He decided to take on a lot more territory and to work out in America, or rather, in the United States, "an epic of liberty" according to the principles of Jacksonian Democracy. It may be that historians have ceased to sing about the Divine Plan and the Chosen People; yet the melody lingers on in the perorations of July Fourth orations and of presidential speeches, even of those presidents who have studied history. And there seems to be a revised version of the theme in Arnold Toynbee's conclusion (10) that history gives us "a vision . . . of God revealing Himself in action to souls that were sincerely seeking Him."

If the old historians had too few concepts, their descendants during the last two centuries, and especially during the last one, have had perhaps too many. This has been due to two developments, or trends if you prefer that word. In the first place, the range of history has been widened to take in virtually all facets of human society. We have moved on from the "drum and trumpet" type of narrative to explore other fields — social, economic, constitutional, institutional, intellectual, scientific, religious, and so forth down a long line. If we are modest in aim we write a history of the English or French or American *people*. The more ambitious of us embark on a study of Western *civilization*; but a glutton for punishment like Toynbee tries to describe more than a score of *civilizations* in ten volumes. Our biographies no longer are confined to saints, sinners, statesmen, and soldiers. A book on *Medieval People* (8) describes a French peasant, a Venetian traveler, a prioress, a Paris housewife, a wool merchant, and a cloth manufacturer. General Grant and General Caesar have had to move over to make room for General Mills, General Motors, the General Will, and the General Strike. In dealing with the sixteenth century we give less attention to Henry VIII's matrimonial revolution and much more to the Price Revolution. Look at any textbook survey on the history of the modern world and you will see how widely we now range — and, in confidence, how thinly the butter is spread over a thousand pages.

In the second place, and as a consequence of the first, historians felt the need for some new kit of tools to help them fabricate a story out of the mountain of raw data they were accumulating. They needed to trace cause and effect, to correlate, to detect interrelations, to synthesize, and even if they had no ambition to evolve a "philosophy of history," they wanted at least to be able to say, "That's how and why it seems to have happened," or even, "That's how things seem to happen."

Some purists, or "scientific" historians as they began to call themselves, stared long and hard at the data, reading and rearranging their notes in the hope that the facts would eventually "speak for themselves" and that the particulars would reveal the generalities which they carried inside themselves. But few, if any, historians ever approached the collection or interpretation of material with a completely blank or open mind. Some wish was father to the forecast and the filing system. Some teacher or book had left an impression that must be either eradicated or strengthened. Love or hatred of some Cause (such as liberty, landlords, or a law) might influence the quest for causality according to whether you had been born (or had become) a little Liberal or a little Conservative. Further, no historian could be entirely ignorant of what people were saying in other disciplines (such as philosophy, economics, biology, anthropology, sociology, or psychology) or in undisciplined controversies about political or economic issues. Finally, only a historian who says Modern History ends in 1273 can escape having his view of the past (or of the future) influenced by the character of the immediate present in which he is living and working. An American historian's choice of facts, emphasis, and interpretation would not be the same in Wilsonian 1913, Hardingesque 1923, depressed 1933, grim 1943, and booming 1953.

Thus historians have fashioned some concepts for themselves and borrowed some from outside. In general we have been rather cautious about the latter, especially if they were grand and cosmic, such as those of Darwin and Spencer on evolution, of Hegel on the philosophy of history, or of Marx on the economic interpretation of history and the all-pervasive dominant influence of the class struggle. We suspect that what is true of ants, polecats, and foxes, or of man as a biological specimen, may have little to do with man as a political and social animal. We regard Hegel and Marx — not to mention some later names — as incompetent to produce philosophies and interpretations of history, because they simply did not know enough history to qualify them for that task. We have not embraced and scarcely flirted with psychiatric approaches, even to biography; and if we regard the philosopher turned historian as a major sinner, the historian turned philosopher may seem little less culpable. In fact, if a historian wishes to consign to the bottomless pit a colleague whose work he dislikes, all he has to say is, "The trouble with him is that he is more of a philosopher than a historian."

Many of the concepts which historians have fabricated or filched are of relatively limited range in time and space. They are, as Heckscher, the Swedish economic historian said of one of them (7), instrumental concepts which, "if aptly chosen, should enable us to understand a particular historical period more clearly than we otherwise might." The list includes a lot of -tions and -isms — Nationalism, Capitalism, Mercantilism, Imperialism, and so on all the way from A to Z; it also includes such labels as the Renaissance, the Industrial Revolution, and the Frontier. Each of these has served a useful purpose by introducing us to *new* phases of the story (such as the Industrial Revolution) or in providing a better tool for analyzing and interpreting old stories (such as struggles for home rule, empire building, and westward movements). The pity is that we have often let a useful servant become a bad master. The tool has become the finished product, the hypothesis has frozen into a dogma. Either we have sought to make a concept so precise in definition and to endow it with such special qualities that it becomes an abstract ideal type, mystical and mythical, whose contact with actual historical conditions is rare and coincidental. Or, on the other hand, we have allowed the concept to become so vague, broad, and imprecise, especially in popular use, that every man can frame his own definition, and the ivory tower becomes a Tower of Babel.

In either case many of these concepts seem to be blurring rather than sharpening our vision of the past, and we would gladly have them scratched out of the academic dictionary. Professor Keith Hancock, the leading student today of modern empires, after counting, in one morning's search, ten different meanings of Imperialism by ten different writers, decided that the word was one which no self-respecting scholar can use (5). My own investigation of Mercantilism leads me to ask, not, What was Mercantilism? but rather, Was there ever any such thing? Professor T. S. Ashton (2), our greatest authority on the era of the Industrial Revolution, protests that the "capitalist spirit," "far from being a phrase suggesting a mental or emotional attitude, has become an impersonal superhuman force. It is no longer men and women, exercising free choice, who effect change, but capitalism or the spirit of capitalism." He quotes some of Schumpeter's *obiter dicta*: "Capitalism develops rationality." "Capitalism produced the mental attitude of modern science." "Modern pacifism, modern international morality, modern feminism, are products of capitalism." So it is with the other -isms; they have introduced a new mysticism into the recounting of plain facts. Hence Ashton resolved that no single word ending in -ism should appear in his latest book, and happened to mention this resolution in an Oxford faculty common room. "Not even baptism?" asked one of his hosts, in that gentle way they have of deflating you at Oxford. The proofs had not yet been returned to the publisher; it would have been easy to substitute "christening"; but Ashton decided to leave the offensive syllables as a warning to himself against vainglory.

So much for the role of concepts in general, and of rather limited ones in particular. Now what of the larger concept of development?

Much that has been said about it by Professors Nagel and DeWitt fits the historian's general understanding of the term. So also does Sidney Hook's definition or description as penned for the Committee on Historiography over a decade ago: "Development is any change which has a continuous direction and which culminates in a phase that is qualitatively new. [Hence the term] should be used to characterize any series of events in thought, action, or institutional arrangements which exhibit a directional cumulative change that either terminates in an event marked off by recognized qualitative novelty or which exhibits in its course a perceptible pattern of growth." If that is how a philosopher sees it, it looks very much like the picture painted by Professor Lane (7), the Johns Hopkins historian, who describes development as those changes which involve passage through successive stages or states, each of which was made possible by that preceding and was prerequisite to that which followed. Further, the movement is one-way. As Lane puts it, "There is no assumption that we will go back from planet to gaseous nebula, from man to ape, from democracy to absolute monarchy, or from one form of class struggle to an earlier form and start over."

Exploring that concept, tracing the steps in development, and seeking for the "historical laws" or "laws of history" which governed the movement were popular exercises among historians during part of the eighteenth century, most of the nineteenth, and the early decades of the twentieth.

In the eighteenth century the French historians of the Enlightenment replaced the Christian interpretation of history by a new dogma based on the idea of progress and having the triumph of reason as its final goal. Unfortunately, they made no attempt to trace the progress, step by step, toward that triumph. Instead, they assumed that earlier ages had been irrational, bound by tradition and superstition, *dark* ages, from which man had only recently been released, enlightened, and converted to the rule of reason by a blinding revelation of truth, as Saul had been on the road to Damascus. Their conceited assumption of their own age's superiority over all others was equaled by their ignorance of those ages, and was often badly jolted when, for example, some critic asked whether Greek art of the fifth century B.C., was inferior to western art of the eighteenth century A.D. Yet the word *progress* stuck in the vocabulary, some of the ignorance was dispelled, and the events of the next 100 or 150 years seemed to prove that progress was a normal characteristic of human development, at least in modern times.

The nineteenth century did a much better job, partly because of the widening interest in social, economic, and political institutions, in mass movements or conditions, and in ideas. The Germans played a leading part, and exported their concepts in the minds and baggage of foreign students who had studied in their classrooms and seminars. Western political institutions were traced from their Teutonic origins in German forest clearings. Economics were tracked along lines of stages or systems: hunting, pastoral, agricultural, industrial; barter, money, credit; house industry, guild, workshop, factory; village, market town, nation, world; and so on. Marx tossed in his list of socioeconomic systems — primitive communism, slavery, feudalism, commercialism, capitalism. Comte, though a pioneer sociologist rather than a historian, drew heavily on historical evidence to trace the evolution of the mind through three states — theological explanation, then a resort to reason, then scientific inquiries that led from mathematics to astronomy to physics, chemistry, biology, and finally to the all-embracing all-explaining science of sociology. Everybody wanted to get into the act. In every field there was a fervent belief similar to that of those historians who thought they could by patient research learn "the character and sequence of the stages through which the economic life of society has actually moved," and even that they could penetrate deeper to discover "the laws of social development." For of course they all believed there were such laws.

How did the historians get on with their search? Frankly, not too well, partly because of the nature of their objective and also because of subjective factors, especially the outlook and temperament of the searchers. Their objective in looking for laws of development was, as Lane puts it, "to ape the natural sciences." They were therefore driven to thinking of history in terms of physics, biology, etc., of laws of nature, of organisms which lived and developed according to pattern. A shocking example was given by one Australian professor. His theory of development was as follows: For long periods mankind jogs along with little or no change in its way of life. Then up pops some startlingly different figure — Caesar, Christ, Mahomet, Cromwell, Napoleon — a *mutant*, the professor called him — who shakes everything up or down, drives or leads his people on to a new plane, which becomes normal until the next mutant turns up. Thus the Great Man theory was dressed up in scientific jargon.

A more ambitious example was provided in the presidential address given in 1923 by Professor Edward Cheyney to the American Historical Association (4). The title was "Law in History"; the theme was that "laws of history there must be." Cheyney gave his guesses at six of them, warning his hearers not to conceive of them as

"principles which it would be well for us to accept, or as ideals which we may hope to attain; but as natural laws, which we must accept whether we want to or not, whose workings we cannot obviate, however much we may thwart them, to our own failure and disadvantage; laws to be accepted and reckoned with as much as the laws of gravitation or of chemical affinity or of organic evolution or of human psychology."

Throughout the address scientific analogies or terms were sprinkled; for instance, "the human race seems to be essentially an organism, a unit," and if any member suffers the whole body of individuals, classes, tribes, and nations is hurt.

Yet one other instance, which had great vogue for at least two decades. Fifty years ago Werner Sombart presented capitalism as a biological entity, characterized by a distinctive organization, technique, and spirit. It was born in the later Middle Ages, had passed through childhood and adolescence by 1750, reached virile manhood during the nineteenth century, but crept into senility, with hardened arteries, toupé, dental plates, and a wheel chair after 1914, and inevitable death not far beyond. Sombart thought he was improving on his intellectual master, Marx, who in his day produced the most complicated, thorough, and influential concept of development we have ever had. Marx in turn got his pattern, not from the natural sciences, but from philosophy. By reading Hegel and occasionally standing him on his head, he got his laws cut and dried. Hegel was deemed right in his stress on dialectic but wrong way 'round when he said that the historians' theme was how the Idea was made flesh, materialized, and worked out in human events and institutions. Rather, said Marx, history's prime concern is with the changing picture of material conditions, especially the prevailing mode of economic production and exchange, and the social organization necessarily following therefrom. On that basis has been built up, and by it alone can be explained, the political and intellectual life of any epoch. And since the social organization was always marked by class divisions, struggles between the two chief classes made up much of every epoch's history. Change the base, the mode of production and exchange; then you will be obliged to change the social organization, and hence the whole political and intellectual superstructure. There will be much strain and friction in the transition and in the changing character of the class struggle. Strain, friction, and struggle make the headlines of history.*

Regarding these concepts of development one may ask two questions. The first is, How do you know that human society is an organism, a unit, or anything else comparable to what the natural scientists explore? The answer is, You don't, or at least the concept is not proved. Even assuming that it were, the second question would be, What sort of laws control development, where have they led, and where will they lead in the future?

Here the subjective factors come into play. For there are sufficient instances to show that the seeker after historical laws is prone to become a legislator, who will make the laws after his own heart, his emotions, or preconceived ideas. He surveys the world around him, approving this, disliking that; and he may then look into the future with hope that what he favors will come to pass or with fear that a nasty current trend will lead to disaster, defeat, disintegration. He may put a fact into a wrong setting, as did the English professor's wife who in 1949 was walking with me down 59th Street in New York City. As we came to a parking lot sandwiched in between two buildings she remarked, with a Londoner's reflex action, "Oh! A bomb site!" The same view makes different impressions on men with different interests. When Guy Stanton Ford, young historian, and Henry C. Taylor, agricultural economist, pulled into Cork harbor in 1899 on their way to Germany for graduate study, Ford looked through the binoculars at the landscape and said, "There's a castle that Cromwell knocked about a bit";

---

* For further discussion of Marxian and other concepts of development in the field of economic history, see H. Heaton, "The Economic Impact on History," in J. R. Stayer, ed., *The Interpretation of History*, Princeton University Press, 1943; "Clio's New Overalls," *Canadian Journal of Economics and Political Science*, Vol. 20 (1954), pp. 476–77; and "Criteria for Periodization in Economic History," *Journal of Economic History*, Vol. 15 (1955), pp. 267–72.

but Taylor's observation was, "Look at those open fields, just like they had in the medieval manor."

Or we may see what we want to see. Stephen Leacock once told of an American married couple who went round the world just before World War I. On their return the husband, an enthusiastic prohibitionist, reported to his lunch club that his outstanding impression was the universal relentless march toward dryness. His wife, an ardent suffragette, told her club that her deepest impression was the irresistible clamor of women in all lands for their political and social rights. Which provoked Leacock to comment that if their forecasts were accurate, it would not be long before the world's women, with votes, and the world's men, without drinks, would stand staring at one another wondering, What next?

Let me illustrate this propensity to prophecy with rather more authoritative examples. In 1912 I heard my history professor, a Quaker, a Liberal, and a disciple of Comte, declare that history was the story of the evolution of peace. That was his inclination, his faith, his hope; but it seemed solidly backed by the fact that since 1815 there had been no Armageddon, no "world war," and it was buttressed by the conviction that even if Britain should lose its power to maintain the *pax Brittanica* the rising might and idealism of the United States, as voiced by such men as Wilson, Bryan, and Carnegie, would ensure for the next century a *pax Americana*.

Or take Cheyney's six laws. His first was the law of continuity; every event goes far back in origin and revolutions do not make all things new. His second was the law of impermanence, of mutability; nothing lasts forever; there is no finality in human institutions, economies, polities, or societies. In these two laws the historian spoke as historian. But in the next four the humane, urbane progressive, speaking in the early 1920's, took over. For the third law was the organic interdependence of individuals, classes, tribes, and nations. His fourth was a "law of democracy, a tendency for all governments to come under the control of all the people." His fifth was a "law of necessity for free consent," and his sixth "a law of moral progress. Obscurely and slowly, yet visibly and measurably, moral influences in human affairs have become stronger and more widely extended than material influences."

This sextalogue enthralled its hearers, who were not unaware of a recently popular prescription in mental therapy propounded by one

Monsieur Coué: "Repeat after each meal the words, 'Every day in every way I am getting better and better and better.'" It reflected the hopes of educated men of good will who were getting over the severe jolt given them by World War I; who had concluded that the world had learned its costly lesson from that tragic experience; and who now believed mankind was getting back on the right ever-upward path, in fact returning to normalcy. Today the laws of Cheyney seem terribly "dated." They read strangely in the light of the events of the last three decades, and the tablet of stone on which the last four of them were inscribed — unity, democracy, freedom, and moral progress — is at least cracked or chipped.

The best illustration of a sublimated libido projecting supreme laws into the future was Marx's forecast that socialism was the inevitable next step in socioeconomic development. All the factors, forces, stresses, and struggles were deemed to be headed relentlessly and dialectically that way, to the next stage, which would also be the final stage, the ultimate step in social change. For when that step had been taken and the bourgeoisie had been destroyed, there would be only one class — the proletariat; therefore no class war; therefore no need for a state as instrument of the ruling class; also no need for a religion to serve as dope administered by the ruling class to keep the oppressed class in a state of torpor; and therefore there would be no more history.

The explanation of this fantastic forecast was, of course, that Marx was a radical, caught up in the welter of social and political unrest of his day. He brought his well-trained mind to provide ammunition for his side in the current agitations, just as I suppose a well-trained physicist may apply his knowledge of nuclear power to kill his wife, crack a safe, or burn all the hostile votes off the papers in the ballot box. Yet the interesting fact is that while academics knew little or nothing about his theory until very late in the nineteenth century, many professors interested in economic history and economics were reaching similar conclusions about the inevitable coming of socialism. In Germany most of them were known as "socialists of the chair." In England they might be good Liberals or Conservatives, yet they felt that socialism was not merely an inevitable development but also a desirable one.

Let me quote the greatest British economic historian of the late nineteenth century, William J. Ashley. In a reply to his fiancée, who had remarked that he seemed to desire industry to be in the hands of the state, he wrote (1):

"I am a bit of a fatalist. . . . Just as in the way in which in the past certain transitions have been prepared by events and have gone through stages, which can be clearly traced, so that after a certain time they became inevitable, and in some cases were then seen to be inevitable, so I think it is with Socialism. Over the history of the last century the development of individualism to its furthest point in industry may be traced, and then the counter-movement setting in, both in philosophic thought and in actual fact. I feel, at the point to which we have got, that the principal branches of production and exchange will ultimately be organized socially is as certain as the rising of tomorrow's sun.

"But broadly speaking, all the great stages in social development in the past have been upward and have helped mankind. And I have faith that this will be so in the future. And then I agree with Comte and St. Paul — with the former that prevision is possible, and that we can hasten and assist the transition, or in the words of the latter that we can be fellow-workers with God. And so I should not stand aside and say 'Well, perhaps it will be so, but I'm rather sorry,' but rather say, 'It must be so, and therefore it must be good, and therefore I must help it.'"

As these "scientific" forecasts were all made seventy to a hundred years ago, we can ask what their batting average has been and consequently how much faith one can have in men who prophesy on the basis of a theory of development. The average is far less than 100 per cent, even in Russia, where the Bolsheviks tried to reach their final stage without letting the economy pass fully through those stages which must precede it according to Marx's route map — scarcely a testimonial to the great master. Further, the promise of a final, permanent, problemless heaven has proved to be unfortunate. In Russia as well as in the Western democratic countries we have learned there is no finality in socialism, no disappearance of crucial problems; and the expounders of development are stumped by the question "Where do we go from here?" As for Sombart's forecast concerning the early demise of capitalism, it looked good in the depressed 'thirties but sounds silly today, for capitalism is a very lively near-corpse; yet it may look different again when we get into the next depression.

Historians have therefore plenty of examples to warn them of the dangers inherent in ambitious comprehensive concepts capable of projection into the future. Even the statisticians have failed us. Their population figures in the 'thirties proved conclusively that the rate of growth was declining, that some countries had already reached a stationary figure, that others, including the United States, were well on the road to one, and that the Western world was doomed eventually to a shrinking and aging population. How were these experts to know that young people would almost overnight in the 'forties go back into the business of producing babies with joyous — even if planned — abandon? The experts' faces are indeed red, and so also would be those of the historians who took their forecasts as scientifically proved, were it not for the fact that we are too busy teaching huge classes composed of these unexpected offspring.

Finally, we simply do not know enough about the past and the present to formulate any concept of development that permits broad, sweeping forecasts. The bigger the canvas the greater the likelihood of inadequacy. If Toynbee tackles all civilizations, it is unlikely that his view of any one of them will be acceptable to the specialist in any of the fields. A Pennsylvania professor of Semitics has questioned his distinction between the Babylonian and Sumerian civilizations, and finds his picture of Syriac society a "conglomerate of loosely assorted elements," while a Chicago Egyptologist rejects his societal pattern of Egypt (9). And so it goes. Our knowledge of many areas, topics, and periods is still so scanty that it only intensifies the darkness. Elsewhere there is very much we do not know, and even are never likely to know. We still have a great deal to learn, even about such centuries as the eighteenth and nineteenth. We will gladly try out any new concept that seems to offer aid in understanding and interpreting. We will endeavor to get ideas from our neighbors in the other social sciences and humanities, but fear we cannot keep up with their pouring out of new ideas, new words, and mathematical formulae. We don't know to which of their men or schools we should listen, for as someone said, "If there are four economists round a table, there will be four ideas, and if Lord Keynes is one of the four, there will be five." We cannot know whether yesterday's doctrines have any validity today, though we suspect that with others, as with us, many of the things written a quarter of a century ago have been put aside as the outmoded works of yesteryear. But at least we are not asleep on the job, and from this symposium I gather that we are in good company.

REFERENCES

1. Ashley, A. *William James Ashley: A Life.* London: P. S. King, 1932.
2. Ashton, T. S. "The Treatment of Capitalism by Historians," in F. A. Hayek, ed., *Capitalism and the Historian.* University of Chicago Press, 1954.
3. Berr, H., and L. Febvre, "History," pp. 357–68 in E. R. A. Seligman, ed., *Encyclopedia of the Social Sciences,* Vol. 7. New York: Macmillan, 1932.
4. Cheyney, E. P. "Law in History," *American Historical Review,* Vol. 29 (1924), pp. 231–48.
5. Hancock, W. K. *Empire in the Changing World.* New York: Penguin Books, 1943.
6. Heckscher, E. F. *Mercantilism,* (Eng. Trans.). London: Allen & Unwin, 1935.
7. Lane, F. C. "The Social Sciences and the Humanities," *Proceedings of the American Philosophical Society,* Vol. 92 (1948), pp. 356–63.
8. Power, E. E. *Medieval People.* London: Methuen, 1924.
9. Speiser, E. A. "The Ancient Near East and Modern Philosophers of History," *Proceedings of the American Philosophical Society,* Vol. 95 (1951), pp. 583–88.
10. Toynbee, A. J. *A Study of History,* Vol. 10. London: Oxford University Press, 1954.

Robert F. Spencer

EVOLUTION AND DEVELOPMENT: A VIEW OF ANTHROPOLOGY

S IR EDWARD BURNETT TYLOR, writing in 1874, defined his position as follows: "The thesis which I venture to sustain, within limits, is simply this, that the savage state in some measure represents an early condition of mankind, one out of which the higher culture has gradually developed or evolved, by processes still in regular operation as of old, the result showing that, on the whole, progress has far prevailed over relapse" (15, p. 32). This is the argument advanced by the scholar who was to become known as the father of anthropology. He equated the concept of development with the evolutionary philosophies of culture that characterized the late nineteenth and early twentieth centuries. It remained for Herskovits to point out both in 1948 and 1955 that had Tylor's suggested concept of development been more widely employed, much of the argument and difficulty surrounding conceptual analyses of culture growth and change might have been in some measure obviated (7, p. 442).

My contribution to this symposium is written from the point of view of the anthropologist whose orientation is primarily toward the understanding of culture and cultures. It is evident from Tylor's remark that the idea of development has a very real and precise meaning for cultural anthropology. The concept is implicit in a discipline that from its earliest beginnings has been wedded to a view of time and temporal sequence. Anthropology at large, in its broadest sense, has aimed always at a comprehension of the processes at work in the development of man in his social, cultural, and biological aspects. The anthropologist conceives himself to be working with human history on several differing

levels. Not the least of these is the concern with man's physical emergence through time, the development in biological terms of the genus
Homo, his growth and spread throughout the world. When to this is
added the concern with human institutions, what men have invented
and devised, what they believe, how they have responded to the complementary poles of nature and culture, it is clear that anthropology,
in its concern with cultural manifestations, is founded in history, and
seeks to comprehend the forces that have shaped humanity and the
differing kinds of human behavior. On this level it asks, What is culture, and what promotes the development of culture?

Despite its recognized historical bent, cultural anthropology has created for itself, especially in recent years, a number of perplexing conceptual problems. It is no longer possible to accept unreservedly
Tylor's hypothesis that the so-called savage state represents an early
stage in the development of human history. Indeed, any anthropologist
who today addresses himself to the task of describing the elements of
primitive society, religion, economics, law or other primitive institutions finds himself faced by the necessity of establishing a frame of
reference in which primitive man is somehow pitted against man in
civilized societies. The problem of primitive culture, inherited from
the point of view which Tylor's reasoning makes explicit, permits no
easy solution. Most modern anthropologists will subscribe to the assertion that primitive man differs, not in kind, as a survival from one of
the bottom rungs of the human developmental ladder, but only in
degree, in possessing a somewhat less sophisticated outlook and more
limited experience because of the absence of the body of accumulated
knowledge and tradition which writing makes possible. By this reasoning, primitive man is simply nonliterate man, and it is now widely
recognized that the roots of a primitive society may reach as far back
in time as do those of the more complex human groupings. However
much the backgrounds of cultural anthropology may stem from the
antiquarian concern with strange customs and unique facts, it is the
patterning of human achievement across the world — culture itself, in
short — which provides the major preoccupations of anthropology today.

If the anthropological discipline is therefore oriented to a time span,
the question must arise of how far one can explain, adequately and accurately, the development of culture as a human phenomenon. To

Tylor and his contemporaries this posed no problem, directed as they were to a conceptual ordering of mankind in terms of a psychic unity that led to a unilinear growth and development of human institutions. To Herbert Spencer, Lewis H. Morgan, Sir James George Frazer, Andrew Lang, and many others, no problem was raised by either the great variety of human attainments or the differing behavioral manifestations of men. All were committed to a view of progress, and all accepted, implicitly or explicitly, the gradual upward trend of man. Nor is this reasoning by any means out of fashion. It could be viewed indeed as an element of Western civilization, of the Faustian ideal of progress, a reflection of a culturally determined concept that holds man to be innately good and improvable.

But no serious student of culture can any longer accept such a view of human developmental history. Two or three schools of thought arose in the twentieth century that effectively demolished the evolutionary structure built by the social theorists of the nineteenth. And if at the present time there is a neo-evolutionism, it is a point of view hemmed about with innumerable qualifications.* It was American anthropology, largely under the leadership of the late Franz Boas, that took a concerted stand against a unilinear interpretation of human development. In the Boas school arises the classic view of historical anthropology, the recognition not of the totality of human culture and its pan-human development, but rather the explanations of the rise and growth of individual cultures themselves. Basically this was an orientation toward the processes of diffusion, the analysis of the results of contact between peoples. Unlike the diffusionism which at about the same period arose in Germany and Austria, for example, notions of the culture-circle and of the world-wide spread of ideas, which Graebner and Schmidt promulgated, and unlike the theory of a single center-source defended by G. E. Smith, Perry, and later by Rivers, the theory of the Boas school was that each culture must of necessity be evaluated in its own terms, that each has its own developmental history, and that it is possible,

---

* That cultural anthropology is again becoming preoccupied with the problems of societal and cultural evolution, this time in multilineal terms, is a recognizable trend. The primary concern is with recurrent phenomena in different cultures and an attempt to come to grips with the causes of such parallel developments (14, 15). The search for laws of cultural development is perhaps promising, and certainly to be contrasted to Tylorian or Marxian teleology. Elicitation of such laws, however, promises to be difficult, but may indeed represent the growing research direction of anthropology.

by comparing related cultures, to understand their components and growth. The Boasian methods became a strong movement of resistance to the evolutionism of Tylor and Morgan. The Boas school objected to any theorizing that was not empirically verified, and in putting forward the concept of diffusion, they struck down the emphases on parallel development which the evolutionists stressed. Most American anthropologists of today no longer concern themselves with the historical reconstructions that are part of the method of Boas. Virtually without exception, however, they have been subjected to Boas' influence. His comparative approach permitted an apprehension of similarities of form and function between societies, of the relative intensity of a culture element, and of the particular phrasing by one culture of a trait shared with a neighboring group. These kinds of comparison in turn permitted the growth of a method of culture history, by seeking to answer questions relating to depth of time and space. Boas' own studies of mythology, Lowie's analysis of Plains Indian age-graded and military societies, and Spier's treatment of the Plains Sun Dance are recognized classic applications — and not the only ones — of this method of historical reconstruction. But it is the methodology which the school of Boas evolved that is of great importance and consequence. It led the way to an evaluation of the direction an individual culture might take, and it presaged an appreciation of the ways in which the cultural parts come to make the cultural whole. More than this, it was the tutelage and influence of Boas that led most pointedly toward the concept of cultural relativism, the view that each culture must of necessity be evaluated on its own premises. This relativism, in turn, led to a rejection of the search for universal laws of culture, holding that they are either nonexistent or, if discoverable, so vague as scarcely to be worth eliciting.

More recently, and apart from the heritage of Boas, other points of view have become influential. On the one hand, the professed lack of interest in history has brought about the "functionalist" approach of Malinowski — the evaluation of a culture and the comprehension of the interaction of its components, the concern with what a culture is, not with how it has become so. This is paralleled in turn by the allegedly more scientifically oriented sociology of Durkheim and his followers, which has led to the search for social laws that characterizes Radcliffe-Brown. Although these influences are to some extent felt by American anthropology, it is to be remembered that Boas, too, is not without his functionalist implications. By holding that the processes of history, operating at random, effect culture difference, he places the emphasis on the role of the individual culture (13, pp. 142–144).

The influence of Boas — and of his students — on anthropology, especially in America, has, it is true, been rather hard on the growth of a concise and specific body of theory. The tradition that came most markedly to the fore was that of field investigation, the gathering, empirically, of facts in living situations of other cultures. The stress on getting the data before the collapse and decline of so many of the so-called primitive cultures, indeed, the emphasis on the necessity of obtaining as complete an array of facts as possible, tended to minimize the concern with problem. Or, if problem could be said to exist, it lay in the analysis of historical factors operative in the growth of a culture or culture area. This traditional interest and background of American anthropologists, perhaps, is what has caused the discipline to lag behind its sister social sciences in the formulation of a more exacting methodology and frame of reference. And it has been this same absence of methodological refinement that has evoked some criticism of anthropological results. If, however, the field of anthropology has made a contribution to the behavioral sciences, it is the important one of cultural relativism and its implications.

Since the historical schemes of the latter nineteenth century came to naught because of the recognition of the remarkable variety of human behavior, contemporary anthropology has shifted its sights and, moving slightly away from Boasian history, has turned its attention to solving the riddle of the nature of culture. It has been said that there are as many and varied definitions of culture as there are anthropologists, a point which would seem to be verified by the recent critical monograph of Kroeber and Kluckhohn (11). Most anthropologists will agree that a fairly basic definition can be reached but that the ramifications of such a concept are boundless. As the study of man, it follows that any and all human problems are fitting areas for anthropological investigation. Social behavior, in itself a prerequisite to culture but in turn channeled by culture, is an intrinsic aspect of such investigatory pursuits. Once the anthropologist began to be somewhat less concerned with history, however, turning to the various questions of function and structure, some of the traditional continuity of the discipline began to be lost. The questions currently being asked come closer to the inquiry "How does the culture act?" rather than to "How does it get that way?" This has meant that even if historical-developmental problems still come to the fore, they tend to be couched in terms of such great variety as to preclude the establishment of any consistent frame of reference.

The result is that anthropology takes on a rather puzzling aspect when the attempt is made to evaluate its contribution to knowledge, to the social sciences, or to history. The sociologist, for example, is troubled that his ethnological colleagues may analyze both the socio-cultural patterns of a remote people and those of contemporary Western society. Or the psychologist is disturbed when projective tests are administered to so-called primitive peoples on an assumption that even though cultures differ, human nature will remain the same and that in consequence such testing is valid in demonstrating the differing effects of cultures shaping personality. Similarly, when the anthropologist invades the realm of documented history and historical philosophy, concerning himself with major trends and movements in the recognized historic civilizations, there is protest from the orthodox historian. Nor are these the only areas of overlapping and conflicting interest. Thus, while no one would argue that each discipline holds a monopoly, and while it might generally be agreed that the study of man itself occupies a significant place in the Comtean pyramid of knowledge, it must be admitted that for anthropology, at least, it is sometimes hard to find the proper niche.

A problem which anthropology has faced in more recent years thus lies in the conceptual difference between diachronic and synchronic approaches. The preoccupation with the former still enjoys a wholly legitimate place, as, for example, in archaeology, and by implication in the more classic types of ethnographic description in the Boasian tradition, which are still being undertaken. A synchronic approach is perhaps best exemplified by the kinds of analysis of culture being currently undertaken by the so-called "British sociologists," themselves ethnographers concerned with more remote societies. Their work carries to a laudable end the empirical traditions begun by Malinowski and suggested in the theory of Radcliffe-Brown. Here is field work at its best, described by Evans-Pritchard as taking place on three conceptual levels. The anthropologist, he notes (5, pp. 61–62), lives among a group, learns its language, its concepts, and its values, and in turn evaluates and translates his experience. He then goes beyond this level of concern with culture, and out of his empirical experience with his group begins to comprehend a structural order. Lastly, he compares his findings with the patterns and structured order of other societies, thereby working toward an understanding of the potential range of human behavior and the reasons for its variations. But although there are a few exceptions, mainly limited to comparisons in a single area, the contemporary British school has not yet realized its ultimate goal of comparison and of social typology. The result is that attention goes to the analysis of structure, not to development. The British approach is mentioned here not because it is a school with special and somewhat limited orientations, but because it represents merely one developed area of interest which has marked parallels outside Britain. Here is a reflection of the attention to "social science" and a departure from the earlier historic or diachronic methodology.

And yet, this is not to say that such differences in aim are fundamental. If it may be agreed that the understanding of culture is primary, that the ultimate consideration of the study of man is description, or as Kroeber puts it (8), descriptive integration, the differences between historical and nonhistorical approaches are those of technique and emphasis, not primarily of method. In short, most modern anthropologists will agree that the task of anthropology is the analysis of culture wholes, of the components which together produce a functioning culture and society. Whether this is done in terms of a comparison of differences or an analysis of single cultures, whether it is done synchronically or diachronically, in large measure depends on choice and circumstances. The result, however, is to produce a phenomenally wide range of problems, from those which relate to such broad issues as the humanistic appraisals of civilization at large and the forces which shape mankind, to those which are confined to the discrete analysis of social, cultural, or biological minutiae.

It is perhaps because of this inherent eclecticism in anthropology that research and the effort to achieve an acceptable frame of reference for investigations have led, especially in the United States, to almost faddist preoccupations. Once the lesson of the Boas school had been taught, once cultural relativism had been established, there came the attempts to evaluate cultures in holistic terms, going back to the initial efforts to appraise cultures which Sapir makes or to the configurational descriptions of Benedict. This trend led in turn to the analyses of personality in culture and the psychiatric orientations which still play an important part in modern anthropological philosophy. Side by side with the psychological view, there grew the interest in acculturation, the "impact" studies relating to culture contact and social change. The proponents of such methods implied they were a panacea and held the resolution of the problem of culture. But while both psychological approaches and the interest in acculturation continue to play an important part in modern anthropological thought, they have in turn been eclipsed by new considerations, as shown by the prevailing interest in values, for example, and the attempts to analyze the content of the value system of a particular people.

But despite these diverse and often far-flung preoccupations, the field of cultural anthropology has not, in the last analysis, repudiated its attachment to history and a general concept of human emergence and development. The comparative method is still an important tool, even though Ackerknecht in a recent paper (1) views with alarm what he considers to be the decline of interest in comparison, the erstwhile key stone of anthropological methodology. For indeed, it was the comparative approach, which antedates Darwin and Herbert Spencer, on which the view of human history was based that characterized both the cultural evolutionists and the Boas school. Kroeber, commenting on Ackerknecht's position, points out that the comparative method has by no means been abandoned, that if human development is to be properly evaluated, its realization must lie in applications, extended and refined, of the comparative methodology (9, 10).

Whatever its ultimate direction, anthropology continues to depend on the heritage of comparison. This method has provided a primary philosophy and is the initial *raison d'être* for the study of man. The comparative method has led, as has been shown, to the realization that cultural phenomena require evaluation in their own terms; that although values are elemental in the determination and organization of human behavior everywhere, human values are not universal. This thought has proved disturbing to a good many students of humanity and has led to the attempts to discover a normative and, as Bidney puts it (2), metacultural "best." But cultural relativism need not be either nihilistic or alarming; it is the lesson of the comparative method, and it leads to the recognition that the societies of mankind have developed out of differing sets of historical circumstances. If applications are sought — as well as solutions to the human problems of contact and conflict — they must lie in the recognition that humanity is characterized by diversity, that men are the respective products of their local cultural trends and development.

It has been recently pointed out (6) that the variously trained students of culture have shown effective cooperation in interpreting particular areas of the world and have been little concerned with worldwide generalizations. This has meant that anthropology, in combining various of its subareas and bringing together ethnology and prehistory, has been able to refine further its concern with human development. This reflects a sharpening of the tools of the comparative method, leading to an understanding of the nature of culture in historic terms. That it is possible to deduce from history the course the future will take or that the development of man as a whole can be analyzed in terms of laws of culture is not implied. It is possible, however, to obtain a view of human history leading to an understanding of why it is that the various cultural manifestations of men have arisen. In terms of observable human behavior, it is becoming possible to see why one human unit stresses its own integrity and achieves a remarkable degree of balance, why one is productive of ideas and another wholly sterile. While it is not conceivable that the development of man follows an immutable course so that the history of one society recapitulates that of mankind as a whole, it is unquestionably possible to treat comprehensively the emergence and development of a single cultural entity. Cultures do seem to possess energy and vitality and each to undergo its own evolutionary course. What the development of each has been, what it shares in common with others, what it has derived from others, aid in the understanding of man at large. This is the basis of man's perspective on himself.

REFERENCES

1. Ackerknecht, Erwin H. "On the Comparative Method in Anthropology," in R. F. Spencer, ed., *Method and Perspective in Anthropology*, pp. 117–25. Minneapolis: University of Minnesota Press, 1954.
2. Bidney, David. *Theoretical Anthropology*. New York: Columbia University Press, 1953.
3. Childe, V. G. *What Happened in History*. New York: Penguin Books, 1946.
4. ———. *Social Evolution*. New York: Henry Schuman, 1951.

5. Evans-Pritchard, E. E. *Social Anthropology*. London: Cohen and West, 1952.
6. Fürer-Haimendorf, Christoph von. "Culture History and Cultural Development," *Yearbook of Anthropology*, pp. 149–68. New York: Wenner-Gren Foundation for Anthropological Research, 1955.
7. Herskovits, M. J. *Cultural Anthropology*. New York: Knopf, 1955.
8. Kroeber, A. L. "History and Science in Anthropology," *American Anthropologist*, Vol. 37 (1935), pp. 539–69.
9. ———. "Critical Summary and Commentary," in R. F. Spencer, ed., *Method and Perspective in Anthropology*, pp. 273–99. Minneapolis: University of Minnesota Press, 1954.
10. ———. "History of Anthropological Thought," *Yearbook of Anthropology*, pp. 293–311. New York: Wenner-Gren Foundation for Anthropological Research, 1955.
11. ———, and Clyde Kluckhohn. *Culture: A Critical Review of Concepts and Definitions*. Papers of the Peabody Museum of American Archaeology and Ethnology, Harvard University, Vol. XLVII, No. 1, 1952.
12. Lewis, Oscar. "Comparisons in Cultural Anthropology," *Yearbook of Anthropology*, pp. 259–92. New York: Wenner-Gren Foundation for Anthropological Research, 1955.
13. Lowie, Robert H. *The History of Ethnological Theory*. New York: Farrar and Rinehart, 1937.
14. Strong, W. Duncan. "Historical Approach in Anthropology," in A. L. Kroeber, ed., *Anthropology Today*, pp. 386–97. University of Chicago Press, 1953.
15. Tylor, Edward B. *Primitive Culture*, Vol. I, p. 32. London: 1874.
16. ———. "On a Method of Investigating the Development of Institutions," *Journal of the Royal Anthropological Institute of Great Britain and Ireland*, Vol. 18 (1889), pp. 245–69.

Social Applications
of the Developmental Concept

John A. Anderson, M.D.

SIGNIFICANCE OF GROWTH AND DEVELOPMENT TO THE PRACTICING PHYSICIAN

THERE is perhaps no professional field in which the concept of growth and development can have fuller meaning than in the practice of medicine. A complete understanding of the patterns of growth and development and the variations in expression of these dynamic processes is necessary in order to define the existence of disease at any time from conception to birth and from birth to maturity. In addition to the responsibility of defining what is pathologic and what is not pathologic, the responsibility of the physician extends further. Society demands that disease be prevented, that it be recognized in its earliest stages, and when it occurs, that the consequences of a permanent nature be prevented. Finally, if disease has produced permanent injury, the necessity of restoring functional capacity to a stage of social and psychologic acceptability is another obligation. None of these responsibilities can be met without a thorough and detailed knowledge of all phases and aspects of the process of growth and development.

In this presentation, an attempt will be made to discuss several meanings that have been given to the concept of growth and development as the accumulating knowledge has been applied to the practice of medicine. The concept has changed throughout the past fifty years as the methods of application of this knowledge have been tested by experience. New terms have arisen which change in their definition, and as they change, a new meaning of growth and development and a new use for the knowledge unfold.

The first knowledge applied by physicians concerned certain measurements related to physical growth and development. The height, the weight, the circumference, and numerous other anatomical data were of great value to physicians in measuring the nature and extent of the growth process in children. On the basis of these data an individual could be compared with a so-called normal or average child. This cross-sectional method of comparison of the specific child provided a certain degree of security to the physician, and this security was transferred to the parents. Physicians were able, to some extent, to show at a given time that growth and development were relatively satisfactory when the individual was compared with a group of other children. It was soon learned, however, that the variations of the group, in height, weight, surface area and the like, were so wide that it was extremely difficult to identify a significant percentage of the group as truly average on the basis of physical measurement alone. No sharp line appeared which would permit a separation of the normal from the pathologic expressions of growth. It was also learned that severe pathologic changes in the growth and development process might occur while yet the anatomical data remained within the range of what might be called average or normal. The limitations of the practical application of the physical data often made the physician uncertain how to interpret the state of affairs of the individual child, and this insecurity often led to his subjecting the infant or child, particularly if too tall, too short, too heavy, or too light, to a battery of laboratory tests and extensive diagnostic studies to exclude the possibility of a disease process. Thus expressed, the physician's insecurity often intensified the anxieties of the parents, who would continue to feel that something was wrong until the child entered adult life, to pass his socially acquired anxieties and his genetic characteristics on to his own tall, thin, heavy, or light children.

The necessity of a new approach became evident as the limitations of cross-sectional comparison were expressed in the practice of medicine. Fortunately, it was decided by several advanced thinkers in the field that a study of these physical processes in the same child from birth to maturity would provide a longitudinal representation of the progress of the child that would permit him to be identified not only in a cross-sectional manner, but also in reference to his own previous progress. Thus it was shown that a given child early in the first months of life would express a pattern of linear growth, and often a pattern of weight in relation to linear growth, that appeared to be peculiar to him. The terms "longitudinal expression of growth" and the "individuality" of the pattern of growth now became defined. Practicing physicians were quick to apply this new knowledge; they began to take measurements of the physical aspects of growth and plotted these for the individual. By such curves of the longitudinal position of weight and height they were able to define for the parents a certain individuality of expression of growth that seemed to be characteristic for their child. As data accumulated and confidence was established, certain physicians made efforts to predict future progress on the basis of the previous longitudinal expression made by the individual child. This concept made it necessary to use the word "normal" with great caution. Certain individuals were found to be so far distant from the median of a cross-sectional representation that their position would be called distinctly pathologic by a cross-sectional comparison. However, when evaluated in terms of pre-existent longitudinal capacity to express growth and development potential, their linear progression was seen to be essentially parallel to that of all others falling within the median or superior zone progression. Obviously, then, this longitudinal method of evaluation provided a more satisfactory method of expressing the presence of a "normal" capacity to progress. It gave physicians considerable confidence as a guide in interpreting to parents a satisfactory state of growth and development. To some extent, it permitted an evaluation of the genetic expressivity within the child. When mild disease of a low-grade nature occurred, a careful evaluation of the longitudinal progression of the growth process at times strengthened the physician's impression, leading to more accurate definitive and diagnostic tests to establish the diagnosis. It was also possible to measure the capacity of the individual to respond following the limitations imposed by an acute disease. Likewise, the impact of chronic diseases on the capacity to progress was more fully expressed when longitudinal comparisons were made.

However, over-reliance on the prediction of individual characteristics from the longitudinal progression of one or more physical attributes soon led to disappointment. As studies have accumulated over the past twenty years, we have learned that we cannot be sure that the pre-existent capacity to progress will persist until maturity even in the absence of disease. A certain percentage of children appear to change in their capacity to proceed, particularly during the spurt period of growth belonging to puberty and adolescence. Those, for instance, that in early life demonstrated a superior capacity to grow in both length and weight soon found themselves, as they approached maturity, in an inferior position relative to the longitudinal achievement of others. This capacity to maintain a channel of a linear nature appeared to become somewhat exhausted during the later phases of growth, and ultimate achievement was not predictable for some 20 or 30 per cent of persons. Likewise, those that had occupied an inferior position in either height or weight or both in the early part of their growth process not infrequently found themselves during the growth spurt of puberty to have moved over into a superior position, continuing in this direction until maturity. There were dangers, then, in the longitudinal process of evaluation as a method of anticipating the nature of the growth process for the specific individual.

As data accumulated, relative not only to the physical aspects of growth and development but also to the physiologic, the mental and neural, the social and psychologic, and many of the counterparts of these, such as the biochemical and the immunologic, it was learned that it was possible to define an individual in a broader biologic sense. As scientists measured against time the longitudinal progress of the development of functional capacities of the body and social, psychologic, and adaptive growth, it was soon learned that reference to one or a few features of the growth and development were inadequate to express fully or to define the child as a whole. For example, a child that manifests a superior capacity to grow from a physical standpoint may sometimes have an inferior functional capacity as regards his gastrointestinal, cardio-circulatory, or some other system. His metabolic activity, as expressed by his need of calories, and his endowment of neural energy, as expressed by activity, may place him in a superior position, whereas his immunologic capacity, as measured by his ability to react to and withstand the innumerable infections that occur during the course of childhood, may place him in an inferior one. When called upon to demonstrate his psychologic, social and adaptive capacities, we may find that this same child represents a superior position. Out of this structure of growth and development, as efforts have been made to evaluate specific phases of it in a longitudinal manner, has come a term commonly used, "the total child concept." Physicians now find themselves with the responsibility of trying to evaluate all these features as they may be expressed in a specific child. This knowledge they must gain by repeated observation over a period of time of the individual expression of the various components of growth and development. A diagnosis of disease and an evaluation of its expression at various stages must be made in the light of the individual capacities of the various processes of growth and development that exist at the time disease strikes. Judgment in the application of specific therapy must also be exercised in the light of the limitations of various physiologic capacities that may have defined or suggested themselves previously by a longitudinal evaluation.

Apart from the responsibility of defining what is normal and abnormal growth and development, or of determining the presence of disease and the impact of disease upon the processes of normal development, this procedure of defining the meaning of "total child" is taking new direction. Out of this arises the recognition of a new responsibility which appears to fall into the hands of physicians dealing with children. Several other forces have led to the assumption of this responsibility. First the physician now caring specifically for children finds that he is spending from 50 to 75 per cent of his time interpreting and guiding the process of growth and development in all its aspects for the well child. The remainder of this time is spent in taking care of the acute and chronic morbid states that occur throughout the growing period. This is particularly true of the specialist caring for children, the pediatrician. As a group, however, pediatricians provide only about 20 to 25 per cent of the care given to children in this country. General practitioners, who constitute by far the greatest number of practicing physicians, provide about 75 per cent of the total care given infants and children. They, too, are called upon to spend about 30 per cent of their time in caring for children and one-half of this in guiding the welfare of the well child.

The necessity of interpreting all aspects of growth and development under the term "total child" has confronted us with new responsibilities. Now as the physician attempts to understand the individuality of the physical and functional aspects of the infant shortly after birth and during the adjustment processes, he tries to convey to the mother and father the necessity of dealing with this child in an individual manner on the basis of his and their interpretation of the kind of longitudinal progress that the child has already demonstrated. Parents often develop the capacity for objective observation and interpretation of these features as they experience them in caring for their infant. As the individuality of the physical attributes or the functional attributes is observed and interpreted by both the physician and the parent, a process of psychologic nearness is cultivated. Rather than experiencing disappointment when preconceived expectancies are not fulfilled, we find parents willing to accept the individuality of the physical or functional response and to anticipate certain kinds of responses on the basis of their previous observations of this child in the early course of his development and adjustment into the family situation. Parents often learn that certain aberrant types of response or behavior may be essentially average in their child on the basis of his capacity to respond in this direction, whereas in another child, such a deviation may be a true expression of pathology. The cultivation of this attitude, beginning as a process of psychologic nearness on the basis of the physical and functional attributes of the child in the early months of growth and development, often helps the parents attain to a degree of objectivity in their approach to the child's individuality. This partially objective approach creates an environment which in turn may permit the child, as he becomes a social being, to cultivate a somewhat objective eye in interpreting the make-up of his parents and the immediate family environment.

The problem of interpersonal relations appears to be one of our largest problems for the future. In initiating the first steps toward good interpersonal relations, the physician may come to play a very important role as he assists the parents in guiding and interpreting the growth and development of their child in all its aspects. Placed as he is in a most intimate and continuing relation with the parents and their child, there are few professional men that have such a good opportunity. Through the application of his skill and his understanding of the processes of growth and development, beginning with the physical and functional attributes and extending through the psychologic, sociologic, adaptive, and educational, he can define the nature of the individual that the parents have the responsibility of rearing to maturity. Through this process he has the opportunity of assisting in creating an environment in which the psychologic distance between the parent and the child can be gradually diminished and the two drawn ever and ever closer as time goes on. The infant in such an environment should thrive; he should develop to his fullest capacity good interpersonal relations with his parents, and subsequently express this satisfactory adjustment within the family constellation and eventually in society. It is in this area that I foresee a future application by physicians of the concept of growth and development.

One cannot help being impressed by the tremendous opportunities and responsibilities confronting the physician today. He has the opportunity of strengthening and of influencing for better or worse the character of our future citizens. He has the privilege of watching over that part of the life of a human being that is of importance in the kind of adult he is to become. It has been stated that "as a man grows older, he becomes more like himself." The rate of change in becoming himself is obviously greatest from birth to maturity.

As one defines liberally and idealistically the function and the responsibility of today's physician and particularly of the pediatrician, it becomes apparent that the disciplines of pediatrics and of human growth are very closely related. It is doubtful whether there is any significant distinction between these two. The study of human growth is in its present state somewhat broader and more inclusive, as it must embrace parts of genetics, anthropology, psychology, and sociology, as well as certain of the basic medical sciences, whereas pediatrics is a clinical science in which the primary responsibility is to practice what is known for the benefit of children. But as Alfred Washburn has said, "The theme of human growth and adaptation should run like a golden thread throughout the years of medical education," and in this aspect pediatrics becomes a field of knowledge that is essentially a subdivision of the broader study of human growth. In pursuing its objectives it is dependent upon the fields of genetics, sociology, anthropology, psychology, and biology for knowledge that may be applied practically to the individual human organism during the periods of rapid growth and development. To observe and guide this process of growth and adaptation is the intimate responsibility and privilege of the physician.

Hyman S. Lippman, M. D.

THE RELATION BETWEEN EARLY CHILDHOOD DEVELOPMENT AND PSYCHOPATHOLOGY

O UR knowledge of psychopathology is based largely on research and clinical studies from psychoanalysis. Freud's early formulations regarding the forces in the psyche interacting with each other, threw new light on the nature of emotional conflict. Dynamic psychology opened up vast areas of research in the clinical fields, especially in psychotherapy. Neurotic illness was no longer classified as a degenerative disease; it became recognized as the logical result of conflicting psychic forces, with understandable causes and specific therapy.

One of the first most significant contributions of psychoanalysis was the discovery that the sex instinct did not manifest itself for the first time during adolescence, but existed from birth onward in different parts of the body, which were called erotogenic zones. These early forms of sex drive were found to be significant in the later development of normal heterosexuality. What up to that time had been considered evidences of abnormal sexual behavior in children were found to be normal stages in the development of the sexual process. Furthermore, there was evidence that unless these early stages were present and ran their course, pathology developed in later sexual adjustment as well as in later emotional adjustment to life.

The resistances which Freud's formulations aroused are well known. Long years of clinical studies which dealt with abnormalities of sexual life, neurotic illness, and character pathology were needed to demonstrate that these formulations were correct — a fact that should not come as a surprise, since Freud's theory of the development of the sexual instinct was a product of many years of intensive clinical research with normal and disturbed human beings.

A brief review of the libido theory which deals with development of libido is necessary, because so much of what we know about the dynamics of neurotic illness is related to this theory. Impressed with the findings of a Hungarian pediatrician who earlier had reported that the vigorous thumb-sucking of some children had the distinct character of a sexual act, and by the fact that many adults with sexual perversions limited their sexual activity to the mouth, which they used as a sex organ, Freud postulated that the libido or energy associated with the sexual process first appeared in the mucous membrane of the lips, tongue, and mouth, where it remained in excessive amounts during the first year. This was the period of oral incorporation, with the infant taking in, getting nourishment and pleasure, by sucking, chewing, and swallowing. The mouth was the center for acquiring a feeling of warmth, acceptance, and pleasure, through which the infant developed a sense of trust and confidence in his state of total dependency.

After the first year, the libido became invested in the skin and mucous membrane of the anal area. This conclusion was derived from clinical conditions in neurotic adults characterized by preoccupation with anal material, and through study of individuals with sexual perversions who used their anus as their sexual organ. The libido at the anal area appeared in greatest amounts in the second and third years of life, which was the period of training and control of elimination. The outstanding characteristics in this period were the tendency to hold onto objects, and learning to let go of objects — retention and expulsion. This was the period when the child showed considerable interest in mastery and control. It was at this time that aggression and sadism developed to a high degree. Florence Goodenough (6) made an extensive study of aggression during this period of life.

From the anal zone the libido became invested in the phallic organs, the clitoris in the female and the penis in the male, during the fourth or fifth year of life. This was the period of exhibitionism, infantile masturbation, and the Oedipus conflict. During this period the child began actively to relate himself emotionally to others.

These three libidinal phases of development constituted the child's infantile sexuality. They were primarily related to gratifications he could find in his own body. It was not until the child reached adolescence that he developed sexual attachments to the opposite sex, achieving normal psychosexual development. Freud considered these phases as theoretical constructions necessary to understanding the dynamics of neurotic illness.

He introduced the term "fixation," which referred to the accumulation of libidinous energy at one of these earlier phases of libido development. The fixation was caused, he believed, in part by constitutional factors, plus the occurrence of emotionally traumatic experiences during the particular libidinous stage.

One of the major factors that produced fixation in the child was the unsolved neurotic conflicts of the parents, whose own early fixations were stirred up by the behavior of the child. Fixation produced a damming of libidinous energy which prevented its forward development to the later normal heterosexual stage — a fact of considerable importance, since all neurotic adults have some degree of disturbance in their psychosexual development.

Freud introduced another concept important in his libido theory — that of regression. He found that when a person whose libidinal development in early life suffered fixation was faced later in life with a reality situation that was traumatic and intolerable, he regressed in his emotional development to the stage where fixation had first occurred. This was observed, for example, when an adult, seized with an attack of hysterical illness, quickly lost his ability to deal with reality, became over-emotional, was unable to leave his home unless accompanied by someone upon whom he could be dependent, and behaved in a manner characteristic of a four- or five-year-old sensitive child. Even more classical was the observation of the obsessionally neurotic adult whose illness Freud attributed to regression to the anal period of libido development where fixation had occurred. Every obsessional neurotic adult described in the psychoanalytic literature, and every obsessional neurotic child known to the writer, has evidenced preoccupation with bowel movements, fecal matter, and the anal region. Their compulsive orderliness, cleanliness, aggression, and sadism were similar to what we often see during the normal course of development of a two- or three-year-old child. It is the one clinical condition in which the suffering continues unless the therapy brings to the surface the underlying unconscious conflicts related to anal fixation.

Later on when psychoanalysis concerned itself with the psychology of the ego, character development was found to be very closely related to problems of fixation, and character types were described. We learned at this time about the oral character with marked dependency needs, the narcissistic character, the obsessional and hysterical characters. These were persons who had character traits sufficiently acceptable to the ego to prevent the breakdown into neurotic illness. Despite the pathology that was present, the individual was able to make a comparatively adequate adjustment to reality.

Freud's libido theory was based almost entirely on a reconstruction of the early childhood experiences of adults in analytic therapy. More recently Anna Freud (5) has reported observations that she and her co-workers made of very young children who lived in the Hampstead Nurseries in England from 1940 to 1945. They were able to observe these children for twenty-four hours a day over a period of months and years. The program was not set up as a research project; the clinical observations were made in the course of their child care. The oral, anal, and phallic stages of these children were observed to merge into each other at the points of transition. They were distinct from each other only in the sense that in each phase the instinctual drives characteristic of that period were more prominent than they were in the other stages. A wider overlapping was observed between the oral and anal stages; the demarcation between the anal and phallic stages was sharper.

Anna Freud noted that children in the Hampstead Nurseries who were exposed to severe traumatic experiences, such as the loss of parents by prolonged separation or death, invariably regressed to an earlier stage. Thus the child who was traumatized at the anal stage of his development soon regressed to the oral phase, sucking and biting, and demanding the dependency care of infancy. Similar findings were reported by nursery school teachers who had been analyzed and who had developed skills in making observations that the untrained observer tended to overlook. Susan Isaacs' classical study of children of preschool age was one of the more notable contributions of this kind (8).

EGO DEVELOPMENT

The development of the child's ego is closely allied to his libido development. Psychoanalytic studies and research have emphasized the emotional relationship between mother and child from the moment of birth. More recent studies have been made of the mother's feelings and fantasies as they affect the child before it is born. There is abundant clinical evidence that healthy ego development depends on a warm, close, intimate, emotional tie between the mother and her child.

It is difficult to speak of ego development during the first six months of a child's life, and most psychoanalytic writers refer to the ego development as beginning in the first half of the second year. In the earliest phases of the infant's life all of his libidinous energy is concentrated on himself — a stage Freud called "primary narcissism."

Anna Freud, in discussing ego development, speculated that after many feedings the infant is probably able to fantasy the food he has enjoyed. When hunger comes he may fantasy his mother, the breast, the bottle, or the milk, and this imagery or fantasy would be the first step in mental functioning. Before long he will distinguish between the fantasy of the object that gave him satisfaction, and the object itself. Early he does not appreciate where he ends and the outside world begins, and as is reflected in clinical material, probably feels that what is good and satisfying is a part of himself; what is painful and unpleasant is outside himself. With his mother's frequently leaving him and returning he begins to recognize that his mother is not a part of himself. Gradually during the second half of his first year he begins to develop the capacity to differentiate. The undifferentiated stage of ego functioning ends at this time. He develops an understanding of his mother's communications and facial expressions, and an object relationship develops which is the child's first love relationship. Ferenczi's article "Stages in the Development of the Sense of Reality" (2) is a most interesting contribution to the understanding of the fantasy life of the child as he relates himself to reality.

Hartmann (7) believes there is a maturation aspect of ego development that has been ignored by most analytic observers, though Freud early referred to this constitutional factor. Hartmann calls this the "autonomous factor," which develops independently of the environment.

In considering ego development one must recognize two regulating principles of normal functioning. The first and earliest is the striving for immediate gratification at any expense. Everything that does not yield pleasure is disregarded. The second is the ability to accept reality with its deprivations and to postpone gratification to a later period. This is only possible when the child can be confident of future rewards. The second principle is achieved primarily through the developing ego by means of its capacity to perceive, to learn, and to plan.

In developing the capacity of integration the ego gradually learns to relate itself to the outside world, testing which of the instinctual drives are acceptable and which are not. The ego sets up a signal of anxiety as a warning that danger exists. This danger may come from within or from the outside world. The ego learns to develop defenses against the instinctual drives which it cannot otherwise master. It develops a force within itself, the superego, which acts as an ally against instinctual drives. All of these accomplishments of integration and synthesis depend on a close warm tie between the child and his parents with whom he identifies and whose standards he takes over.

In the study carried on at the Hampstead Nurseries, Anna Freud and her co-workers found that when the children regressed in their libido development, they also suffered ego regression, returning to earlier stages of ego development. The most recently acquired ego functions were the first to suffer in the regression; this affected speech, bowel and bladder control, and forms of locomotion. The children became clumsier, less well coordinated, more primitive in their modes of play, and functioned according to the pleasure principle. These findings are familiar to children's physicians during periods of acute illness.

Many behavior disorders can be traced directly to disturbances in the ego development, and with the exception of those owing to constitutional and organic factors, all are due to pathology in the mother-child relationship. Many studies indicate that infants who are unwanted and unloved are slower to develop a secure hold on reality. A certain amount of denial and frustration is a requirement for healthy ego development, but these frustrations must come from someone who loves the child. The child who is seriously deprived of affection and care invariably becomes disturbed.

René Spitz (12) showed that infants beyond the age of six months living in institutions, accustomed to seeing their mothers frequently and then suddenly deprived of their mothers' visits for long periods of time, developed severely withdrawn behavior having the character of an acute depression. He called this condition an "anaclitic depression," since the pathology resulted from the loss of dependency support from the mother. During the depression the child's ego accomplishments suffered serious regression, often irreversible.

Beata Rank and her co-workers (11) demonstrated that infants who fail to receive the mothering they need during the first weeks and months of life often develop a state of extreme and total inability to relate themselves to objects. They are unable to differentiate between themselves and the outside world. Their ego development remains blocked at a primitive level. Leo Kanner (9) had earlier described such children, whom he called "autistic" because they were almost completely withdrawn from the outside world. Beata Rank found that most of these psychotic young children, whom she calls "atypical" rather than autistic, had parents who suffered from severe forms of regressive mental illness. She ascribed the narcissism of the child to the narcissistic illnesses of the parents. She and her co-workers discovered a form of therapy which depends for its success on the most intensive, intimate, warm relationship between the therapist and the child. The therapy, which may last from one to three years and sometimes longer, seeks to convince the child that it is safe for him to trust another person and to develop an affectional tie. When this is finally accomplished, ego development becomes possible for the first time in the child's life. Studies such as these by Beata Rank, and the pioneer work of Hartmann and others on the ego-structure in psychosis, have paved the way to the discovery of methods of treatment that help the psychotic to develop emotional contacts with others, a first step in becoming well.

Only a small percentage of children deprived of affection in early life develop psychotic illness. Most of them develop varying degrees of secondary narcissism which interfere with their ability to relate themselves to others. In its more severe forms, narcissism can produce serious character disturbances that limit the individual's capacity to enjoy life.

Because of its significance in the social and emotional life of the individual, we may consider the development of aggression as a separate entity, even though it is closely related to the development of the instinctual life and of the ego. It is difficult to understand normal and abnormal psychological development without understanding the role played by aggression and destructive tendencies and attitudes. These play an important part in the production of neurotic illness and criminal behavior. In contrast to those schools of thought which regard aggression merely as a result of frustration arising from the environment, psychoanalysis maintains (4) that "aggression is one of the two fundamental instinctual drives (sex and aggression, life and death instincts)." Psychoanalysis looks upon aggression as an inborn instinctive drive which develops spontaneously in response to the environment, but is not produced by it.

The component of aggression is necessary to deal with a hostile environment in the struggle for existence. Sexual aims could not be reached without the component of aggression. Aggression is needed in every phase of the development of the sexual instinct, and is so bound to the erotic instinct that to separate them is often difficult. During the oral libidinous stage, aggression is reflected in the insatiable greed with which the child attacks the mother's breast and body; in his biting and screaming, and throwing himself into a rage. During the anal period, defiance and aggression are at their peak, and his possessive hold on the mother is exhausting. He destroys the toys he cherishes, and the animals he loves have to be rescued from him. During the phallic period of libido organization the child tries to dominate his sexual object by means of his aggression, and also uses this to protect it. He attempts to impress and subdue his sexual object.

The fusion of aggression with sexual urges is normal. When either one is excessive abnormal behavior manifests itself. Pathological forms of aggression occur in the unloved, rejected child, whose aggressive behavior is often uncontrolled and vicious, filled with destruction and hate. The rejected child has little remorse or concern about the damage or suffering he causes. His behavior can be explained by the absence of the libidinous factor which must be fused with the aggressive urges if they are to be kept under control. Neither punishment nor bribes have much effect on youngsters of this kind. Nothing short of caring for the causative factor — the absence of neutralizing affection — will check the wanton aggression. When affection is available to the child, provided it can be accepted by him (which is not always the case), the naked aggression is neutralized. Unfused, unneutralized aggression is what we see in persons who are capable of perpetrating tortures on others and of committing sadistic murder.

There are other striking evidences of pathological aggression which result when children are deprived of early mothering. Lawson Lowrey (10) found that infants who remained in large institutions during the first two or three years of their lives were rarely able subsequently to make a healthy emotional adjustment to life. Their hostile, destructive behavior, combined with insatiable demands for affection, made it impossible for substitute parents to keep them in their homes for long periods of time. Dr. Lowrey was the only one of several working with such children who felt that their pathological behavior was not irreversible. Recently Beres and Obers (1) described a few successful adjustments of early institutionalized children, achieved after several years of heroic effort by exceptional foster parents who were able to gratify the great needs of these children. It is interesting in this connection that accompanying the aggression of this group of children was an inability to relate to others, a tenuous hold on reality, and an inability to learn — all products of defective-ego development.

Pathological aggression which results from the absence of fused libidinous energy is not always directed against the outside world. Often the aggression is directed against the individual's own self. In an article "The Unwelcome Child and his Death Instinct" Ferenczi (3) makes the following statement: "Children who are received in a harsh and disagreeable way die easily and willingly. . . . if they live, they keep a streak of pessimism and an aversion to life." This mechanism probably plays an important part in most suicides. Ferenczi also refers to a speculation which Freud once made, that the absence of the libidinous component was responsible for the unconscious attempt at self-destruction in the epileptic attack.

Psychopathology and early normal development, then, are closely related to each other. A faulty development of the instinctual drives, of the ego, and of aggression so profoundly conditions the child in his early life that unless the conditions which produced the faulty development can be materially changed, later emotional illness is inevitable.

An early recognition of serious deviations in development demands immediate action to remove those factors which block normal development, at a period in life before the conditioning has become deeply fixed. Whenever it is evident that an infant or child is deeply rejected, intensive efforts must be made to help the parents accept the child. When the rejection is so marked or the parents so emotionally involved that they cannot respond to attempts at therapy, it is important for the future emotional development of the child that he be removed to a setting which can provide the essentials for normal development.

Freud concerned himself from the outset with the psychology of normal mental phenomena as well as the abnormal. Present psychoanalytic research on early childhood development is directed to the understanding of the normal child as well as the abnormal. The goal of this research is the prevention of psychopathology, and the evolution of a program that will help to prevent neurosis, psychosis, and criminal behavior.

REFERENCES

1. Beres, D., and S. Obers. "The Effects of Extreme Deprivation in Infancy on Psychic Structures in Adolescence," *The Psychoanalytic Study of the Child*, Vol. 5 (1950), p. 212.
2. Ferenczi, S. "Stages in the Development of the Sense of Reality," in *Contributions to Psychoanalysis*. Boston: Richard C. Badger, 1916.
3. ———. "The Unwelcome Child and his Death Instinct," *Internat. J. for Psychoanalysis*, Vol. 10 (1929), pp. 125–29.
4. Freud, A. "Instinctual Drives and Human Behavior," in R. M. Loewenstein, *Drives, Affects, Behavior*, pp. 259–77. New York: International Universities Press, Inc., 1953.
5. ———. "Observations on Child Development," *The Psychoanalytic Study of the Child*, Vol. 6 (1951), pp. 18–30.
6. Goodenough, F. L. *Anger in Young Children*. Inst. of Child Welfare Monogr. Ser. No. 9. University of Minnesota Press, 1931.
7. Hartmann, H. "Mutual Influences in Development of the Ego and the Id," *The Psychoanalytic Study of the Child*, Vol. 7 (1952), pp. 9–30.
8. Isaacs, S. *Social Development in Young Children*. London: George Routledge & Sons, 1933.
9. Kanner, L. "Problems of Nosology and Psychodynamics of Early Infantile Autism," *Amer. J. Orthopsychiatry*, Vol. 19 (1949), pp. 416–26.
10. Lowrey, L. G. "Personality Distortion and Early Institutional Care," *Amer. J. Orthopsychiatry*, Vol. 10 (1940), pp. 576–85.
11. Rank, B., and D. McNaughton. "A Clinical Contribution to Early Ego Development," *The Psychoanalytic Study of the Child*, Vol. 5 (1950), p. 53.
12. Spitz, R. "Anaclitic Depression," Ibid., Vol. 2 (1946), pp. 313–42.

John C. Kidneigh

THE CONCEPT OF DEVELOPMENT WHICH UNDERLIES THE SOCIAL WORK HELPING PROCESS

D EVELOPMENT may be recognized by social workers as referring to several kinds of processes. In one sense it may be regarded as historical development; in another, as social process; in another, as the development of a social value system; in another, as personality development with the concomitant biological, psychological, and social components. Social workers tend to emphasize the importance of dynamic social interaction and hence focus upon the phenomena of *relationships* as central to their concept of the *nature* of human nature.

This paper will present briefly a concept of development which holds the concept of relationship central. But if one is to see this idea in perspective, and from the same "staging area" as does social work, it is necessary first briefly to present two other considerations, namely, the development of social work as a profession and the development of social work education.

THE DEVELOPMENT OF SOCIAL WORK AS A PROFESSION

Social work as a profession is the product of this century, although its roots are well established in the history of earlier times. In those earlier days there was a widespread practice of giving alms to the "worthy" poor, not so much for the benefit of the recipient as for the salvation of the giver's soul. To some extent, this relatively unenlightened attitude toward giving persists to this day. As people began to take responsibility for the welfare of their neighbors through activities which were called "charity," "poor relief," "philanthropy," and "social reform," and particularly after there appeared a body of paid personnel who served as agents for groups of philanthropists, it began to be apparent that the welfare and rehabilitation of the recipient of aid should take precedence over the salvation of the soul of the almsgiver.

At this point earnest students of the problem of philanthropy began to clarify a dilemma. On the one hand, it was contended that the objects of charity were inferior human beings, that their poverty resulted from their own lack of intelligence or morals. On the other hand, it was contended that poverty and human maladjustment arose from society itself and from forces beyond the control of the individual, such as the dislocations arising from industrial revolution, depressions, wars, and similar phenomena of social disorganization or reorganization. The paid personnel who served as agents for groups of philanthropists came to the conclusion that neither of these views was wholly tenable. Sometimes personal inadequacy could largely account for the suffering and unhappy state of the individual. Sometimes societal conditions could be blamed for the individual's plight. More often both forces seemed to be at work. Hence, human problems could best be solved by working with the unfortunate on a case-by-case basis, helping individuals to marshal their own and the community resources toward a solution of their individual and family problems. Simultaneously efforts had to be made in social reform which would assist the community to take such steps in community organization and to adopt such social policy and programs as would tend to reduce or eliminate the hazards of poverty, sickness, unemployment, delinquency, discrimination against minorities, and the like.

Thus it became clear that social workers had to secure tested and usable knowledge about man and his potentialities, limitations, and development as a biological organism, a psychological creature, and a social being. At the same time social workers had to secure tested and usable knowledge about society and its potentialities for change, its limitations, organization, standards, values, culture, and processes of social change. If social workers were to help a person become or remain "normal," it became important to know the dynamics of the social process and *how* to influence it. Social work has tended to turn to the social sciences for knowledge of man and society, often to find a fractional, underdeveloped, and somewhat confusing state of affairs. The contribution of social science to a social practice like social work has been considerable, of course, but far less than has been needed. As the social sciences mature, social work may be expected to improve. A considerable development has occurred, however, somewhat independent of the social sciences.

Social work programs began to appear in various forms, some primarily adopting the case-by-case method for the solution of human problems — from which the modern method of social casework evolved, and some primarily adopting group action methods — from which the modern methods of social group work and social community organization work evolved. Later as the agencies became large in size, and particularly as social work programs under governmental auspices developed, the modern methods of social work administration evolved. Throughout these developments, as social agency leaders sought to understand the problems with which they grappled, there was a slow development of social work research methods.

Social work has regarded itself as a "practice" rather than a "field of study," and as an "art" or "applied science" rather than a "pure science." It dates itself as a modern profession from the appearance of Richmond's *Social Diagnosis* (11), published in 1917, and the organization of the American Association of Social Workers in 1921 under the presidency of C. C. Carstens, who was followed in that high office by such illustrious pioneers as Owen R. Lovejoy, Harry L. Hopkins, William H. Hodson, and Frank J. Bruno.

At first social work was concerned with the victims of personal inadequacy or social injustice; that is, the poor, the indigent sick, the orphaned, the handicapped, members of minority groups, the delinquent, the criminal, the inebriate, unmarried mothers, the poorly housed, and social outcasts. But as social workers applied their helping skills to these cases, and as they engaged themselves in social reform activities looking toward more general solutions of social problems, it became ever clearer that these clients were *human* like others in the community, and hence that social services should not be restricted to the extremely maladjusted and unfortunate but should be used in the community at large to help prevent social breakdown and human suffering at an earlier point.

At first, social work programs appeared in highly specialized or fragmented forms. Each of the programs tended to focus on a single problem. That is, there would be a program for helping the worthy poor, another for unmarried mothers, another for the hospitalized indigent sick, and still others for orphans, for children having problems in school, for crippled children, for emotionally disturbed children, for neighborhood problems, and for reducing discriminatory practices against minority groups. As the American community became aware of a particular social problem, it proceeded to create another social work program or agency to deal amelioratively and specifically with that particular problem.

In large measure this kind of highly specialized social work program persists to the present time, and is explained in part by the nature of the vested interests of founders, endowers, and lay boards, by their methods of financing, by sectarian auspices, and by similar factors bearing upon the life and continuity of a given social work agency. Despite the phenomena of special agencies for narrowly defined kinds of social problems, the general trend is away from such highly specialized agency forms. The trend is toward social agency programs that see the individual and family whole within the context of group and community life. The trend expresses itself in three ways: (a) the merger of two or more specialized agencies into a single multifunctional agency, such as the merger of family and children's service agencies among those supported by private funds, or the merger of several separate specialized governmental agencies on township or city level into a single multifunctional county or state social welfare agency; (b) the expansion of a specialized agency to a broader function, such as a probation service expanding to a family relations court service; and (c) closer collaboration between existing specialized agencies through a system of joint planning and coordinated service, such as is fostered by social agency and community welfare councils.

Parallel to this trend from narrowly specialized to more comprehensive approaches to human social problems has been a comparable trend in professional development. As social work emerged from a period where it was strictly a volunteer service of good-neighborliness, the paid worker or philanthropic agent appeared. Later these paid workers were to become a profession emancipating itself from the narrow sponsorship of a few philanthropists, in order to render professional service on behalf of the whole community. At first it was thought that each special program required a uniquely specialized worker. Hence, social workers were given a wide variety of titles, "friendly visitor," "visiting teacher," "probation officer," "relief investigator," "community worker," "adoption worker," "social consultant," and "psychiatric social worker." In time the similarity of methods used, the emerging commonness of purpose, the establishment of professional associations, and the development of social work education brought a marked trend toward professional unity. The most recent evidence of this unity is the formation of the National Association of Social Workers, which replaced seven preceding professional associations in the field. While some of the various titles given earlier to social workers persist to the present as historical remnants, the commonly accepted title "social worker" now covers the range of positions calling for professional social work skills.

It can be said, then, that social work began with a series of specialized forms and developed toward a comprehensive unity. In this respect the course of its development differs from that of certain other professions (1). Medicine, for example, seems to have begun with a broad, inclusive function and developed toward a variety of subfunctional specializations.

At this point one may properly ask what is the correct definition of this developing professional field? Obviously it concerns itself with the relationships between persons, and between individuals and various groups or social systems. Its interests lie not only in knowing or understanding those relationships, but also in knowing what can be done to assist individuals and groups to find solutions to their problems.

Life for individuals, for groups, and for communities is a continuous series of problem-solving events. Each problem is made up of a constellation of factors. A solution requires the ability to understand or diagnose the constellation and to rearrange its elements, eliminating some of them at times, sometimes adding to them, so as to bring relief from tension or unhappiness. In most instances individuals, groups, and communities are able to find a solution to their problem without special technical help. But at times they need it. The function of any service profession is to give such special service whenever the problem falls within the functional area of the profession's competence. Whenever the problem of an individual, a group, or a community involves personal, social, or economic adjustment, it falls within the social worker's purview. The social worker's skills in social casework (4), social group work (15), social community organization work (10), or social work administration (14) can help the individual, group, or community find a solution. Modern social work can, therefore, be defined as a professional service rendered to people for the purpose of assisting them as individuals or as groups to attain satisfying relationships and standards of life in accordance with their particular wishes and capacities, and in harmony with those of the community (12). This modern definition stands in sharp contrast to the concept of social work at the opening of this century.

SOCIAL WORK EDUCATION

Education for social work has reached its present state of development after a relatively short but rapid rise from apprenticeship training (6, 7). Formal education for social work at first adhered very closely to the needs of voluntary social agencies and differed little from the concept and content of apprenticeship training. In fact, the first schools of social work were established under the auspices of social agencies rather than of universities. This focus began to change during the years from 1915 to 1920. The emphasis shifted to professional preparation based upon scientific knowledge and the development of scientifically oriented methods of helping individuals, groups, and communities.

The most fundamental of the influences producing this change was the growing awareness of the need for deeper knowledge about man as a biological organism, a psychological creature, and a social being, as well as a need for deeper knowledge about society, social processes, and social organization. Logically this awareness led to a demand for practitioners possessing a broad liberal education with some concentration in the social sciences, and, to a lesser extent, the biological and medical sciences. The social work field took the decisive step in 1935 of requiring the Bachelor's degree as a prerequisite to entry into professional graduate social work education. This placed social work as the first service profession, and as yet one of the very few, to establish so high a standard for entry into the professional school.

Another powerful influence was the establishment of schools of social work within the university framework. This furthered a recognition of fundamental knowledge upon which professional study should be based, brought about the gradual relinquishment of the concept of training for specific agency needs, and fostered the development of helping methods applicable to a variety of social work programs of service. The presence of a school of social work in the university has concurrently contributed to the stimulation of other disciplines, encouraged their interest in social problems, and resulted in some enrichment of their development.

A considerable influence upon the development of professional social work education has been the demand for individual readjustment to changing conditions of life and the establishment of social reforms. These have called for a variety and volume of social work services scarcely contemplated by the pioneers of the profession.

One additional important influence on the development of social work education can be mentioned. An association of Schools of Social Work was formed in 1919 for the purpose of expediting an interchange of information. By 1932 this association issued a "minimum curriculum" statement, and thenceforth admitted to membership only those schools that offered a course of study which included the "minimum curriculum." Admission to membership became equivalent to being "recognized" or "accredited." The professional associations of practitioners established membership requirements which included education in an accredited school; hence, any school desiring to qualify its students and graduates for admission to a professional social work membership association sought to become accredited. As a result, the accrediting authority in the field of social work has played an enormously important role in the development of social work education.

The successive curriculum policy statements that have served as the basis for accrediting mark off the several steps of change and development. From the concept of a "minimum core" there has been a movement toward broader areas of study. Concepts of integration and progression of learning underlie a two-year graduate professional program of study based upon a four-year undergraduate liberal education about man and society. In social work six years of college and university preparation are now regarded as the minimum adequate preparation for entry upon professional practice. The four years of undergraduate pre-professional study should be devoted to the acquisition of a broad liberal education, with some concentration in the biological and social sciences. Through the discipline of these four years of study the student should acquire a basic knowledge of man and society. An ideal undergraduate program of study would include courses drawn from the biological sciences, including human genetics and public health, as well as courses on individual personality development and human behavior drawn from psychology and sociology. Additional courses would deal with the social, political, and economic forces. Concurrently a knowledge of the scientific method should be acquired, along with some of the tools for analyzing problems.

Following his pre-professional preparation, the social work student enters the graduate professional school to acquire disciplined methods for helping individuals, groups, and communities who need and seek professional service. The three broad areas of study now required in an accredited (9) school of social work are: (a) knowledge and understanding of the social services, their development, and their relation to social order, to social change, and to community needs; (b) knowledge of human behavior, needs, and aspirations, and (c) knowledge, understanding, and use of social work methods involving social casework, social group work, social community organization work, social work administration, and social work research (17).

THE "RELATIONSHIP" AS CENTRAL TO DEVELOPMENT

Along with the development of social work as a profession and the development of social work education, there has emerged a concept of development as related to men and society which conditions social work goals and methods. The remainder of this paper presents briefly a tentative conception of man as a behaver (in contrast to conceptions of man's behavior) and of social systems in process (in contrast to descriptions of social organization).

It will be remembered that modern professional social work appeared upon the American scene after classical economics with its theory of the "economic man"; after Comte had presided over the birth of sociology; after Tylor and Bastion had laid the groundwork for anthropology; and after psychology had separated itself from philosophy. Sociology, anthropology, and psychology were markedly influenced by Darwinism and biological science. One might mention, for example, Spencer or Durkheim in sociology, Frazer or Tylor in anthropology, and McDougall in psychology. Slowly but surely the theories of unilineal cultural evolution and instinct psychology, so widely accepted in the nineteenth century, became discredited. They were replaced by an almost confusing array of social-scientific theories of culture, social organization, developmental, comparative, and gestalt psychology, culture and personality, psychoanalysis, and so on. During this period there seemed to be a considerable lack of communication between the social sciences, each developing almost independently of the other. Recent evidence indicates that the several social sciences, fortunately, are seeking a *rapprochement* (3).

As the several social sciences were parting company, modern social work appeared upon the American scene. This was almost immediately after Franz Boas, with considerable success, had combated theories of unilineal evolutionism, geographic and economic determinism, the organismic analogy, the concept of the group mind, racism, instinctivism, and theories of primitive mentality. The emergence of modern social work was almost concurrent with the rise of developmental psychology and psychoanalytic theory. It coincided also with the period when sociology was preoccupied with the study of social problems, a period to be followed by the rise of scientism in sociology. That social work, in its attempt to find a body of usable theory about man and society for its professional task, should experience difficulty in selecting and ordering the contributions of the social sciences was to be expected. And so one finds social work borrowing ideas from a variety of sources, testing these ideas against the practical situations encountered in working with people, and modifying the contributions accordingly. But social work did not limit itself to borrowing from the social and biological sciences. It also borrowed from other service professions, notably medicine and psychiatry, law, and teaching. And to the constellation that emerges from all the borrowing something also has been added.

It is interesting to note that the first great published study from which modern social work dates itself was titled *Social Diagnosis* (11), and that "the person worked with" by the social worker is referred to as the client. Obviously the word "social" expresses the major focus of concern. The word "diagnosis" was borrowed from medicine and implies the application of knowledge and a scientifically oriented method of arriving at a definition of the situation. The term "client" was borrowed from law because it seemed to imply a relationship of equality, with helpfulness toward, and identification with the person, group, or community being helped, and possessed less of the implication of control, superiority, or direction than was then associated with the term "patient."

As the profession emerged from its lay past, the focus gradually came to be the welfare of the individual for his own sake in the interest of society rather than the measures to deal with specific social problems, such as poverty, alcoholism, or crime. Social work came more and more to be a conscious application of democratic principles with an increasing understanding of the dynamics of human behavior and of the social process. This focus separated social work from the social sciences in one sense, while demanding a *rapprochement* in another sense. While psychology was preoccupied with human behavior and how to measure certain parts of it in order to generalize or predict certain behavior outcomes, social work was concerned primarily with the behaver and with methods that would be effective in helping the behaver. While sociology was concerned with social problems and social organization, and most particularly with research methods that would describe or predict social organization or reorganization, social work was concerned primarily with the social systems (families, groups, or communities) themselves, and with methods that would be effective in helping the social system as a behaver. While anthropology was concerned with patterns of culture and with the descriptions of given cultures, social work was concerned primarily with the impact on individual personalities of their own or conflicting culture patterns, and with the practical problems of acculturation. While political science was concerned with patterns of governmental organization and political process, social work was concerned with the conscious application of democratic principles to individuals and groups of individuals in their everyday life. While economics was concerned with the supply of and demand for material goods, social work was concerned with the victims of economic processes. In drawing these contrasts, I do not mean to imply that the various social sciences were not interested in the behaver and were solely preoccupied with the behavior. Nor do I mean to imply that social work is not concerned with a knowledge of behavior but solely preoccupied with the behaver. It is the *focus* or *emphasis* adopted by the social worker which leads me to articulate that the concern of social work is primarily an interest in the behaver as such. Knowledge *about* the behavior is not in itself enough when one is charged with *doing* something in working with the human subject.

In constructing a concept regarding the human behaver and his development, social work has screened the contributions of various fields of knowledge through a double-meshed screen. One of the screens has been the empirical test of practical experience. The other screen has been the social value system of social work — central to which is a deeply held belief in the essential dignity, worth, and right to self-determination of the client. Both of these demand a continuing warmth toward others, a deep concern for human welfare, and professional self-control that maximizes the client's power to use his own and the community's resources for a solution of his problem.

Because these factors have operated, social work has tended to draw heavily from psychological theory, especially psychoanalytic theory, and from sociological theory in coming to a generally accepted idea about the human behaver and human development. However, the influence of economic and political theory and of anthropological theories of culture and personality have also been felt. I will not try definitely to place the origins of the several ideas that make up the constellation, but will present in summary outline some of the essential components of the social work conception.

Man is a biological organism whose physical body develops according to a predetermined plan not yet fully understood but within a pattern the main outlines of which are known. Within these physical and biological limits he becomes human through a process of learning to relate to other human beings. He is, from conception to death, a part of one or more social systems. Further, he is human because he internalizes the social systems of which he is a part. The very beginning of life for any given individual (which is at the point where the ovum is fertilized by the sperm cell) results from a social act within the context of a relationship between mother and father — a two-person social system. Throughout gestation, while tremendously important biological developments take place, the individual is a part of a two-person social system consisting of himself and his mother. At birth and for some time thereafter he learns to be human by being a part of a most important social system — his family. As he becomes a member of an increasing number of social systems, he acquires human qualities by the internalization of the realtionships he has had with each of the several social systems. Throughout his life he is under the influence of his relationship to others within the variety of social systems of which he is a part. Thus we can say that man is human by virtue of the development of relationship skills, and that this development is primarily a *social* process, the whole, of course, being held within biological limits and based upon physical and intellectual abilities and aptitudes that are predetermined in the genetic structure. These basic abilities are variable among different persons, constituting a range of capacities among human beings. But the important point is that growing and developing, which may be viewed as a biological and psychological process, becomes *human* growing and developing when the factor of relationships is introduced. The "learned" behavior is the internalization of these relationships. Hence, how a person *feels* determines to a great extent his behavior.

Because there exists such a complexity of social systems in which the individual may find or place himself, it is obvious that there can be no absolutely uniform pattern of development for all human beings. But because there are sufficient similarities in the social systems of any culture, it is possible to discover certain norms against which any individual may be compared.

It is fortunate that the biological and psychological sciences have established or charted some norms in a few important areas. The biological norms, beginning with human embryology and running on through the norms of the fetal period, birth, infancy, childhood, latency, adolescence, adulthood, and aging, mark off convenient guideposts. The psychological norms of behavior and intelligence provide another set of convenient guideposts. The psychoanalytic norms of psychosexual development provide another set. Each of these sets of norms has its social relationship aspect. Despite this there remains a lack of reasonably definitive norms concerning the maturation of relationship skills.

In search of a useful frame of reference about the development of individuals, social workers have tended to accept formulations which are in comformity with biological and psychological theory but which emphasize or articulate the relationship phases or norms. The formulation of psychosocial development set forth by the Mid-Century White House Conference on Children and Youth expresses this emphasis clearly (16). The overlapping stages of development are labeled: developing a sense of trust; developing a sense of autonomy; developing a sense of initiative; developing a sense of duty and accomplishment; developing a sense of identity; developing a sense of intimacy; developing a parental sense; developing a sense of integrity. It will be noted that this formulation is not inconsistent with biological or psychological theories of developing, but is expressed in terms of social relationships.

The social systems of which any given individual is a part tend to become institutionalized. That is, the relationship between the individual or group and the larger whole of the system tends to become defined. As a consequence social workers have been interested in social organization and social change, particularly when the resources of organized social groups can be used for human betterment, or when social change for human welfare is indicated. Norms for this kind of phenomenon are not as yet fully developed. In general, however, the nature of social change as expressed through the modification of social institutions seems to express itself through a cyclical process. As Chapin (2) has formulated it, there are three discernible phases.

The first of these phases is characterized by stability, adherence to well-known and well-accepted rules, provisions for enforcing the established ways of doing things, and an identification of the established mores and folkways of the community with emotional, religious, and political sanctions. As changes occur, such as those ushered in by technological inventions, this rigid and well-established system becomes increasingly less adequate for meeting the social problems that arise.

The second phase is characterized by experimentation, the breaking away from certain established procedures, the proliferation and multiplication of organizations and methods that are attempts to cope with new conditions, and the breaking up of rigidities in law and custom that seem inadequate for the times. This phase is often referred to as the time of social progress, when new ideas, new inventions, new techniques, new ways of meeting problems in an increasingly complex society are looked upon as the most important contribution any individual can make. In time this increasing complexity and multiplicity of agencies, organizations, and associations becomes unwieldy. It is recognized as less efficient than it could be.

A third phase is characterized by attempts at integration, merger, consolidation, coordination, rationality, "efficiency and economy," and other measures which attempt to make things orderly and integrated. This means a new set of mores and folkways, a new orderly, rational approach, and the further it goes the more and more it assumes the characteristics of the first phase — but on a different plane.

When one combines the concept of individual development with the concept of social change, it becomes obvious that the integrative task of becoming a mature human being through the internalization of social relationships is considerable. A bewildering variety of relative successes or failures in this integrative task eventuates. Where the most important social systems, such as the family and certain primary groups, have maintained themselves with reasonable stability, retaining a quality of emotional warmth and security, the integrative task is more likely to be accomplished successfully. Where change and reorganization of social systems, especially family and primary groups, proceed at too rapid a pace, the integrative tasks are multiplied. Aberrant personalities as well as aberrant social systems become more numerous. Social workers are often called upon to assist individuals, groups, and communities where the integrative process has been disturbed. Social work attempts to *work with* the relationship problems of individuals *through* a relationship which is consciously controlled, and marked by warmth, consistency, and respect.

We can summarize the social work concept of development by saying that it is based on scientific data; that the organic, psychogenetic theory of personality is fundamental; that social relationships within the context of social processes of change are of primary importance. Social workers following these concepts assume that the objects of study and "treatment" are individuals and social systems, not organisms and aggregates. The personality is a whole. The whole and its parts are mutually related, the whole being as essential to an understanding of the parts as the parts are to an understanding of the whole. Personality is both biological and cultural. From this point of view social workers engage in the process of helping individuals, groups, and communities in the problem-solving continuum which is life (13). From this point of view social workers approaching the problems of social adjustment regard as indispensable the study of social relationships, psychosocial diagnosis, and social "treatment," i.e., the offering of social services (5) aimed at helping the individual, group, or community to attain satisfying relationships and standards of life in accordance with their particular wishes and capacities (8).

REFERENCES

1. Bruno, F. J. *Trends in Social Work.* New York: Columbia University Press, 1948.
2. Chapin, F. S. *Contemporary American Institutions.* New York: Harper, 1935.

3. Gillin, J. P., *et al. For a Science of Social Man.* New York: Macmillan, 1954.

4. Hamilton, G. *Theory and Practice of Social Casework.* New York: Columbia University Press, 1940.

5. ———. "The Underlying Philosophy of Social Casework," pp. 7–23 in C. Kasius, ed., *Principles and Techniques in Social Casework. Selected Articles 1940–50.* New York: Am. Assn. of Social Workers, 1954.

6. Kendall, K. A. "Education for Social Work," pp. 170–75 in *Social Work Yearbook.* New York: Am. Assn. of Social Workers, 1954.

7. Kidneigh, J. C. "Education for Social Work," pp. 158–70 in *Social Work Yearbook.* New York: Am. Assn. of Social Workers, 1951.

8. ———. "People, Problems, and Plans," *Social Service Review,* Vol. 25 (1951), pp. 181–88.

9. *Manual of Accrediting Standards.* Council on Social Work Education, 1953.

10. Murphy, C. G. *Community Organization Practice.* Boston: Houghton, 1954.

11. Richmond, M. E. *Social Diagnosis.* New York: Russell Sage Foundation, 1917.

12. *Social Work Yearbook.* New York: Am. Assn. of Social Workers, 1954.

13. Towle, C. *Common Human Needs.* Washington: Federal Security Agency, U.S. Social Security Board, 1945. Reissued by Am. Assn. of Social Workers, 1952.

14. Trecker, H. B., R. Glick, and J. C. Kidneigh. *Education for Social Work Administration.* New York: Am. Assn. of Social Workers, 1952.

15. Wilson, G., and G. Ryland. *Social Group Work Practice.* Boston: Houghton, 1949.

16. Witmer, H. L., and R. Kotinsky. *Personality in the Making.* New York: Harper, 1952.

17. The complete curriculum policy statement is included in K. A. Kendall, *op. cit.,* pp. 174–75, as well as in the *Manual of Accrediting Standards,* 1953.

Willard C. Olson

DEVELOPMENTAL THEORY IN EDUCATION

D EVELOPMENT is a master concept in the field of education, formal and informal. The present paper will present some ideas with a strong factual basis in an attempt to extend the area of the known by theoretical extensions which are at times of a speculative and controversial character.

The definitions of such words as *growth, development,* and *maturation* are not completely standardized, particularly when one moves from one field of specialization to another. Growth as increase in size or amount is fairly standard, and we can apply this indiscriminately to growth in inches or pounds or abilities in school subjects. Growth is an appraisal of the process of change, and is often used to include the concept of increased complexity as well as change in size. Some have preferred to use the term development to describe changes in complexity, using it with a meaning similar to differentiation in biology. Maturation is frequently confined to sequences and patterns which are innate and over which no external influence has any power. Maturation includes the fact that frequently the nervous system anticipates a new function, i.e., the environment does not create the function. The progression is assured by internal factors, and the environment supports the changes but does not generate them. The racial inheritance is accomplished through maturation. If one wishes to specify social inheritance as environment, the child comes into it through a process of acculturation.

The maturation process describes the potential capacities of the individual, but experience determines the expression in development. We do not usually see the full significance of this interaction in the commonly nurtured and much practiced areas such as motor development and size increase, but regularly do so in those areas in which there is presence or absence or highly variable amounts of it, as in reading, music, and swimming. Maturation is thus the internally determined aspect of development. Time in and of itself increases many powers, but experience, practice, and learning are needed for an effective use of the maturational power. It is this "hen and egg" circular character which frequently confuses educational practice. If you emphasize maturation, practice says, "Wait, it will be more economical and effective." If you emphasize experience, practice says, "Start at once, you must produce the readiness." The best judgment of the moment suggests that "Pace, maturation, and learning go best hand in hand."

In the field of education we have ample justification for using the term development as an end product under the combined influence of nature and nurture, in which nature defines the maturational pattern and in which nurture insures changes in size in the sense of growth and complexity. It is in this sense that one speaks of child development and the curriculum, with the curriculum as something through which nurture is provided for the development of the child. In this sense it is proper to speak of developing abilities to read, to compute, to run. Maturation, growth, and development involve time as an important dimension.

A few persons are inclined to dismiss as unimportant in practice the attempts to understand growth and development in terms of both its components of nature and nurture. It cannot be dismissed so lightly, for concrete information and a point of view make substantial differences. The first effect is found in the behavior of the teacher, whether he delays, forces, or paces. A second important effect is found in the behavior of the parent, as to whether he holds the school responsible for presence or absence of reading at age seven, for example. The third effect is found in the attitude of society which is very ready to blame a specific practice or find a scapegoat when it is believed that single solutions are available. In the absence of a substantial body of reliable knowledge, the teacher may feel frustrated and guilty, the parent anxious and demanding, and society critical, using lack of attainment as an excuse for inadequate support.

The task of this report is first to define and illustrate some concepts of development, and then to elaborate upon them as they affect the practices of schools. No attempt will be made to treat the whole range of developmental concepts as they find expression in the educational process. Some oversimplification may be helpful for orientation.

DEVELOPMENTAL EQUATIONS

When we consider development operationally, we can define it by the following simple formula:

1. Maturation $\times$ Nurture $=$ Development

Equation No. 1 is sufficiently elastic to allow within the meaning of maturation not only gross physical factors, but also the visceral and activity drives, and the physiological concomitants of emotions. The concept of nurture is broad enough to include within it all the social learnings that come about by association with the mother, the family, the neighborhood, and the community. The equation is too simple if thought of only as a factor system. It is in reality a dynamic interactive system, in which the attained development in turn interacts with both nature and nurture to produce complex effects. The stream of energy flow which we call behavior and the level of achievement are thus determined by both endogenous and exogenous factors and come to constitute a dynamic system.

If now for purposes of educational development we become interested in achievement and consider nurture as experience, we can write an equation for our simplest case, i.e. the case of absence of experience. Presence and absence of reading experience in a deprived culture would be a specific illustration. The formula becomes:

2. Maturation $\times$ Zero nurture $=$ Zero achievement

Our most common case will be where every child in school has an opportunity for an experience which we can designate as a constant supply. If we substitute for maturation a complex assessment of growth potential, our end product in achievement will be determined solely by individual differences in maturational factors. Thus, under conditions of constant supply, the achievement is a variable. The equation will be as follows:

3. Variable maturation $\times$ Constant supply nurture
$=$ Variable achievement

Often it can be demonstrated that conditions vary so that nurture is actually a continuous series from absence to the maximum that an organism can take. With constant nature the environmental supply determines the achievement according to the equation:

4. Constant maturation $\times$ Variable supply nurture
   $=$ Variable achievement

Equations 1 through 4 are clearly too simple an answer, for there appears to be evidence for "differential uptake." This results in an enhancement effect, because the differentials, once established in achievement, in turn so modify the organism as to make it more selective, permitting more rapid uptake in some and less rapid in others. In effect, then, the constant supply is surely a myth, since children will seek a larger or smaller supply from what is available, as in the following equation:

5. Variable maturation $\times$ Differential uptake of nurture
   $=$ Enhanced variable achievement

In effect, then, the product we know as development in education is an achievement in which neither rate nor supply is constant, and in which the outcome in individuals may consist of various mixtures of the two.

The present development or achievement in the above equations is essentially what people mean when they are talking about readiness, which is neither sheer nature, maturation, nor sheer acquisition from the environment, nor anything completely within the powers of the person to produce.

It may come as a surprise to have one consider the provisions for stimulus-induced learning in the same category as nurture, such as food and water. It will be helpful to think of this distinction in terms of the extent to which a function is central in the survival of the organism, and the extent to which it is peripheral. Physiological regulation, or homeostasis, tends to regulate the nurtural requirements needed for survival. This self-equilibration permits the organism to survive within a range of requirements for food, water, oxygen, and temperature. Exceeding these limits is lethal, and one cannot talk of development on a presence or absence basis for these requirements. Although not as central, the acquisitions and adaptations of the organism have a survival value also. Some are near the core or center and others are so peripheral as to make presence or absence of little consequence under some conditions. Spoken language is an achievement that comes almost as readily as eating and sleeping; nurture in this respect has an inevitability about it in any society. The skills for survival under conditions of lush supply need little attention — they just come naturally. Under other conditions the organism is forced to create the conditions. This is more than simple adaptation and often involves a deliberate nurturing process.

THE NATURE OF THE EVIDENCE

There is much evidence to support the general theory back of the writing of such equations as those preceding. At the University of Michigan much evidence is found in longitudinal, multi-discipline studies of children in the University School. A frequent method of description has been to translate samples of growth into age units. Thus individual growth curves are constructed to show growth in height (HA, height age), weight (WA, weight age), bone (CA, carpal age), strength (GA, grip age), dentition (DA, dental age), intelligence (MA, mental age), and achievement (RA, reading age). The average of these is called organismic age (OA).

Figure 1* describes the growth of three groups of boys who were selected at age eleven as fast readers (RA four and a half years or more above CA), as intermediate readers (RA clustered at CA), and slow readers (RA two years or more below CA). The data for girls are similar on a relative basis, but at somewhat higher average levels on an absolute basis. The curves in the figure will be assumed to represent the end product in development at any point in time of variations of the equation maturation × nurture = development. The assumption of strong maturational factors is supported by family studies and by components of organismic age that are resistant to planned change. The solid line represents the comprehensive sample of growth known as organismic age, and the broken line gives the reading age which is used as a sample of achievement.

When one studies the differences between the children in the three groups and their counterparts in many other studies, progress toward

* From Harriett Kraemer Beck, *Relationships of Emotional Factors in Early Childhood to Subsequent Growth and Achievement in Reading.* Publication No. 2323 (Dissertation Abstracts) University Microfilms, Vol. 11 (1951), p. 283.

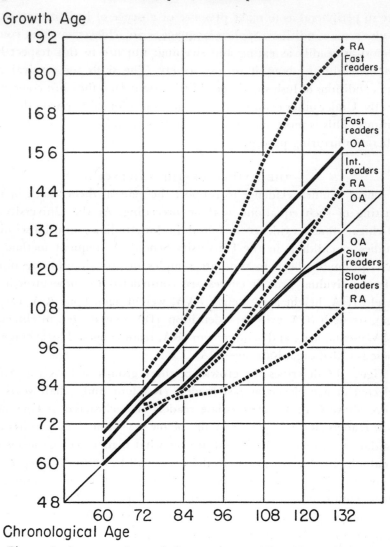

Growth Age

Chronological Age

Figure 1. A comparison of three groups of boys in organismic age and reading age at successive chronological ages

a theoretical system can be made. These associations will be described subsequently.

First, however, let us see if any kind of case can be made for enhanced achievement in which variable maturation with selective uptake makes for a differential supply of nurture and results in enhanced achievement. Some of the possible comparisons are in Table 1. Here the organismic quotient $(OC = \dfrac{OA}{CA} \times 100)$ at ages 8 and 11 is used to determine a theoretical reading age with chronological age regarded as constant nurture. When this value is compared to the obtained reading age, the differences suggest that differential uptake of nurture exists. Whether this is actually a process or a statistical artifact cannot be determined without much more study. It is of interest, however, that in our longitudinal studies we regularly find the largest standard deviations in these areas most responsive to environmental differences — e.g., reading as compared to mental age, mental age as compared to physical measures, and weight as compared to height.

Let us now move to more general theory by a model detached from any particular set of findings.

Table 1. Comparisons of Theoretical and Obtained Reading Achievement for Boys Selected for High, Intermediate, and Low Status in Reading

	At Age 8				At Age 11			
	OQ	Theor. RA	Obt. RA	Diff.	OQ	Theor. RA	Obt. RA	Diff.
High	119	114	124	+10	119	157	188	+31
Intermediate	107	103	93	−10	108	143	145	+ 2
Low	98	94	82	−12	95	125	108	−17

A MODEL OF INDIVIDUAL DIFFERENCES IN DEVELOPMENT

The graphic schematic model in Figure 2 shows the growth of one highly developed child (A), one who is just average (B), and one who is below average (C). Chronological age is on the x axis and growth age or organismic age is on the y axis.

We can now set up a series of concepts involving known facts surrounding the model. These are of varying degrees of generalization, and each should be preceded by the qualification "other things being equal." The model is based on the assumption that the growth represented by the curves represents a composite according to the equation Maturation $\times$ Nurture $=$ Development. Viewed alone it appears as a relatively static model with much stability and continuity. Injected into a social field, however, the children represented become dynamic in the sense of relationship to other individuals and to meeting the requirements of each situation.

Growth Age

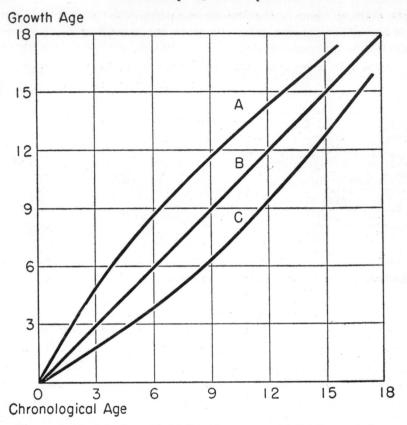

Figure 2. Model of rapid (child A), average (child B), and slow (child C) growth according to the equation
Maturation × Nurture = Development

What general theory can be built about the model in the illustration?

PRINCIPLES IN HUMAN DEVELOPMENT

Concepts that will stand the test of universality, of experiment, and of prediction are hard to come by in a field governed by multiple causation. When stated, such concepts are limited in the sense that other postulates may in part account for the phenomenon. There is always something of an indeterminant character when variable individuals experience variable nurture.

The following postulate comes close to having generality: "For all achievements which increase with chronological age, the rapidly growing child will yield the achievement earlier, and the slowly growing child will achieve the status later than the average child of a given age."

From such a postulate one can predict in advance the individual differences that will exist, the factors that must be observed in an adequate experimental design, and the constant errors which must be allowed for or adjusted. We can predict in advance the results of many types of experiment. With such a postulate a person can predict, as an average trend at least, many of the types of data that can be secured in a classroom group or even in physiological experiments. The basic evidence needed for the predictions is a fairly accurate account of age change. For example, knowing that emotional outbursts decrease in number and severity with age, we can predict that a child showing such outbursts will have many characteristics of the slowly growing child. Some of the objective findings on associations with the model furnish a basis for more general theory.

ASSOCIATIONS WITH THE MODEL

Here are some operational associations and deductions from the model. It should be noted that the effects are not only in the model as constructed, but also in the matrix of all the associated factors that go into the loading of the model. The differences shown have important associations with socio-economic status, social acceptability, responsibility, levels of interests, reaction to frustration, age of accomplishment of developmental tasks, and many valued traits of character and personality. The differences also run in families, and are remarkably resistant to planned change, although reflecting changes in design over the years.

More specifically, A as contrasted with C will be higher in social age, will be advanced in interests, and will be superior in social status in the group. C, contrasted with A, will have more behavior problems whether checked by self, teacher, parent, or associates. Child A as contrasted with Child C will be characterized by more active, seeking behavior in general, including motivation for achievement. His appetite and interest in food will be greater, although calories per unit of body weight will be less in accord with the age trend.

The associates of A will be more like A than they are like C, and similarly, the associates of C will be more like C than like A. The rationalization of the association may be in terms of social status, interest, values, levels of development, or comparable skills of achieving or performing.

Some examples of the significance of the associations for other systematic approaches can be illustrated.

THE MODEL AND PSYCHOANALYTIC THEORY

Psychoanalytic theory emphasizes the fundamental maturational significance of the aspects of human life concerned with ingestion, excretion, reproduction, and the ramifications of these in interaction with the environment. Psychologically, development comes to be represented by the Id, the Ego, and the Superego. Within the developmental cycle dominance of a phase is often identified, such as the prenatal, neonatal, oral (first year), anal (1 to 3 years), phallic (3 to 5 years), latency period (5 years to prepuberty), prepuberty and adolescence, and adult. Adult character has been described in terms of the trauma of a period or the dominance of one aspect over the others.

Observations I have made suggest that insights are added and some mistakes corrected when the theory of the model is also utilized. Thus children like C of the model will remain later in each of the above phases, and problems of conflict, coercion, and repression will be more prominent. The significance of clinically and hospitally selected children for general theory requires correction for the downward selection of the sample in such populations. With such adjustments the conflicting evidence on the significance of early childhood experience and child rearing practice might, by allowance for the theory of the model, make more systematic sense.

The theory of the model, of course, allows for both cultural and biological factors, effects, and interrelationships.

THE MODEL AND FRUSTRATION-AGGRESSION THEORY

In classic frustration-aggression theory one has two opposing courses, one of which is restraining. Operationally, frustration occurs when there is interruption in progress toward a goal. The consequences may be aggression, regression, physical strain, and tension. In reference to the model we can make some predictions in accord with the theory. The theory demands that the effects be related to the strength of the tendency, the extent of the thwarting, the frequency of frustrated responses, and the competing tendencies resulting from anticipation of punishment. Biosocial theory affirms that Child C has greater frustratability, a greater past frequency of frustration, will be frustrated by less difficult environmental factors, and will have more competing tendencies for avoidance. This appears to be in accord with the facts when C is constrasted with B or A.

THE MODEL AND THEORIES OF INTELLIGENCE

The conflict in emphasis between those psychologists who see in individual differences a large element of human biology, and those social psychologists who see the differences among people or groups of people as primarily determined by the culture, is most dramatically illustrated in the attempt to produce so-called "culture fair" tests. In such work, the experiences attributable to a particular social class position have been studied in a meticulous manner, and tests that differentiate social class experiences have been excluded. After this work is done, it is of interest to note that large individual differences still remain among the children of all social class positions, that these individual differences far transcend the average differences between social class groups, and that the reapplication of so-called "culture fair" tests, as contrasted with the contaminated tests, still produces differences in the same direction.

The model allows for the fact that intelligence must be nurtured, that under a constant supply of nurture A will be contrasted to C primarily by maturational factors, and that with varying degrees of deprivation in the nurtural supply (with constant maturation) the end product in development will vary. More commonly the end product will be determined by the complexities of variable maturation multiplied by variable nurture.

RECONCILIATION OF EXPLANATORY THEORIES

It appears clear that mistakes or at least a constricted view will be held when there is a focus on a single, self-contained system.

For example, a psychoanalyst recounts an incident in a progressive elementary school in which there were a number of cases of reading retardation. He reports the lack of progress made by conventional remedial reading methods (traditional learning theory) with the employment of objective diagnostic measures, instrumentation, and practice. He calls this approach a mistake since psychoanalytically his diagnosis was that the children were suffering from severe repression of the scotophilic (looking at feces) tendencies. Work with the parents revealed that such repression had been common in the socialization of the children.

The theory and observations associated with the model inject an additional dimension of explanation which assists in understanding these two conflicting diagnoses, both based on correct observations.

We have only to note that the retarded readers under discussion regularly tend toward C in developmental characteristics. They will indeed have learned less well (less learning potential in terms of growth age as contrasted with chronological age). They will also have persisted in the anal phase longer (delayed over-all growth), and will thus have created more anxiety in parents (conflict of expectation and readiness), and will have been subjected to more repressions.

INDIVIDUAL PREDICTIONS VERSUS EXPLANATORY PRINCIPLES

The model and associated theory may be criticized since the relationships referred to are often small. One should recall, however, that explanatory principles are commonly based on small differences. It could not be otherwise in a world of multiple causation.

The student of total growth regularly finds small coefficients of correlation between all measured structures and functions. These give important support to the idea that there are underlying factors in development which express themselves in various ways. Some investigators have disparaged the significance of these relationships for a theory of development in education, since they are not of a size as to be very helpful in individual predictions, where the goal is to predict the status of a person in a group. Before one disparages these small coefficients as a basis for an explanatory system, he should ponder the large differences produced at the extremes. It is often at the extremes, including the gifted, the mentally retarded, the delinquent, and the disturbed, where theoretical insights are sought, and practical programs constructed.

The schematic model may be criticized properly as oversimplifying many very complex problems in genetics and nurture. The science of organized complexities may be better brought out by the graphs of growth for individual children. This has been done and is being done in the hope that there may also emerge "laws of the case" as well as laws of populations.

The geneticists are moving from a single-gene theory to a polygene theory, where multifactorial genes combine to produce a continuous change among individuals in an attribute rather than the discontinuity that might be indicated by a single-gene approach. As we go into a molar type of study of the child, we are concerned with such ideas as design, pattern, shape, form, configuration, or morphology. When such ideas are applied to a child, they seem to have reality in terms of his behavior. His pattern or shape thus has some significance for his behavior in addition to the actual amount or substance of things present. Thus, there is special significance in having a child with a very highly developed intellect but with less adequate general growth support. Such children have been described as "a high-powered motor in a light chassis." Similarly, a child characterized from birth by apathy and lack of strength reflects this in the totality of his behavior in play, and even in retardation in a subject such as reading, where he may have a high intellect which should, from average predictions, produce outstanding achievement. His apathy and weakness is a part of a patterning of significance in understanding his behavior and achievement. The significance does not depend on a pronounced statistical correlation for children in general between strength as measured by a dynamometer and ability to read. The attempt to analyze the substrata of development by sampling, as in the model, commonly reveals important trends for both the individual and for a population sample.

THE TASK OF EDUCATION

For purposes of education it is necessary to translate concepts of development into principles to guide practice and into practices which exemplify the concepts and the principles. In the body of developmental theory should be included also findings or facts, each often of limited applicability, yet supporting in some degree the more general concept. The planning of the nurtural environment commands the attention of curriculum specialists and is the everyday activity of the classroom teacher. But the physical environment, however well planned, is still insufficient, since process is also a part of the environment. The management of the child and the environment, and the process of bringing the two together are commonly thought of as the art of teaching. It has been the custom, because more easily translated into operations, for the curriculum expert to stress the environment with such imperatives as he could get from the nature of society and the nature of the person. Usually it is impossible to do this with a high refinement of detail in adaptation to individual differences. Since this is difficult some curriculum specialists seem to ignore individual differences. Others emphasize process to the extent that the innocent bystander seems to perceive that some specialists think that method is all important. Witness the controversy over phonics and other methods of teaching when evidence is not very good that any single method will explain the differences between children! If we could reconcile ourselves to the fact that absolute standards are impossible, with variable nature and variable nurture, we should take a step ahead on the affective side of education. The adjustment of expectations to the individual differences that exist among children increases satisfaction and productivity rather than improves tested performance.

When one proceeds deliberately to set up a program for the development of children, it is necessary to introduce additional concepts of values and directions. Understanding is the goal at the theoretical level but is insufficient at the practical level. The step to practice in implementing the differences described here may be illustrated by concepts of seeking, self-selection, and pacing.

SEEKING, SELF-SELECTION, AND PACING

The idea that there exists a "wisdom of the body" that enables children to make wise choices in matters educational has led to direct demonstrations and a whole theory of curriculum and method in education. Choice by the learner from a total environmental supply of experiences becomes of larger importance as compared to assignments on the part of the teacher.

The healthy child is naturally active, and he is engaged almost continually while awake in an active exploration of his environment. He seeks from that environment those experiences that are consistent with his maturity and his needs. Other aspects, even though present, are ignored, for he does not react to them and therefore does not learn appreciably from them. Since children grow at widely varying rates, it is impossible to say that they will be ready for a particular experience at a specific age. We can, however, trust the seeking behavior to tell us much about the readiness of a child for an experience. This is evident even in the first year of life as the child begins to understand, later as he begins to talk, and in his early responsiveness to pictured materials found in the home. The longer the children have an opportunity to grow and the more experiences that they have, the more different do they become and the less ready are they for a common experience — either in terms of difficulty level or in terms of interests.

Throughout nature there is a strong tendency for life to be sustained by the self-selection of an environment appropriate to the needs of the plant, animal, or human being. If the appropriate environment does not exist ready made or is inadequate in some major respects, the human being also works creatively for the conditions that advance his well being. Investigations show that infants have great ability to regulate the amount and timing of their food intake to harmonize with their needs, and that they accept and reject foods on the basis of flavors, consistency, or quantity, in ways appropriate to their maturity.

If young children in the preschool period are turned loose in an environment in which there exists a variety of stimulating objects, each child will tend at appropriate times to react to some of the material, but he will react differentially according to the rapidity with which he is maturing. Thus, in such an environment, the more mature child will spend more time with books while, for a period, such materials will be ignored by the less mature child even though he is of equal age. In later years children select books from an environment supply in accord with both maturity and interest.

Pacing refers to the teacher's acts which ensure that each child is provided with the materials upon which he can thrive. It also refers to the attitude which expects from the child only that which he can yield at his stage of maturity. Just as the concept of self-selection has back of it a psychology of motivation, so the pacing approach has back of it concepts of the nature of success, incentive, and productivity. Studies of learning and productivity in relationship to the goals that are set suggest that the child will continue to strive when success is clearly within his grasp. He will start avoiding the experiences which are at a level of difficulty clearly beyond his present attainments. The teacher's task is to guarantee that every classroom situation, or its immediate surroundings, will have in it tasks which are interesting in terms of intrinsic content, and at the same time cover a range of difficulty as great as the variability in the human material with which he deals.

SUMMARY

Developmental theory has major significance for education viewed as bringing together the maturational forces within the child and the nurture needed for development. A series of equations describe the differences found among individuals in the absence of nurture, under constant supply, under variable supply, and under the condition of differential uptake based on previous learning. Concepts of development are illustrated by data on boys who read at high, intermediate, and low levels. A graphic, schematic model is presented with factual associations and generalizations of significance for developmental theory. Concepts of seeking, self-selection, and pacing are described as ways in which theory may be translated into practice.

Index

INDEX

Ackerknecht, E. H., 221
Action sequences, 150
Activity level, 30–32, 70
Adaptation: in homeostatic mechanisms, 98; related to perception, 96–97
Adjustment: and variability of behavior, 61; patterns of, 232
Affectionate nurture, and child's identification, 155, 159
Aggression: and sex drive, 241; development of, 235, 240–42; in dogs and chickens, 73; pathological, 241–42
Anaclitic depression, 240
Analogy: in science, 9, 27; transfer of information by, 186
Anatomic ontogenesis: defined, 110; modifications of the concept, 110–14
Analytical procedure: in behavior studies, 79–80; in study of development, 50–51
Anthropology: compared with history, 215; theories reviewed, 215–19; relation with other social sciences, 219
Appetitive behavior, 98–99
Arber, Agnes, 7, 28
Ashley, W. J., 210–11
Ashley-Montagu, M. F., 110
Ashton, T. S., 204
Autism in children, 240
Autonomous factor in ego development, 238
Avoidance behavior: in dogs, 69; and stimulation, 98–99

Barker, R. G., 26
Barron, D. H., 131
Bastian, A., 251
Bayley, Nancy, 135
Beck, Harriett, 263
Behavior: and social expectancy, 34; contrasted with structure, 149; definition in terms of function, 60–61; determinants of change in human, 151–52; development of efficiency, 33, 35; dimensions of human, 149–51; electroencephalograms, 67; functional differentiation, 59–60; hereditary factors, 54; instigations of, 150; neonatal, 66, 89, 93; of monsters, 63; origins of, 54–58; plasticity and phyletic levels, 95; prenatal, 55–56, 87, 91; relation to growth and structure, 32–33; selectivity as property of organism, 33–36; structural basis for, 55; studied by isolation method, 95; variability as essential property of, 62. *See also* Function

Behavior development: characteristics of, 55; comparative approach to, 79–80; human vs. animal, 50; maturation vs. experience, 86–89; phylogenetic approach to, 80–82

Behavior differentiation: and development, 54–58; growth of form, 32, 63–65; genetic factors, 68–72; in relation to time, 62–68; social factors, 72

Behavior norms, use in social work, 255

Behavior organization: and principle of cumulation of effects, 39–40; limits on, 35–36; prenatal, 56; resulting from biological processes, 83; self-stimulation in, 86–89; species differences in capacity for, 101–2

Behavior theory: concern of experimental psychology, 166–67; and developmental problems, 170–72

Behavior variability: and adjustment, 61; and habit, 61–62; concept in genetics, 61

Benedict, Ruth, 221

Beres, D., 242